HARLEY-DAVIDSON Performance Parts Directory

Dave Mann

DEDICATION

This book is dedicated to four great Americans who couldn't be with us today:
Buddy Rich
Mickey Thompson
Steve McQueen
Stevie Ray Vaughn

First published in 1993 by Motorbooks International Publishers & Wholesalers, PO Box 2, 729 Prospect Avenue, Osceola, WI 54020 USA

Motorbooks International books are also available at discounts in bulk quantity for industrial or sales-promotional use. For details write to Special Sales Manager at the Publisher's address

Printed and bound in the United States of America

Library of Congress Cataloging-in-Publication Data

Mann, Dave.
Harley–Davidson performance directory / Dave Mann.
p. cm.
Includes index.
ISBN 0-87938-774-2
1. Motorcycle supplies industry—Directories. 2. Harley–Davidson motorcycle—Parts—Directories. 3. Harley–Davidson motorcycle—Performance—Directories. I. Title.
TL448.H3M36 1993
629.227'5—dc20 93-25843

On the front cover: A sharp FXRS Sport owned by Bruce Fischer is poised for a run up the coast. This Low Rider Sport has aftermarket exhaust, ignition, and more, including a nitrous oxide system with a chrome nitrous tank. *Ron Hussey*

CONTENTS

ACKNOWLEDGMENTS

A word of appreciation is due to the people who responded promptly to my requests for information about their businesses. Without their cooperation this book could never have been completed. Thanks to everyone who sent photographs, catalogs, and other information for the book.

There are over a hundred people to thank. In particular, Dale Nungesser, John Dangerfield, John and Pam Hanzlick, Larry Smith, Mark Everitt, Mel Magnet, Michael Dapper, Paul Wiers, Rick Nail, and Tony Reif helped out while I was working on this project.

To all of you, as well as Bill Frye and all of the other "just down-home folks" at the Apollo Restaurant in Harrisburg, North Carolina, thanks.

HOW TO USE THIS DIRECTORY

To find a particular company, look it up in the main section of the directory. All companies, and most of their products and services, are listed in alphabetical order.

To find particular types of products and the companies that make them, turn to the Component Manufacturer Section near the back of the directory.

To find companies in a particular geographical area, look in the section called Manufacturers and Fabricators listed by Area, at the end of the directory.

Important Notice for Manufacturers and Fabricators

The second edition of this book is being prepared now. If you would like your company to be included (free of charge), or if you want your company's description updated, send black and white (preferred) or color photographs of some of your products or work, and a copy of your catalog (or a description of your products and services) to Dave Mann, in care of the publisher.

Introduction

The main goal of this directory is to provide Harley-Davidson enthusiasts with the most complete listing possible of high-performance equipment made for (or that can be installed on) their motorcycles. Manufacturers and fabricators from Australia, Canada, France, Germany, Holland, Italy, Japan, New Zealand, Scotland, Sweden, the United Kingdom, and the United States are represented in these pages. There are companies here that are relatively new, and some that have been around for decades.

The Harley-Davidson community has always seemed to be broken up into segments. We have the chopper guys, the dirt-track racers, the drag racers, the OEM suppliers, the restoration crowd, the road racers, the salt flats racers, and the touring riders. News rarely travels from one camp to the others as it should. This brings us to another goal of this directory—to bring Harley people all over the world a little closer together, or to at least let them hear about each other.

To make this directory more complete, I have included a few companies that do not produce components but provide various services for performance-oriented Harley-Davidson owners, such as race engine building and repair, cylinder head modifications, development work, dyno time, custom fabrication, and complete race bike construction.

Not everything in these pages is designed specifically for Harley-Davidsons. A few components such as some of the brakes, forks, and wheels are made for motorcycles in general, and require some machining to adapt to your bike. But after all, if you're scratch-building a bike you won't be expecting everything to just bolt together. My own interest in lightweight components, road racing, and drag bike chassis design as well as race car technology led to some of the more exotic equipment being included here, even though some of it isn't intended specifically for Harley-Davidsons. I would rather provide too much information than not enough.

To make information easier to find quickly, all of the products described on a particular page are described in alphabetical order. No company was given preferential treatment over any another. Performance companies were invited to submit product photos for the directory, thus, you'll see photos only from those companies that chose to supply shots. Not everyone chose to do so.

After the main section of the directory you will find lists of the manufacturers of specific components, which you can refer to for a better idea of what's available in a particular field. These component manufacturer lists are included as quick reference guides, with descriptions of particular products found in the main section of the directory.

With much of this equipment coming from outside North America, a few words about dealing with these suppliers are in order. When dealing with someone who might not speak English, it's always best to contact them in writing first. For information on making international phone calls, call your operator and make sure of the right country code that precedes the actual phone number.

Don't forget you might be dealing with small companies—many of the companies in here are run by one or two people. When you call them, you won't get a receptionist—in fact it might ring for a while before you get an answer because the only person in the shop is welding or machining when you call. Don't let this discourage you from doing business with them. Just be considerate and reasonable by getting right to the point so they can get on with their work.

Due to the large number of manufacturers and products involved in this project, there isn't enough room here for detailed descriptions about what fits what. For example, throughout the directory you will see a particular component described as being available "for Big Twins and Sportsters," or "for Shovelheads." That's just to get you in the ballpark. Unless it says otherwise, assume that it's for late-model bikes and then follow up with a well-informed dealer or the manufacturer for specifics about your particular application.

It should be mentioned that much of the equipment listed in this book has been designed exclusively for racing and is often sold without any warranty. In many cases this equipment will not be legal for street use. Also bear in mind that it is the nature of many performance parts to be very lightweight and designed for a shorter lifespan than original equipment. Who knows—you may even get away with running some featherweight three-spoke magnesium wheels on your FXRS touring bike. But nobody is likely to recommend that you do unless they're eager to make a sale. And if you read about some real neat stuff in here and then go out and buy a 120-inch blown alcohol engine for your street bike, don't complain about tune-ups and mileage.

The idea for this directory occurred to me back in 1988, while I was trying to stuff an Evolution Sportster engine into an XR-750 chassis. (The chassis was eventually sold when I couldn't locate a crowbar big enough to do the job.) At that time there was no single book or catalog that could tell me where to get every component needed to scratch-build a high-performance Harley. Working full-time as a machinist kept me from doing anything about the idea for the directory until January of 1992, when this project began.

I enjoyed working on this project, and was particularly happy to provide some well-deserved publicity for the "little guys" in the industry who lack the advertising budgets of the big companies we already knew about.

I have tried to treat all of the companies equally, listing them in alphabetical order, with all of them receiving coverage that was as equal as practical. Despite my writing over six hundred letters and spending over $3,000 on phone calls in the eighteen months I worked on the book, more than 140 of the companies listed here did not respond to my requests for product information and photographs.

Hopefully now that everyone can see what this directory is all about they will realize that being listed in here really is good publicity that costs nothing more than a letter and a few pictures.

More than 250 letters asking for product information and pictures were mailed on the same day back in April of 1992, and the first manufacturer to respond was Amp Research, who beat everyone else by at least a week.

All of the manufacturers' claims were scrutinized, and in some cases they were toned down. Many people were very modest and just sent pictures and a few words. But the point here is that virtually all of the superlatives in this book are my own.

For those of you who work with computers, this project was done entirely on my Macintosh. This book went from my computer disk directly to the editing and graphics departments at Motorbooks International without first having been manually retyped into the editing or typesetting equipment. I mention this because I wanted to give credit where it's due—if it hadn't been for the Macintosh's being so easy to use, I would never have even considered writing this book. In case you are interested in computers, this was submitted on disk as a 585k document (without photos), containing just over 81,000 words.

Some very knowledgeable people will read this directory. I hope that some of you will take the time to point out anything in here that you find incorrect or misleading. The single most important goal here is to provide accurate information for Harley-Davidson enthusiasts. Since this is the most complete book of its kind, it might as well be good, too.

Your suggestions for manufacturers whose components should be considered for the next edition would be welcomed, as would information about anything in here that you find is outdated or just plain wrong. (But don't write to ask questions—I don't have time to answer them.) You can reach me by writing to Dave Mann, in care of the publisher.

This directory will continue to evolve in its future editions, with more manufacturers and performance products being added. Tentative plans call for it to be redone every other year, with the next edition to be published near the end of 1995 (although I hereby reserve my right to burn out and buy a Ducati).

One other thing. After the book was submitted to the publisher it was edited by two other people, so I didn't have total control over the end result. But trust me—when this book left my place, some parts of it were funny.

—Dave Mann
Dallas, Texas
October 1993

Part One

Master Index of Manufacturers

This manufacturer's index lists companies in the directory and what they manufacture. (Companies appear in alphabetical order through the directory, the same as in this index.) As many of their components are mentioned as possible, but in some cases only a company's more popular products are mentioned to due space limitations.

Most components are mentioned in alphabetical order, both in this index and in the main section that follows.

Directory of Manufacturers

Accel Performance Products

Accel manufactures the Thunder Twin fuel injection system as well as a complete line of performance ignition components for most recent Harley-Davidsons that includes battery eliminator kits, ignition coils, control modules, regulators, rev limiters, starter drives, solenoids and relays, spark plugs, and spark plug wires.

Battery eliminator kits provide a way to do away with the weight of a battery without switching over to a magneto system. These kits only work with the Accel generator-style solid-state voltage regulator on a generator-style engine.

SuperShaft crank pins, pinion shafts, and sprocket shafts are turned from aircraft Durabar 60 steel and ground to an extremely smooth finish after some sophisticated heat-treating. The crank pins are available in four versions: for Big Twins from 1981 and up; for 1941-1981 Big Twins; for 1981-1990 Sportsters; and for 1954-1981 Sportsters. Pinion shafts come in six versions, for Big Twins from 1958 to 1986 and Sportsters from 1957 to 1985. There are four types of sprocket shafts: for late 1981 to early 1985 Big Twins; for 1972 to early 1981 Big Twins; for 1957-1976 Sportsters and for 1977 to early 1981 Sportsters.

Rev Master rev limiters use a DIP switch for setting the engine's rpm limit and are housed in a chrome-plated 4 3/4in by 2 1/2in enclosure.

Starter drive units are designed to replace the stock versions and feature five-roller clutches with hardened receivers and stainless steel springs.

Thunder Twin fuel injection systems are presently designed to be used exclusively with the Crane #1-1100 cam, with versions for other cams to follow. They have been tested on the dyno as well as for emissions. The digitally-port-injected systems provide fuel control and ignition control simultaneously. The Rivera Engineering catalog describes the Thunder Twin system in detail.

Accel Performance Products
P.O. Box 142
Branford, CT 06405-0142
(203) 481-5771
FAX (203) 481-7603
Catalog available

Accutronix Racing Products

Mike Malone and the staff at Accutronix manufacture a variety of CNC-machined billet aluminum components for Harley-Davidsons, including billet aluminum triple clamps for Narrow Glide and Wide Glide forks.

These triple clamps feature shallow milled slots and can be supplied with or without adjustable steering stops and handlebar riser mounting holes.

Accutronix Racing Products
17650 North 25th Avenue, #1
Phoenix, AZ 85023
(602) 993-2675
Catalog available

Advanced Racing Technology

ART products include combustion chamber inserts, cylinder heads, slipper clutches, computers, engine plates, intake manifolds, magneto drive systems, supercharger kits, and throttle assemblies.

Cylinder heads are billet aluminum four-valve, designed for Evolution Big Twin Top Fuel bikes. These heads are supplied with ART rocker arm assemblies, rocker box covers and stainless steel exhaust manifolds.

Computers are designed for drag racing, with three models available. The Tek-1, Tek-3 and Tek-10 computers provide varying degrees of data, taking up to 250 samples per second.

Magneto drive systems are designed to use twin Mallory Super Mag 3 or Mallory Super Mag 4 automotive magnetos.

Supercharger kits are based on the Opcon Autorotor screw-type supercharger. Your stock primary cover is sent to ART and modified to accept the double Gates drive V-belts. Induction is through an S&S Super G carburetor and an ART custom billet aluminum intake manifold. This is a complete kit that comes with

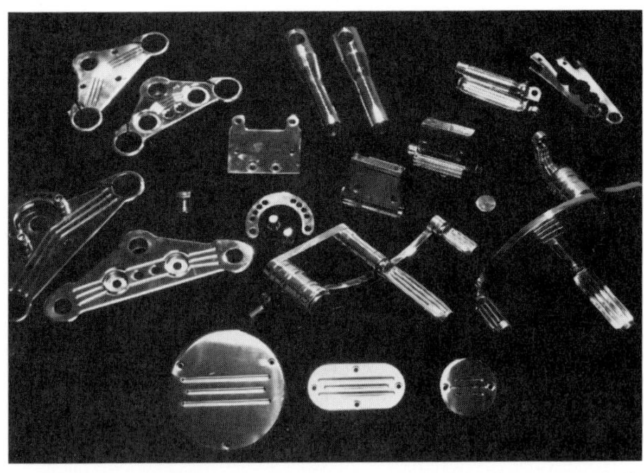

Accutronix components include (clockwise from top left) triple clamps with or without adjustable steering stops, regulator mounts, handlebar risers, master cylinders, footpegs, brake and clutch levers, forward controls and primary inspection covers.

The ART (Advanced Racing Technology) multiple-stage slipper clutch—assembled…

…and disassembled.

ART (Advanced Racing Technology) throttle assemblies can be provided for 7/8in or 1in bars and provide only 1/5-turn of travel in case you're in a hurry.

These products give you an idea of the kind of work ART is capable of.

Air Flow Research can likely improve any Harley-Davidson heads, which can be returned bare or complete with your choice of components. Both racers and manufacturers count on Air Flow Research for expert cylinder head analysis and design work.

detailed instructions. ART is establishing a dealer network to provide customers with competent professionals who can install their supercharger systems.

ART is also the exclusive North American distributor for the Opcon Autorotor motorcycle superchargers from Sweden, which are described under Opcon Autorotor.

Jim Fox uses three-dimensional CAD-CAM equipment to design his company's products, which are CNC-machined on five four-axis machining centers. Jim also makes use of a digitizer, which can take a complex, three-dimensional part and measure all of its dimensions and contours so it can be duplicated with computerized machining equipment. The ART resident machinists include Cynthia Fox, Gary Long, and Gary McMurray.

ART can provide custom fabrication, racing cylinder head modifications, and complete motorcycle construction to order. They are closely involved with several NASCAR Winston Cup and NHRA Top Fuel teams.

Advanced Racing Technology
5857 Jefferson Avenue
Newport News, VA 23605
(804) 245-3455
FAX (804) 247-3297
Literature available

Air Flow Research

Known for decades as a leading race car cylinder head supplier, Ken and Scott Sperling and the staff at Air Flow Research offer expert cylinder head modification services. The Air Flow Research shop contains an aluminum foundry, modern machining and welding shops, and a dyno. They also provide design and prototype work for racing teams and OEM suppliers.

Air Flow Research
10490 Ilex Drive
Pacoima, CA 91331
(818) 834-9010
FAX (818) 890-0490

Air Tech

Air Tech manufactures fiberglass fairings and gas tanks for Sportsters and XR-750s. Fairings are produced for 1982-and-up Sportsters as well as XRTT vintage road racers. The Sportster fairings are available as packages that are complete with a larger gas tank and a new tail section and rear fender.

Gas tanks can be supplied for 1982-and-up Sportsters, the XLCR and in dirt-track as well as road racing styles for the XR-750. The dirt-track XR tanks are replicas of the originals, as are the 6.5gal XRTT tanks.

Air Tech also manufactures fiberglass components for other companies in the motorcycle aftermarket industry.

Air Tech
3052 Industry, Suite 109
Oceanside, CA 92054
(619) 757-3366
Catalog available

Akront

Akront's popular extruded aluminum motorcycle rims are distributed in North America by Cosmopolitan Motors, who stocks them drilled and ready for lacing, in virtually any size up to 5 3/4in wide. While complete Akront wheels are not manufactured, Cosmopolitan can supply—on a special-order basis—Akront rims intended for modular wheel manufacturers. These rims have a flange in the center of the rim for the center section to attach to.

Cosmopolitan Motors, Inc.
301 Jacksonville Road
Hatboro, PA 19040
(215) 672-9100—information
(800) 523-2522—orders only

Alliance Composites, Inc.

Joel Otto and the crew at Alliance manufacture exhaust systems, fairings, gas tanks, swing arms, mufflers, and wheels for road racing motorcycles. All of these components are made from lightweight carbon fiber.

Their first product designed specifically for Harley-Davidson motorcycles was a slash-cut muffler weighing only 6oz. Wheels are offered in 17in diameter, intended for road racing. Alliance is primarily a supplier to the aircraft industry, and has produced a number of race car parts as well as complete bodywork for Ducati road racers.

Alliance Composites, Inc.
760-6 Eighth Court
Vero Beach, FL 32962
(407) 562-6333
FAX (407) 562-2109

American Classics

American Classics is owned by John Fisher along with Don and Pat Perrine. In addition to providing performance engine building and custom fabrication, they have one of the few shops in the Northwest that offers dyno time and consulting work for serious racers.

Fabrication services include heli-arc welding and a complete machine shop. They also do frame modifications, custom aluminum gas and oil tank fabrication, and complete race bike construction.

American Classics
1721 LaBounty Drive
Ferndale, WA 98248
(206) 380-2428

Amp Research

Amp Research manufactures the Power Clutch kit, which is claimed to reduce the effort needed to operate Harley-Davidson clutches by about 40percent. It's available in versions that fit Evolution Big Twins and Sportsters. The kit uses a patented system of a pair of gears and a spring, with the spring helping the gears to rotate. It's an elegantly simple solution to an old problem.

Installing the Power Clutch is pretty simple, too. You check your clutch cable's free play as given in your owner's manual, or set it using a quarter for a feeler gauge between the end of the cable and its perch on the lever; remove the mirror; remove the screw for the anti-rattling device and replace it with coupling studs; bolt on the Power Clutch; adjust the self-locking nut which sets the position of the lever relative to the bars; lube the lever and the cable pivot and you're done.

Some earlier models which don't have the anti-rattling device will call for a new clutch lever with H-D part number 45066-85. The system can be supplied in black with a billet or cast body. Chrome plating is also available as an extra-cost option. The gears are both mounted on sealed ball bearings, with the whole package designed to require no maintenance.

Amp Research
1855 Laguna Canyon Road
Laguna Beach, CA 92651
(714) 497-7525
FAX (714) 497-0284

Andrews Products, Inc.

Andrews Products is headed by John Andrews, whose company manufactures a complete line of cams, ignition coils, and valve gear for virtually all Big Twin and Sportster engines, as well as their gears and components for most Harley-Davidson transmissions. Other products include an accelerator pump kit for 1980-1988 Keihin carburetors, oversize and undersize cam gears for all Big Twins and a silicone spark plug wire kit.

Cams are available for Panhead, Shovelhead, and Evolution Big Twins, all Sportsters, and the XR-1000. A wide variety of profiles are offered for most street or strip applications.

Four-speed Big Twin transmission components include a 2.44:1 first gear set; a 2.60:1 first gear set; a 1.35:1 third gear set; stock ratio second and third gears; 1-2 and 3-4 shift forks and shift clutches; replacement mainshafts for 1970-1985, 1965-1969 and 1937-1964; as well as countershafts for 1977-1981 and 1976-and-earlier.

Five-speed Big Twin transmission components include a close-ratio 2.94:1 first gear set; stock-ratio first, second, third and fourth gears; replacement transmission shafts for 1985-and-up and 1981-1984; and countershafts for all five-speeds.

Transmission pulleys fit all Big Twin five-speed belt drive transmissions and come in two versions: a 29-tooth for a nine-percent underdrive over stock; and a 34-tooth for a six-percent overdrive.

Other Andrews components include solid lifter conversion kits for Shovelheads and aluminum or chrome-moly pushrods for most Harley-Davidson engines.

Andrews is one of the best-equipped companies in the aftermarket motorcycle cam industry, with some sophisticated and powerful computer software used for designing cams and for controlling their Landis 3L CNC cam grinder. The Landis 3L is the standard cam grinder in the automotive OEM industry, but Andrews is the only "small" company in the United States that is using one. Production and custom cams can be designed and manufactured on a quick turnaround basis, thanks to the efficiency of the CAD-CAM design and manufacturing equipment Andrews uses.

Andrews Products, Inc.
5212 North Shapland Avenue
Rosemont, IL 60018
(312) 992-4014
FAX (312) 992-4017
Catalog available

Arias Industries

Arias (pronounced "AIR-ease") makes a complete line of forged pistons for Harley-Davidsons. While their main focus is competition, Arias pistons are also suited for street use if chosen correctly.

Racing pistons are available for virtually all production Harley-Davidson engines. They can also be custom-built according to the customer-specified size and configuration. Also, Rivera Engineering can supply special big-bore Arias pistons in 3 5/8in and 3 13/16in bore sizes with unfinished domes, for those who prefer to handle that part of the machining themselves.

Street pistons are forged from the same grade of aluminum as the competition versions. They are available for all Evolution engines as well as Shovelheads and iron Sportsters. Specialized pistons for supercharged Harley-Davidson engines can also be supplied.

Back in 1956, Nick Arias opened a shop that specialized in manufacturing high-performance automotive pistons. In 1972 he came up with a big-block Chevy cylinder head with hemispherical combustion chambers that became popular in NHRA drag racing, and he went on to develop and produce what has become one of the most popular monster truck and tractor pulling engines.

Arias Industries
13420 South Normandie Avenue
Gardena, CA 90249
(213) 770-0055
FAX (310) 310-8203

Arlen Ness

Arlen Ness and his staff have a complete line of components that include air cleaner covers, axles, bodywork made from ABS and fiberglass, brake components, cable clamps, engine covers, exhaust systems, footpegs, frames, gas cap covers, handlebars, handgrips, headlights and taillights, intake manifold clamps, kickstands, levers, license plate frames and mounts, master cylinders and covers, mirrors, oil tanks, seats, shift levers, swing arms, triple

Akront rims are popular among modular wheel manufacturers. *Cosmopolitan Motors*

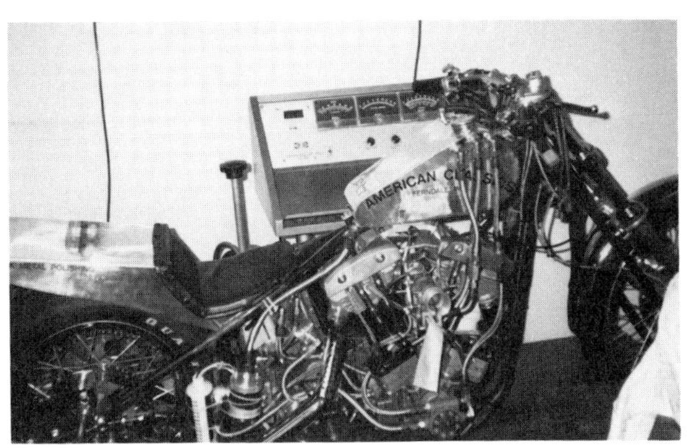

The bike features American Classics sheet metalwork along with many hand-built components.

American Classics campaigns this 96in injected alcohol Shovelhead drag bike, shown on their dyno.

Gears that allow you to select the ratios in virtually any four-speed or five-speed Big Twin or Sportster transmission are accurately machined by Andrews. This set is of gears and transmission shafts has been designed for five-speed Evolution Sportsters.

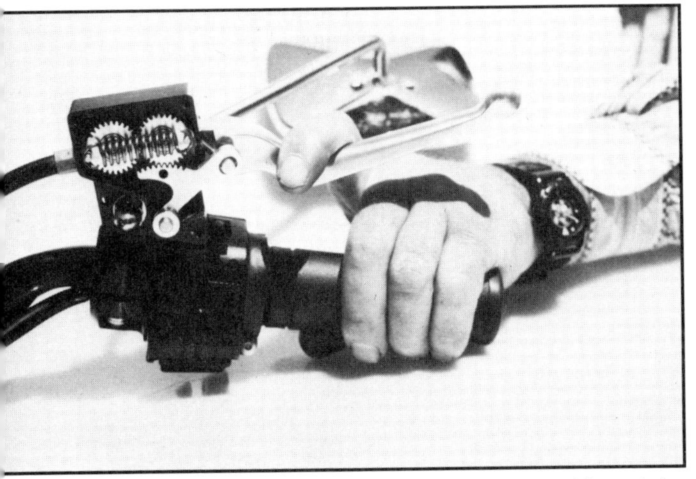

Before disengaging the clutch, notice the position of the spring on the gears in the Amp Research Power Clutch mechanism.

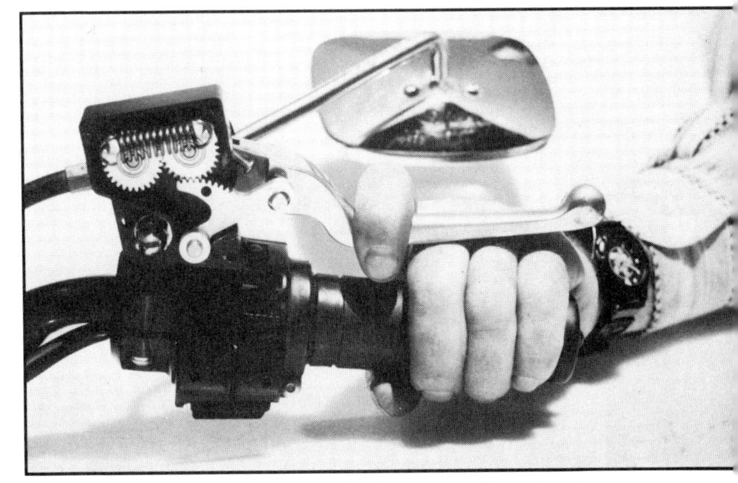

When the lever is pulled, the spring has moved up, helping the gears in this Amp Research Power Clutch mechanism to rotate.

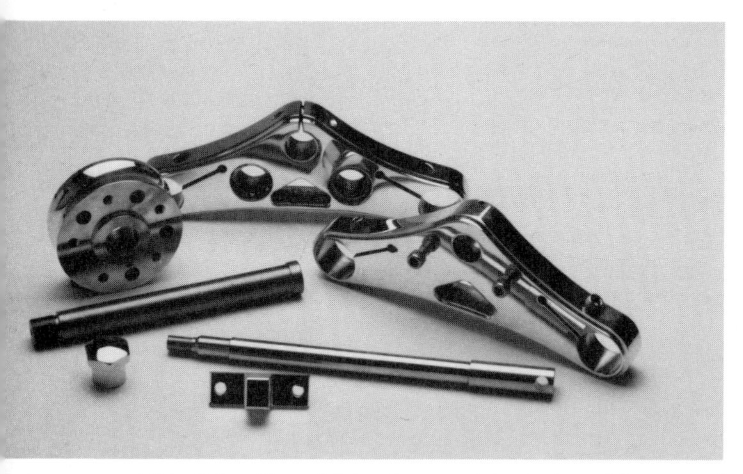

This Arlen Ness triple clamp set is designed to convert stock 39mm forks to Wide Glide width. Shown here are the polished billet aluminum triple clamps and disc spacer, the steering stem, front axle, headlight bracket, and top nut. A second disc spacer is available for dual-disc bikes. *Carmina Besson*

Auto Meter's 5in Pro-Cycle Monster tach has 10,000rpm range and memory recall.

While they might not lower your quarter-mile times, the Ness-Tech billet aluminum Flamed components shown here may make you feel quicker.

Auto Meter's 3 3/4in Pro-Cycle tach has 8000rpm range and memory recall.

clamps, and voltage regulators. Most of these components are available for Big Twins and Sportsters.

ABS and fiberglass bodywork includes quarter fairings, wedge-shaped air scoops that mount ahead of the front engine mounts (which are also available in sheet aluminum versions) and a wide variety of fenders. Cable clamps are CNC-machined from solid aluminum. They wrap around the frame tubing and are designed to hold a cable close to the tube, running in the same direction.

Exhaust systems include drag pipes with or without mufflers and two-into-one systems with Cycle Shack or SuperTrapp mufflers. These and other systems are available for Softails, FXRs, FXs, and Evolution Sportsters.

Frames are available in several versions, all of which are built from 4130 chrome-moly tubing. A replacement frame for five-speed rubber mount FXR models provides lighter weight combined with the look of a lowered four-speed frame and fine workmanship. The FXR frames accept the stock engines and transmissions, running gear, swing arms and pegs; other hardware and accessories must be purchased or fabricated. A four-speed swing arm frame shares most of the features of the FXR frame. It provides a 2in lowered seat height and is available with a horseshoe oil tank. The wildest Ness frame is the new Smoothtail. Styled long and low like a drag bike, it accepts Softail rear shocks and the 1986-and-up FXR engine and transmission. A choice of two-front end geometries is available: a 35-degree head angle with a 2in stretch; and a 38-degree head angle with a 5in stretch. Tubing is 7/8in diameter 4130 with a .188in wall thickness.

Intake manifold clamps are available in versions for 1948-1978 and 1979-and-later manifolds. The earlier versions have a machined relief for the stock O-ring. All are two-piece cast brass construction and are offered in polished or chrome finishes.

Swing arms are available to fit FXRs, Softails, and all Ness frames. Like all Ness frames, they are made from 4130 chrome-moly tubing. A version for Softail frames looks especially good.

Triple clamps are available for Wide Glides, 39mm forks, and the older 35mm models. CNC-machined from solid aluminum, they are beautifully polished.

Voltage regulators were co-developed by Arlen Ness and Accel. Seven versions are available to fit Big Twins from 1970 and up and Sportsters from 1977 and up. Designed to provide maximum heat dissipation, they feature large, closely spaced cooling fins and a chrome-plated finish.

Arlen builds complete custom bikes to order for customers all over the world, and has been known to sell his creations right off the showroom floor.

Arlen Ness
16520 East 14th Street
San Leandro, CA 94578
(510) 276-3303
(510) 276-3395
FAX (510) 276-3534
Catalog available

Atlas Precision Tool & Die

Dick Ellavsky at Atlas Precision builds lay-down frames for Big Twin and Sportster drag bikes. All frames are custom-built to order using chrome-moly tubing. Atlas is a fully equipped machining and welding shop that can provide design, fabrication and repair services.

Atlas Precision Tool & Die
16091 Kamana Road
Apple Valley, CA 92307
(619) 242-9111

Auto Meter Products, Inc.

Auto Meter manufactures the Pro-Cycle tachometer for all Harley-Davidson applications. This tach can be supplied with a 3 3/4in or 5in face, with or without the memory recall feature. Recall allows you to press a button for a readout of the highest rpm you've turned since the last time you checked. A fifth version (with a 10,000rpm range and 5in face) has a shift light that comes on at a pre-set rpm.

Pro-Cycle tachs are shipped with a Dyna S ignition adapter to ensure compatibility with single-fire or dual-fire ignition systems. Auto Meter now manufactures and includes their own unique mounting bracket that provides excellent shock-absorption.

Auto Meter Products, Inc.
413 West Elm Street
Sycamore, IL 60178
(815) 895-8141
Catalog available

Avenger Wheels

On a special-order basis, Frank Gaffney makes lightweight modular wheels for drag bikes. These are usually made with three narrow spokes and have a distinctive appearance.

Avenger Wheels
3022 Community
La Crescenta, CA 91214
(818) 248-7394

Avon Tires, Ltd.

Avon manufactures a complete line of tires for most motorcycle applications in a variety of sizes. Models designed for Harley-Davidsons include the H-rated 16in and 19in Roadrunner Universal, the 19in and 21in Speedmaster Mark II rib, the S-rated traditional SM Mark II and wide whitewalls. Avon also manufactures Kevlar-belted tires, radials, sidecar tires, and models designed for vintage racing.

The Auto Meter LTM Performance Analyzer allows racers to record, playback, and study engine performance, and can provide help with variables such as clutch set-up, gearing, shift points, and tire slipping. Each micro-cassette can store up to thirty minutes of running time on each side. The LTM allows playback with any Pro-Cycle tach.

Avon V-rated Super Venom AM 18 tire sizes include 120/80 V 16 (front and rear), 130/90 V 16 (rear), 150/80 V 16 (rear), and 100/90 V 19 (front and rear).

Avon's H-rated Roadrunner AM 20 (front; left) and AM 21 (rear; right) tires are designed to be used together and provide durability and good mileage. Fronts come in seven 16, 17, 18, 19, and 21in sizes. Rears come in five 16, 17, and 18in sizes.

The classic 19 and 21in Speedmaster Mark II rib front tire from Avon is available in 325 S 19, 350 S 19 and 300 S 21.

Avon Tires, Ltd.
Bath Road
Melksham, Wiltshire SN12 8AA
United Kingdom
Phone 0225-703101
FAX 0225-707880

Avon Tires, Ltd.
407 Howell Way
Edmonds, WA 98020
(206) 771-2115—information
(800) 624-7470—orders only
Catalog available

Axtell Sales, Inc.

Ron Dickey at Axtell Sales manufactures the Mountain Motor big-bore kits for all Evolution engines, which include pistons and cast-iron barrels. Mountain Motor kits can be built up as follows:

Big Twin engine kits

Bore (in)	Stroke (in)
Cu. In.	cc
3.500	4.250
81.77	1340
3.625	4.250
87.72	1437
3.812	4.250
97.00	1589
3.812	4.500
102.71	1683

Sportster engine kits

Bore (in)	Stroke (in)
Cu. In.	cc
3.812	3.812
87.01	1424
3.812	4.500
102.71	1683

The kits with 3.812in bore require boring out the cases to accept the larger cylinders. Although this takes the project well beyond a simple bolt-on operation, it can be handled by lots of machine shops once the engine has been pulled and stripped down to the cases.

Axtell could have used aluminum for their cylinders but chose cast iron to take advantage of its mechanical stability throughout the operating temperature range.

Axtell Sales, Inc.
1424 S.E. Maury
Des Moines, IA 50317
(515) 243-2518
FAX (515) 243-0244
Catalog available

Bad Bones

Bad Bones manufactures a line of accessories that includes brake discs that are made from 7075-T6 aluminum, plated with titanium nitrate. The claimed weight is 1.9lb per disc. Also available are the Magnum Jet carburetor, a line of exhaust systems and oil tanks. Aluminum oil tanks are for Softail frames, and come complete with braided stainless oil lines and standard threaded fittings.

Bad Bones
18457 Amistad
Fountain Valley, CA 92708
(714) 964-0049
FAX (714) 964-0340

Baisley Hi-Performance

Dan Baisley at Baisley Hi-Performance specializes in Harley-Davidson cylinder head modifications. He also manufactures a line of roller-bearing rocker arms as well as a valve spring compressor tool, valve springs, valve stem seals, and valves.

Complete cylinder head services are available, including flow bench testing, O-ring conversions, porting and all of the related development work and machining. Used by many successful racers, Baisley "Pro Street" heads are the result of decades of research, testing, and racing.

Roller-bearing rocker arms are manufactured from your stock rocker arms on an exchange basis. Introduced in the late eighties, these are the only roller-bearing rocker arms that are built this way. Dan offers this conversion for all years of Evolution, Shovelhead, and Panhead Big Twins as well as all Sportsters and XR models. All versions are returned with the stock rocker arm geometry and ratio. Evolution versions (only) can be set up for corrected rocker arm geometry, with your choice of 1.7:1, 1.8:1 or 1.9:1 ratios.

Valve spring compressor tools are used and recommended by numerous respected racing engine builders and are likely the finest made for working on Harley-Davidsons. They allow you to save time when tearing down and assembling cylinder heads by accurately measuring the spring pack in a few seconds, and can also let you measure the piston dome valve pocket thickness. They come complete with an adapter ring, a cup, and a dial indicator; with optional adapters for other makes of engines also available. Hand-made and assembled, they can be mounted on a bench or a wall and have a shipping weight of about 50lb.

Valve stem seals are available in a new Viton version for all Evolution engines as well as in Teflon for virtually all Big Twins and Sportsters. The Teflon seals were designed with more contact area and can last up to three times as long as stock seals. Valves are available for all years of Evolution, Shovelhead, and Panhead Big Twins as well as all Sportsters and XR engines. They can be supplied in original and oversize diameters or as blank stem valves with large head diameters.

A dedicated racer, Dan was the first to get a gas Harley-Davidson down into the eight-second bracket in the quarter-mile, riding his twin-engined drag bike to an 8.70 ET at over 156mph back in 1978.

Baisley Hi-Performance
5804 North Interstate
Portland, OR 97217
(509) 289-1251
FAX (509) 296-4980
Catalog available

Bandit Machine Works

Bandit is run by John Magee, who designed and now manufactures the RaceCase transmission, the Superclutch, and transmission trap doors for Sportsters. Bandit also builds a limited number of chassis every year which, like most Bandit products, are for serious Harley-Davidson drag racers.

The Superclutch is available for Big Twins from 1941 to 1993 and also for all 1971-and-later iron and Evolution Sportsters as well as the XR-1000. Wet and dry versions are made and a full line of related components are available.

RaceCase transmissions are intended for fuel or gas Harley-Davidson drag bikes. The RaceCase can be supplied with a variety of ratios with two, three, four, or five speeds. This is a fully-automatic, sliding-gear design, housed in a case that is machined from billet aluminum. Reliability is achieved through beefy design and excellent materials.

Bandit Machine Works
222 Millwood Road
Lancaster, PA 17602
(717) 464-2800
FAX (717) 464-4465
Literature available

Barnett Tool & Engineering

Mike Taylor and the staff at Barnett manufacture quality cables, clutches, and tools for Big Twins and Sportsters.

Cables are available for virtually every Harley-Davidson application, as stock replacements or in stainless steel.

Barnett, which has been in business since 1949, released their "K" series of clutches in 1992. These feature Kevlar plates, which was chosen after a search to find an alternative to asbestos. Testing demonstrated Kevlar outlasting semi-metallic by a factor of three and asbestos by a factor of twelve.

Tools include diaphragm clutch spring compression tools and compensating sprocket nut tools.

Barnett Tool & Engineering
P.O. Box 2826
9920 Freeman Avenue
Santa Fe Springs, CA 90670-0826
(310) 941-1284
FAX (310) 946-5887
Catalog available

Bartels' Performance Products

Bartels' can provide their own cams, exhaust systems, fiberglass parts, gaskets, manifolds, pushrods, rearsets, shocks, and sprockets for Evolution street and race bikes. Bartels' can also supply dyno time (at their shop and on location) along with engine modifications such as boring, blueprinting, twin-plug conversions, and performance valve jobs. They also build street-legal XR-70 replicas with Champion frames powered by Evolution Sportster engines, and sell their own bike covers, posters, tools, and T-shirts. Here's a look at some of their performance parts.

Cams are available for all Evolution engines. BP 20 is a mild Big Twin grind that is strong up to 5,200rpm; and BP 40 is a high-performance cam with more midrange and top-end power. Performance cams for Evolution Sportsters are available for the four-speed, BP 140, and the five-speed, BP 145.

Exhaust systems are available in many versions in addition to the Sportster road racing system shown here. Most are flared duals with slash-cut ends, available for all late-model bikes.

Fiberglass parts include road racing fairings, gas tanks, and seats. Fairings are reproductions of the factory KR fairings, available in two versions: the two-piece 1963-1967 (which can also be supplied for Evolution Sportsters); and the one-piece 1968-and-1969 version. Replica seats are made for the 1970-1974 XR-750 road racer and the 1963-1967 KR road racer.

Gasket kits were developed for high-compression engines and are made for Evolution Big Twins and Sportsters. Each kit is available in versions with a choice of .027in or .043in copper head gaskets, and also includes a pair of cylinder base gaskets, four O-rings, and sealant.

Intake manifolds to replace the stock versions are designed to do away with the compliance fitting leakage problem. Available for all Evolution Big Twins and Sportsters and polished inside and out, they are compatible with the stock Keihin, Mikuni, and Screamin' Eagle carburetors.

Pushrods are adjustable, machined from 4130 chrome-moly and heat-treated. Available for all Evolution Big Twins and Sportsters, the Big Twin versions are designed for bikes with milled heads and are made .125in shorter than stock.

Rearset kits are designed to bolt onto Evolution Sportsters without any drilling. They are completely polished after being machined from aluminum. The rear master cylinder is moved up to improve cornering clearance. Available in four-speed and five-speed versions, these are complete kits that come with all mounting hardware, brake and shifter levers, and instructions.

Shock absorbers are made exclusively for Bartels' by Progressive Suspension in a 15in length to provide improvements in cornering clearance and handling for all Evolution Sportsters. Bartels' can also provide progressively-wound fork springs, and complete suspension upgrade kits that include the shocks, springs, spacers, and fork oil.

Tools include a rear wheel stand with a pair of casters, designed for Evolution Sportster road racers. The stand includes a pair of small tabs with a hole which are to be welded onto the swing arm. Locking pins go through the stand and the tabs to hold the bike in place. The bike can be rolled around with the stand in the lowered position

Baisley's Evolution Pro Spring Kits are intended for racing applications with high-lift cams.

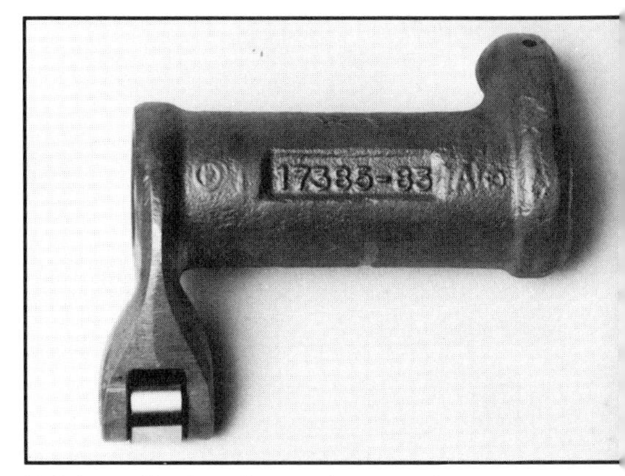

Baisley roller-bearing rocker arm for XR-750 and XR-1000 engines.

The Baisley Pro Street valves and seals are available for all 1948-and-later engines.

This FXR has been set up with Bandit's Superclutch, the most popular clutch in the Gas Harley-Davidson drag racing classes since its introduction in 1987.

The Bandit Machine Works Superclutch is a proven performer.

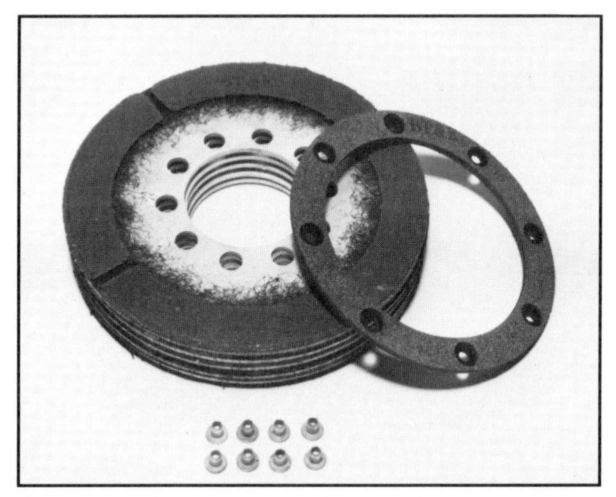

Barnett clutch kits are manufactured for virtually every Harley-Davidson.

This Bartels exhaust system was designed for Twin Sports racing. Also shown are Bartels' rearset kit and shocks. (The stand shown here is not the locking version described in the text.)

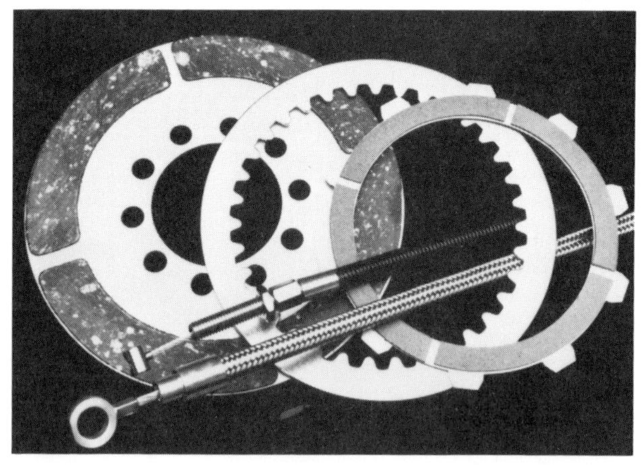

Barnett has a complete range of clutch components, along with cables and brake lines.

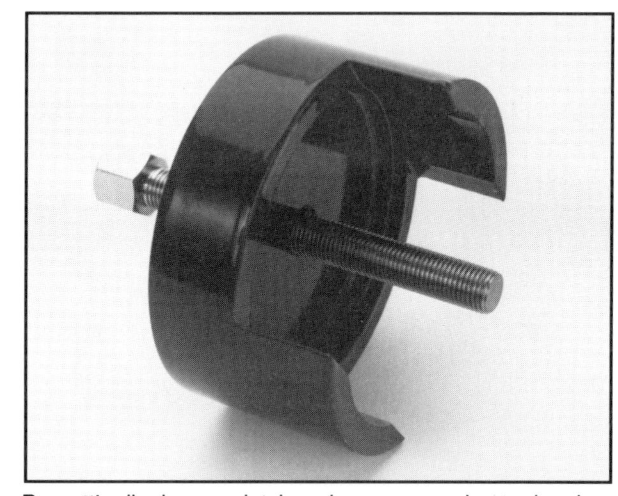

Barnett's diaphragm clutch spring compression tool makes it easy to remove and install the retainer ring to get at the clutch plates. The HD-1 (shown) fits 1990-and-up Big Twins and 1991-and-up Sportsters. The HD-2 fits Sportsters from 1984 through 1990.

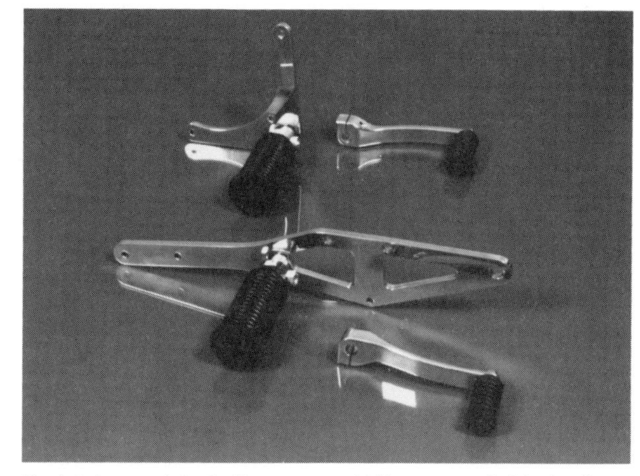

Bartels' complete bolt-on rearset kits are available for four-speed and five-speed Sportsters.

and then lifted up at the back end.

XR-750 owners can find a complete stock of factory replacement parts for 1972-and-up bikes at Bartels', who have been working on them for decades. While this book was being fabricated several new components for KR racers were under development at Bartels'. These include crank pins, pinion shafts, and sprocket shafts.

Bartels' is run by Bill Bartels, whose Bartels' Harley-Davidson has been known as the racing-oriented Harley-Davidson dealer in the Los Angeles area, with parts and service departments catering to street riders and serious racers. Their mobile dyno has been seen at Sturgis and at AMA Camel Pro and Twin Sports races all over the United States.

Bill and his staff have made a significant contribution to the sport. Bartels' sponsors the 1990 AMA Camel Pro Rookie of the Year Mike Hale and the legendary Jay Springsteen on the AMA Camel Pro Grand National dirt-track racing circuit; and Nigel Gale, the 1990 AMA Twin Sports road racing champion and winner of the 1992 Daytona and Mid-Ohio Twin Sports races.

Bartels' Performance Products
8910 Washington Boulevard
Culver City, CA 90230
(310) 842-8081—information
(800) 747-1151—orders only
FAX (310) 842-8083
Catalog available

Bellucci Racing, Inc.

Bellucci Racing manufactures lightweight titanium valves for racing engines, and will build specialized Harley-Davidson valves to order.

Bellucci Racing, Inc.
126 East Irving Park Road
Bensenville, IL 60106
(708) 595-4923

Ben's V-Twins, Inc.

Veteran drag racer Ben Edwards specializes in high-performance engine and transmission modifications exclusively for Harley-Davidsons. Ben can provide all racing engine building and repair services for Big Twin and Sportster owners.

Ben has built and raced numerous drag bikes over the years. His bike was built around a frame from Truett's Frame Works, which has proven reliable in an estimated 1,000 passes. Ben is building a new Pro Gas bike for the 1994 season and plans to use another Bonnie Truett frame.

Ben's V-Twins, Inc.
1926 Remount Road
Charlotte, NC 28208
(704) 358-8741

Bentec AB

Based in Sweden, Bentec builds two-speed transmissions for Harley-Davidson drag bikes. These are extremely durable, intended strictly for serious drag racing with an air shifter. High gear is direct drive; while the first gear can be changed to provide ratios of 1.38:1 or 1.47:1.

Nungesser Engineering is the exclusive distributor of Bentec transmissions throughout the United States.

Nungesser Engineering
515 East Tenth
Box 829
Belle Plaine, KS 67013
(316) 488-3688

Billet Bilt

Five-speed Big Twin transmissions can be fitted with a complete kickstart kit from Billet Bilt. These kits are designed for easy installation and are CNC-machined from 6061-T6 aluminum plate.

Billet Bilt
P.O. Box 83203
Phoenix, AZ 85071-3203
(602) 869-0206
(602) 993-2194

Billy Budde's Custom Motorcycles

Billy Budde has come up with an electronically-timed fuel injection system kit that can be supplied for all Big Twins and Sportsters. Complete instructions and all hardware are included, along with a control box with five controls: front idle mixture; rear idle mixture; vacuum; deceleration; and a high-speed scale for the fuel curve. This last control allows the rider to adjust the system while riding, locking it in position once dialed in; and also provides the ability to compensate for changes in cam, displacement or whatever.

The injector body is cast from 356 aluminum and contains only one moving part—the throttle shaft, which is mounted with sealed needle roller bearings at each end. The system is designed to provide instant throttle response and uses two sensors (one for vacuum, which is in the control box; and another for air temperature, which is mounted on the air cleaner). These sensors alter the fuel mixture according to the engine load and air temperature. This system is compatible with all ignition systems.

Billy Budde's also does all kinds of custom work, including performance engine modifications, fabrication, machining, painting, heli-arc welding, and wiring. Custom frames for any Harley-Davidson engine can be built to order for street bikes or drag racing.

Billy Budde's Custom Motorcycles
15640 East 14th Street
San Leandro, CA 94578
(510) 276-0739
Literature available

Bill Wiebler Enterprises

Bill Wiebler has built dozens of winning XR-750 dirt-track racers. He can provide custom components for XR-750s that include disc brake carriers, clutch parts, exhaust systems, distributor type battery ignition systems, intake manifolds, and oil tanks. In addition to being a master mechanic, Bill has a dyno as well as complete machining and welding facilities. He can provide performance cylinder head and piston modifications, complete XR-750 construction, frame design, and Evolution engine modifications.

Bill Wiebler Enterprises
7519 Sportsmans Drive
Mapleton, IL 61547
(309) 697-1579

B&G Racing Computers

Bruce Huggard at B&G makes the computer systems that are used by Jim McClure and several other top drag racers.

These computers have three parts. First, the system reads pressure altitude (from the altimeter), temperature and humidity, and then computes the density altitude. Secondly, the density altitude is used to suggest changes to the fuel system, including the bypass pill, supercharger overdrive, the fuel pump, jetting, total nozzle area, and nitro percentage. B&G computer systems are available in two basic versions, differing in the type of altimeter. Bruce provides free software updates and is good about helping racers using his system who are stuck with a problem.

B&G Racing Computers
4213 North 18th Place
Phoenix, AZ 85016
(602) 274-2537
Literature available

B&J Transmissions

B&J transmissions are used on many successful Harley-Davidson drag bikes. Designed and built in California by Bob Batten and Jerry Beebe, they are available with two, three, four, or five speeds. All B&J transmissions use components that are CNC-machined from the highest-quality billet materials available, along with machined cast-magnesium cases. B&J also have a complete line of air shifters and related components.

B&J Transmissions
P.O. Box 2170
38 West Henderson Avenue
Porterville, CA 93258-2170
(209) 781-1064
FAX (209) 781-2422

B&K Cylinder Heads

Brad Oehler at B&K specializes in all cylinder head modifications for drag racing and high-performance street bikes. Brad has also developed some billet aluminum cylinder heads which can be supplied in two-valve or multiple-valve configurations.

Brad doesn't run your average cylinder head shop. Before putting an engine on his dyno, it's not unusual for him to mount accelerometers on the connecting rods. B&K heads can be seen at work on the 1991 ProStar national champion Bill Furr's Top Fuel Harley drag bike, which has turned a 7.26-second ET at 188.35mph in the quarter-mile.

B&K Cylinder Heads
1004 West Market Street
Bloomington, IL 61701
(309) 827-0485

Blackmon Racing Products

Chuck Blackmon machines rearsets for Evolution Sportsters that can be used for racing on dirt tracks and road courses. These are designed not only to provide a riding position that is better suited for competition but to stand up to the abuse of serious racing.

As a testament to the durability of these rearsets, in May of 1993 I watched a Twin Sports road race where Scott Zampach cut a fast corner a bit too tight and smacked a pylon hard with his shift lever. The lever bent but he was still able to shift easily. Zampach, who rides to win, had done this before with some more popular, weaker rearsets, which caused him to fall behind when the broken lever left him stuck in one gear.

Chuck is a Twin Sports road racer who finished third overall in the 1992 racing season.

Blackmon Racing Products
106 Effie Drive
Greenwood, SC 29649
(803) 223-8677

Bob's Cycle

Bob Hemmings manufactures fiberglass fenders and dummy gas tanks for Harley-Davidson drag bikes.

Fender selection includes the FXR rear fenders, which are made in widths from 8.5in for Pro Stock to 15in for Top Fuel. All of Bob's products are normally supplied in a white gel-coat finish.

Bob's Cycle
713 South Emerson
Indianapolis, IN 46203
(317) 356-4045

Bonneville Engineering

Having worked on Harley-Davidsons professionally since 1967, Mac McCluskey at Bonneville Engineering in Arizona has specialized in making custom aluminum cylinders to order since 1981. He can set you up with the barrels you need for any Big Twin or Sportster engine, for any application. These are manufactured completely in-house and beautifully finished.

Mac's shop name was inspired by his favorite race track.

Bonneville Engineering
P.O. Box 4841
Huachuca City, AZ 85616-4841
(602) 456-9050

Bartels has two-stage, two-into-one exhaust systems available for all late-model Harley-Davidsons.

Shown here in a Nungesser Engineering chassis, the Bentec transmission case is an aluminum casting with steel threaded inserts added for durability.

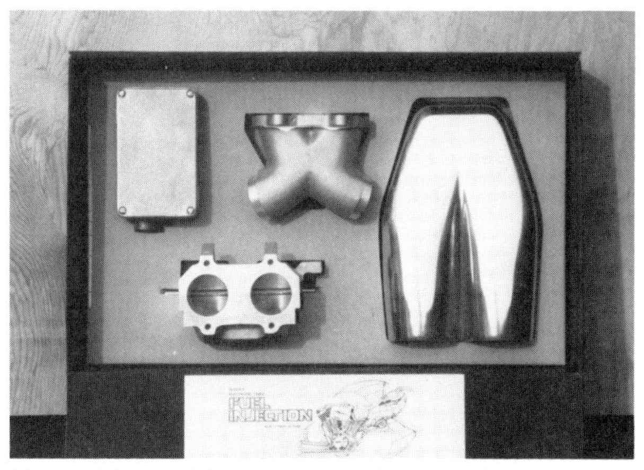

The Budde fuel injection system is a complete kit that is also compatible with superchargers and turbocharger systems.

When installed, the Budde system is a sanitary package. Air cleaners can be supplied in two styles—as shown here, or in a stock-appearing design.

The B&J three-speed (top) is built in a case measuring 7 3/16in in diameter by 8 1/8in wide, and it weighs 40lb. The two-speed (bottom) case measures 5 1/4in diameter by 7 1/2in, and weighs 23 pounds.

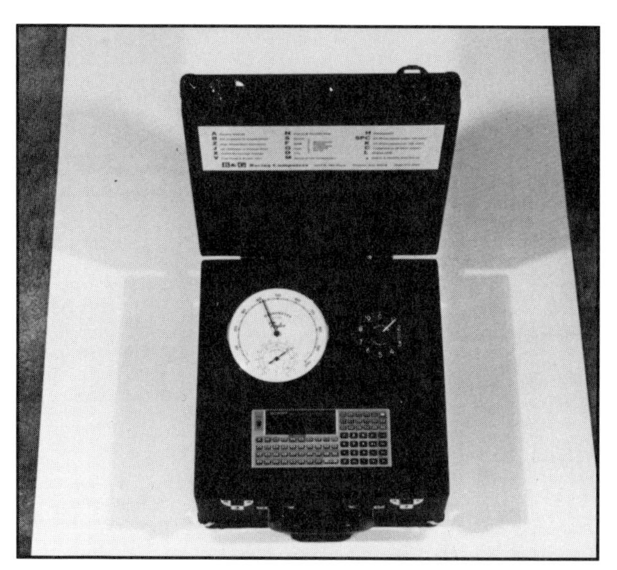

The B&G Deluxe computer system is a versatile system, aimed at serious drag racers.

Blackmon Racing rearsets are used by many winning Twin Sports racers, including Chuck (whose bike is shown here) and Scott Zampach, the 1991 and 1992 Twin Sports national champion.These rearsets provide your choice of three different positions for both the shift lever and the brake pedal. The shifter is exceptionally strong, providing a wider attachment surface area than is found on some other rearsets. *John Dangerfield*

All of Bonneville Engineering's aluminum cylinders are made for specific engines and applications, and are shipped ready to bolt on.

This FXE Shovelhead with a Bub dual system sits beside the Shovelhead-powered Tenacious, the fastest single-engined motorcycle in the world.

Bonneville Engineering's complete big-bore kits can be supplied for virtually any Harley-Davidson.

Brad Foote Gear Works leaves the transmission's end plate oversized around the edges so the fabricator can machine it to fit the particular chassis in which it will be used.

Shown here on an FXRP, the Brilhante Company KF Supercharger may be the most practical, reliable and thoroughly-researched supercharger system ever offered to Harley-Davidson owners.

Brad Foote Gear Works, Inc.

Brad Foote Gear Works is run by Stewart Ward, who co-designed and hand-builds these transmissions for Big Twin drag bikes. To keep the cost reasonable, they are designed to fit inside the original five-speed transmission case (as well as the beefier Sputhe #8501 four-speed case). It's described as a "three-speed automatic", since once you launch you shift under full power without using the clutch. First gear is 2.5:1, second is 1.5:1 and top gear is 1:1, providing 40percent and 33percent gear drops. The splined clutch hub is ready for a Bandit clutch. The final drive sprocket is on the right side of the bike, which can be positioned to clear a 10in tire.

Custom-made final drive sprockets are also available from Brad Foote Gear Works. As a matter of fact, industrial gears are the main product at the shop, with some of them standing over six feet tall.

Stewart campaigns a beautiful turbocharged alcohol Big Twin drag bike that features stock 80ci displacement, titanium valves, and a Hahn turbocharger and injection system, set in a custom-built Race Visions chrome-moly chassis. In 1992 Steward rode it through the quarter-mile in 8.09 seconds at 168mph. Determined to do even better, he is now running the turbocharger with 35lb of boost.

Brad Foote Gear Works, Inc.
1309 South Cicero Avenue
Cicero, IL 60650
(312) 242-1070
(708) 652-7700
FAX (708) 652-4140

Branch Flometrics

Jerry Branch at Branch Flometrics offers a complete cylinder head modification, porting and dyno service for owners of Big Twins and Sportsters as well as the XR-1000 and the XR-750 Grand National engines. Jerry's ideas work well enough for him to have been chosen to do the porting on all of the factory XR-750 and XR-1000 heads.

Evolution heads can be given complete new combustion chamber configurations. After cleaning, the stock chambers and spark plug holes are welded in using aluminum filler rod. After cooling, the heads go to the vertical milling machine, where the new combustion chamber and spark plug holes are machined in.

Branch Flometrics
5556 Corporate Drive
Cypress, CA 90630
(714) 827-1463
(714) 827-5340
Literature available

Brazos Valley V-Twin

Jon Marchman is a Harley-Davidson drag racer, engine builder and custom fabricator. He does a lot of work on cylinder heads and fuel injection systems for gas, alcohol, and nitro engines. Jon also offers custom components and complete drag bikes built to order.

Brazos Valley V-Twin
7614 Woodsman Trail
Houston, TX 77040
(713) 466-0189

Brembo

Brembo brake components include master cylinders, floating cast-iron discs, and a wide variety of calipers. Brembo is now making systems for Harley-Davidsons that feature lightweight floating discs, and six-piston calipers that are machined from solid aluminum billet. With a standard triple-disc set-up, your bike could have twelve brake pads on the front and six on the back. The weak links in the braking power of a bike equipped with a system like this will be traction and the rider—not the brakes.

The finest of their large selection of brake discs have aluminum center sections that keep the weight down and are allowed to float laterally to avoid binding. All of their discs are machined from Meonite, a secret formula of cast iron. This allows the discs to maintain their size and shape under high temperatures.

Brembo brake components are used by BMW, Ducati, Laverda and Moto Guzzi and have been used on many Grand Prix race-winning bikes. They are distributed in North America by Slater Brothers.

Brembo S.p.a.
Via Provinciale 8
24030 Paladina (BG)
Italy
Phone 035-541231
FAX 035-544403

Slater Brothers
P.O. Box 1
Mica, WA 99023-0001
(509) 924-5131
FAX (509) 928-0918

Brilhante Company, Inc.

The Brilhante Company offers complete supercharger kits that have been specifically designed for Harley-Davidsons. These are available for FXRs, Softails, and Evolution Sportsters.

Brilhante supercharger kits are offered in street and racing versions. They differ mainly in the length of the rotors and case—the Max-15 street superchargers use 6.5in rotors; while those on the Max-30 racing superchargers are 9.5in long. The Max-15 street supercharger systems include new primary covers that accommodate part of the supercharger drive unit. Some flexibility in the mounting of the supercharger itself is provided.

Brilhante Company supercharger kits were developed by Dr. Lee Perry, who told me, "While the volume of air forced into the engine is one issue, it is only part of the story. A supercharger system must be engineered so that the supercharger is harmonious with the engine."

Brilhante Company, Inc.
3283 Motor Avenue
West Los Angeles, CA 90034
(310) 838-5901—information
(800) HOT-BIKE—orders only
FAX (310) 836-8664

Bub Enterprises

Bub is run by Denis Manning, who specializes in manufacturing a complete line of exhaust systems for a wide variety of Big Twin drag and street bikes in addition to late Sportsters. They can set you up with duals or a two-into-one system for anything from a Shovelhead to a Softail. Bub exhaust systems are available in chrome or black.

All Bub exhaust systems are fully tested on the dyno and fully road-tested before going into production. Bub glass-packed mufflers are rebuildable and can be supplied with your choice of flat or reverse cone end caps.

As Denis says in his literature, "We make pipes for bikes. That's all we do. We don't import them from Asia and we don't have someone else design and build them. We don't use aggressive marketing techniques and we're not a division of a big corporation. And we don't festoon our name all over the sides of the mufflers. Performance means power, but it also means great sound, good looks, fit, something you can feel, and something that will last. Our pipes are designed and built with performance in mind, not the bottom line. They're pipes for the chrome and steel heart of a Harley."

Denis built four of the seven fastest motorcycles in history, two of which are single-engined Harley-Davidsons. At Bonneville in 1970, the late Cal Rayborn rode a Sportster-powered streamliner to a new absolute speed record for single-engined motorcycles at 265.492 mph. This bike was featured in the classic movie "On Any Sunday" and is now in the Indianapolis Motor Speedway Museum. In 1986, Dan Kinsey rode a Shovelhead-powered streamliner to over 290mph at Bonneville, which remains the fastest single-engined motorcycle in history.

Bub Enterprises
22573 Meyer Ravine Road
Grass Valley, CA 95949
(916) 268-0449
Literature available

Buchanon's Frame Shop

Kenny Buchanon and the staff at Buchanon's build and repair laced wheels for all motorcycles. They have an exceptional stock of rims and spokes and can build custom wheels using your choice of components. Aluminum rims are available from Akront, Borrani, D.I.D. and Sun and can be supplied, drilled with their own equipment, or undrilled. Buchanon's also provides a frame repair service and has alignment jigs for most Harley-Davidson frames.

Buchanon's Frame Shop
629 East Garvey Avenue
Montery Park, CA 91754
(818) 280-4003
FAX (818) 280-4106
Literature available

Buell Motor Company

What's more American than a new Harley-Davidson? Some think it's a new Buell. Erik Buell and his staff build America's sport bikes, the Buell RSS 1200 and the RS 1200. They feature fine handling, innovative engineering, and some of the finest components produced. These motorcycles are available through selected Harley-Davidson dealers.

Erik Buell, the founder, designer, engineer, and president of the Buell Motor Company, began producing his own motorcycles with Harley-Davidson engines in 1985. Both of the 1993 models have XLH-1200 Sportster engines and transmissions. As with the previous Buell motorcycles, vibration is taken care of with a unique frame design that suspends the engine from above, along with engine mounts that allow some vertical movement.

These are the first production motorcycles to have D.O.T.-approved stainless steel brake lines. Other features found on both models include WP Racing upside-down forks and single rear shocks, Performance Machine six-piston calipers, SuperTrapp stainless exhaust systems, hand-laid fiberglass bodywork, and tool kits. Touring riders can specify soft luggage and different handlebars that provide a more upright riding position. The total package has earned some high praise from those who have ridden them. If there is a limitation to the Buell it would be the stock Sportster engine—but it's not too hard to turn one into a 90hp Gentlemen's Express.

In early 1993, the Harley-Davidson Motor Company became a stockholder in the Buell Motor Company. At that time, Buell ceased production of the 1993 models so they could concentrate on developing the 1994 bikes. The new models had not yet been introduced as this book went to the publishers, but the added backing promises to help make future Buell motorcycles even better than what you see here.

Buell Motor Company
214 Jefferson Street
Mukwonago, WI 53149
(414) 363-3767
FAX (414) 363-7566

Burchinal's Performance

Burchinal's Performance is run by Chris Burchinal, whose specialty is building custom Harley-Davidson street and drag bikes to order.

Chris also offers modification and repair services for Big Twin and Sportster owners, and produces a line of CNC-machined aluminum components.

An Evolution Sturgis with a Bub two-into-two system benefits from improved performance along with classic looks.

Bub's two-into-one collector systems can be supplied for all years and most models, including dressers and Softails.

Buell is known for outstanding paint, as shown (albeit in black and white here) on the 1993 RSS 1200. It's done up in transparent Ruby Red over a silver base.

Buell design improvements are implemented as needed and can be fitted to earlier models. The 1993 models featured tool kits and optional touring equipment, including soft luggage and taller bars.

Burchinal's Performance
1924 South Anaheim Boulevard,
Suite C
Anaheim, CA 92805
(714) 991-4772

BW Billets

BW is run by Jerry Webster, who manufactures a variety of components that are CNC-machined from solid aluminum. A BW billet aluminum belt final drive guard is pictured under Pat Kennedys Custom Motorcycles (in Arizona; one of their distributors). Other products include transmission plates for four-speed Big Twins and triple clamps.

BW Billets
1334 West Collins Avenue
Orange, CA 92667
(714) 639-8750

Cal-Products

Owners of four-speed Big Twins can replace their worn shift linkage with cast-aluminum shift levers from Cal-Products. These levers use sealed ball bearings to improve durability. Levers are available to fit the FL and the Wide Glide. A second version, for 1979-1985 FX models, includes special shoulder bolts for installation.

Cal-Products four-speed transmission cases greatly improve the strength of the stock Harley-Davidson transmissions. Weighing 3lb more than the stock cases, these are CNC-machined 356 aluminum castings with beefy reinforcing ribs that are similar to those on a GMC supercharger.

Also available is an early-style case for custom applications and 1941-1979 transmissions. This case provides the outboard bearing support as was used on the 1965-1978 cases. All Cal-Products transmission cases have track lugs cast into the bottom of the case to provide resistance to side-torque loads.

Rivera Engineering distributes Cal-Products.

Rivera Engineering
6416 South Western Avenue
Whittier, CA 90606
(310) 692-8944
FAX (310) 699-3943

Cam Corp

Cam Corp is run by Doug Libby, who will custom-machine high-performance cams for any Harley-Davidson engine. Stock Big Twin cams can be reground with Doug's Blueprint Plus design, which can be provided on a two-day turnaround. Cams are also available for vintage Harley-Davidson restoration projects.

Cam Corp
435 B2 Air Park Road
Edgewater, FL 32132
(904) 426-0670

Carl's Speed Shop

Carl's Speed Shop has been involved with high-performance Harley-Davidsons since 1969. It's headed by Carl Morrow, who does all kinds of custom work along with his son Doug and the rest of the crew. Carl looks after complete or partial engine building and dynamic balancing as well as modifications and repairs to heads, carburetors and magnetos for street and strip.

Carl's custom exhaust systems are available for most late-model Big Twins and Sportsters. In 1992 Carl introduced his own CDI magneto, which fits 1970-and-later Big Twins and 1971-and-up Sportsters. These can be supplied for conventional or four-plug applications.

For part of the shop's research program, Carl has several Harley-Davidson drag bikes and has also been a regular competitor at the Bonneville salt flats. He also does consulting work for S&S in developing new products.

Carl's Speed Shop
9339 Santa Fe Springs Road
Santa Fe Springs, CA 90670
(310) 941-9385
(310) 941-5208
FAX (310) 941-5988

Carrillo Industries

Fred Carrillo and his staff make a line of high-performance connecting rods for all Harley-Davidson engines (except for the XR-750) that are suitable for applications from street riding to Top Fuel racing.

All Carrillo rods are made from fully machined forgings, being Magnafluxed for imperfections before any machining is done. The material used is known as Carrilloy, which is essentially a clean version of an alloy comprised of chromium, nickel and molybdenum.

Forging is used to provide control over grain integrity and direction. The standard raw forging used to manufacture a Harley-Davidson female connecting rod weighs a full 9lb before machining, and is then machined on all surfaces to its approximate size. This is followed by a unique heat-treating process that ensures extraordinary hardness properties. Finish machining is next, then the races and bushings are installed, followed by shot-peening and finish honing. In 1992, Carrillo made several subtle changes to their Harley-Davidson rods to improve strength and weight.

Carrillo Industries
990 Calle Amanecer
San Clemente, CA 92672
(714) 498-1800
FAX (714) 498-2355

Carroll Racing Products

Bud Carroll manufactures Champion frames for dirt-track racing and street bikes. One of Bud's latest projects is an XR-style chassis for Evolution Sportster engines. These chassis allow owners of late Sportsters to fit

The heart of the 1993 Buell was its powder-coated, 19lb frame. One of the most rigid among production motorcycle frames, it was built entirely from heli-arc-welded chrome-moly tubing. The rear shock was laid under the transmission, with a hydraulic preload adjuster that allowed adjustment without tools or removing any bodywork.

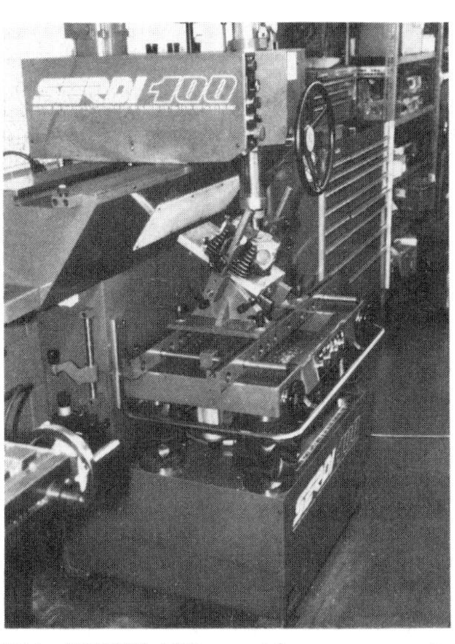

This SERDI 100 machine represents part of the significant investment Carl has made to be able to provide top-quality Harley-Davidson cylinder head work.

This picture isn't reversed—the engine is. One of the Carl's Speed Shop project bikes uses a transmission that was intended to be driven from the other side. Rather than reverse the engine rotation, they flipped it around. The chassis was done by Kosman.

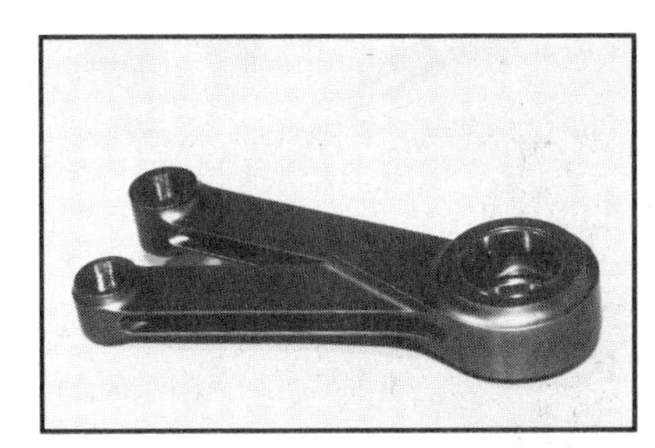

Carrillo Harley-Davidson rods ought to be strong enough for anybody, and are fine examples of excellence in mechanical engineering and industrial design.

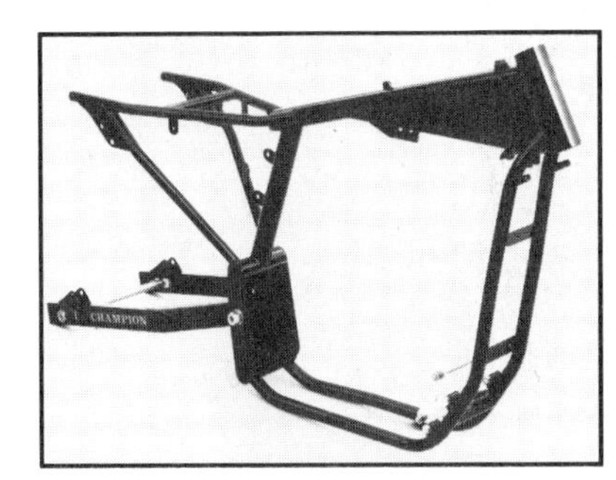

Built from chrome-moly tubing, this Champion frame from Carroll Racing accepts Evolution Sportster engines and components.

This work of art was designed and fabricated in Iowa by the talented people at The Chrome Horse.

Four gallons of nitro per pass equals sixteen gallons per mile. But what amazes me is that Tator actually has the nerve to let the clutch out while the engines are running.

This Shovelhead street bike has been treated to some outstanding detailing. C&L built the frame and exhaust system and also provided the paint and assembly work.

Conti Super Twin front tires are offered in 3.25 H 19 and 3.00 V 21 (shown). Rear sizes are MT 90 H 16 and 4.00 H 18.

Conti Tour TK16 front tire sizes include 130 90 H 16, 120 90 H 18 and 100 90 H 19.

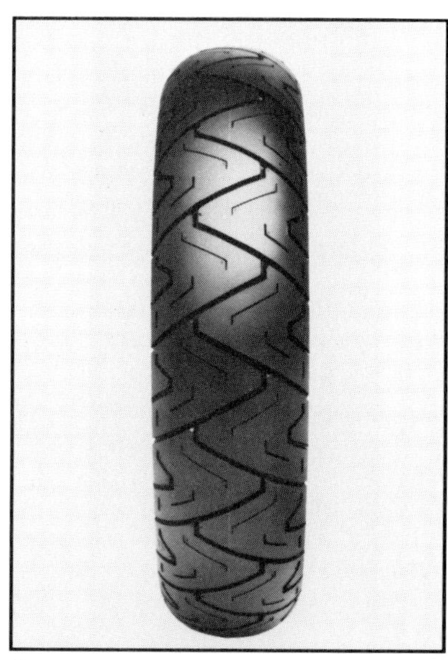

Conti Tour TK17 rear tires come in 150 90 H 15, 130 90 H 16, 140 90 H 16, 130 90 H 17 and 120 90 H 18.

most of their stock components to the new frame along with new XR-750 Grand National-style bodywork.

Carroll Racing Products
18700 Normandie Avenue,
Unit C
Gardena, CA 90248
(310) 327-3432

The Chrome Horse

The Chrome Horse is run by Gary "Tator" Gilmore, a successful and dedicated drag racer who has an awesome drag bike and a fine shop that can do anything for street and strip Harley-Davidsons. This shop is a good example of why this directory was needed. Here we have a group of talented and dedicated racers who do excellent work but are only known to those who follow Harley-Davidson drag racing. Tator pledges to keep his customers up with the latest technology at a fair price.

Some of the services available at The Chrome Horse include assembly, clutch hub balancing, custom frame building, custom painting by Skinny, double plug conversions, dyno work, engine blueprinting, engine balancing, engine breather timing, engine case repairs, engraving, fabrication of just about any component, fin repairs, fuel injection system engineering and installation, flow bench testing done on a SuperFlow flow bench, flywheel shaving and truing, frame repairs, glass beading, head porting and resurfacing, honing on a Sunnen hone, line boring, no-lead conversions, pressure testing, restoration, rocker arm geometry changes, rod rebuilding, scraper rebuilding, valve jobs with up to five angles done on a Myra head machine, valve spring clearancing, welding, wheel lacing and balancing, and whatever else is called for.

The shop also buys and sells used parts and complete Harley-Davidsons. They are also working with Sifton and S&S, testing new developments and products on the drag strip.

They maintain a complete stock of Russell braided hose and hose ends, and are now manufacturing their own line of high-performance engine gaskets.

In 1985, Tator was one of the founders of the American Motorcycle Racing Association. He won the AMRA Top Fuel championship in 1986 and 1987 and was the runner-up in 1988 and 1989. He campaigns a wild Top Fuel drag bike that's powered by two 112ci Evolution engines which must be putting close to 700hp on the ground. The earlier version that was sponsored by Coors Light through the 1989, 1990, and 1991 seasons turned a 7.92 at 177.24 on it back in 1990. With the new bike, Tator has his sights set on being the first Harley-Davidson rider to hit 200mph in the quarter-mile.

The Chrome Horse sponsors the annual Iowa All-Harley Drags, which are held on the Fourth of July weekend in Humboldt, Iowa.

The Chrome Horse
18 Fourth Avenue East
Spencer, IA 51301
(712) 262-8910
Catalog available

C&J Precision Products, Inc.

On a special-order basis, Jeff Cole at C&J builds frames for XR-750 race bikes and Sportsters. Using chrome-moly tubing and fine workmanship, C&J has built frames and swing arms for many successful dirt track racers.

C&J Precision Products, Inc.
1151 East Mission Road
Fallbrook, CA 92028
(619) 728-1707
FAX (619) 728-7652

C&L Hog Shop

While most of this shop's work is for street bikes, most are built with performance in mind. In addition to providing custom bike building and fabrication services, Lou Falcigno at C&L builds custom exhaust systems and frames to order. C&L can also provide some of the finest custom paint anywhere.

C&L Hog Shop
1315 North U.S. Highway 1
Fort Pierce, FL 34950
(407) 464-5623

Classic Chassis

Classic Chassis offers a good variety of stainless steel fasteners. They can provide complete engine building hardware kits for Big Twin and Sportster engines, and also have a good selection of fasteners in S.A.E. fine and coarse threads as well as metric. Stainless steel header bolts and grease fittings are also available.

Classic Chassis
P.O. Box 53
Glenview, IL 60025-0053
(708) 724-7033
Catalog available

Classified Motorcycle Company

Dan Wilson at Classified has designed exhaust systems for FXRs and Softails. He also builds custom laced wheels to order and has developed a couple of cosmetic kits for Evolution Sportsters.

The first version gives the late Sportster the appearance of an old Vincent from the early Fifties. It includes laced 18in wheels with Akront aluminum rims, an aluminum gas tank, seat, a stainless steel two-into-one exhaust system, a new headlight and taillight, stainless steel fenders, and the necessary brackets. The second version has styling inspired by the XR-750. It includes a 3gal aluminum gas tank and a fiberglass tail section that is reinforced with steel tubing.

Classified Motorcycle Company
P.O. Box 565
Carmel Valley, CA 93924-0565
(408) 659-0329

Claymore Racing

Claymore builds all-out Evolution Sportster road racers that can be supplied as a bare frame, a rolling chassis or as a complete road racer or street-legal cafe racer.

Spondon Engineering in the United Kingdom builds frames and swing arms for Claymore, using the same heli-arc-welded aluminum tubing construction they use on the frames they build for the Norton F2 superbike. Upon arriving in Sweden, the fully-polished frames are built up with some of the finest road racing components available, including an Öhlins single rear shock absorber that lies horizontally, just to the left of the rear cylinder. The bodywork includes a full fairing with detachable lowers which, along with the style of the seat and tank, is reminiscent of the Yamaha TZ-250 road racers.

The Claymore H-D road racer appeared in the April 1993 issue of *Cycle World* magazine.

Claymore Racing
Egilsgatan 8A
753 34 Uppsala
Sweden
Phone 011-46-18-2608-80

Cobra Engineering

Cobra offers a line of "Boulevard Exhaust" systems for Evolution models. These are supplied in a chrome-plated finish in five styles: bell, fishtail, slash-cut, tapered, and turnout. All Cobra systems feature 3in-diameter mufflers.

Cobra Engineering
4760 East Bryson Street
Anaheim, CA 92807
(714) 779-7798
FAX (714) 779-2191

Colony

Colony specializes in fasteners for Harley-Davidsons and also offers pushrods along with various chassis and engine replacement components. Fasteners are chrome-plated stock replacement items, which are available for virtually every application on a custom Harley-Davidson. Pushrods are machined from aluminum alloy tubing, available for use with hydraulic or solid lifters in eleven different versions. They can be supplied for 1936-1947, 1948-1952, 1953-1965, 1966-1983 and 1984-and-up Big Twins as well as 1957-1984 Sportsters.

Colony
1300 Industrial Parkway North
Brunswick, OH 44212
(216) 225-3410—information
(800) 321-3412—orders only
FAX (216) 225-9412
Catalog available

Competition Drive Lines

Competition Drive Lines builds the Competitor clutch and belt primary drive kits for Harley-Davidsons.

Competition Drive Lines
11779 Cardinal Circle
Garden Grove, CA 92643
(714) 530-0786
Catalog available

Competition, Inc.

Lonnie Isam at Competition, Inc. in Houston custom-builds four-cam Big Twin engine cases and barrels which are designed for serious drag racing. With this equipment you have the option of going up to a 6in stroke.

Competition, Inc.
8318 Braniff Street
Houston, TX 77061
(713) 644-4922

Competition Motorcycles

Carl Pelieter at Competition Motorcycles in Idaho specializes in engine work for all Harley-Davidsons, from cylinder head modifications to balancing. In addition to engine modifications, Carl manufactures aerodynamic fiberglass body kits for FXRs.

Carl's Evolution Sportster has run a two-way average speed of 176mph at the Bonneville Salt Flats.

Competition Motorcycles
3602 1/2 Chinden Boulevard
Boise, ID 83706
(208) 344-7580

Continental Tire

Continental Tire imports and distributes tires for street riding and touring, in the basic 16", 19" and 21" sizes and three types—the Conti Blitz for a compromise between sport and touring tires, the six-ply Conti Tour for loaded touring, and the Conti Twin for rain and durability.

Front Conti Blitz tires are available in 110 90 H 18, 3.25 H 19, and 110 90 H 19. Rear Conti Blitz tires are available in 150 90 H 15, 120 90 H 16, 130 90 H 16, 140 90 H 16, 4.00 H 18, 120 90 H 18, and 130 90 H 18.

Continental Tire
General Tire, Inc.
41 Strong Street
Wallington, New Jersey 07057
(201) 471-8890

Cougar Customs

Andy Ryder at Cougar in Scotland builds custom exhaust systems, frames, swing arms, and triple clamps to order for Big Twin and Sportster owners. While much of their work is for street bikes, the shop is capable of supplying racing frames to the customer's specifications, either heli-arc-welded from mild steel or bronze-welded from Reynolds 531 tubing. Cougar also offers custom fabrication work and welding.

Cougar Customs
Upper Polmaise, Stirling
Scotland FK7 9PU
Phone 0786-65778

Cougar milled these billet aluminum triple clamps and machined the steering shaft for a customer's street bike.

This Cougar custom frame wasn't built for Harley-Davidson power, but it shows the kind of work Andy likes to turn out when the customer calls for it.

Big Twin cams like this are made by Crane for E.C.S. Engineering and Head Quarters. *E.C.S. Engineering*

One of the latest products from Custom FRP is a complete body for Pro Stock drag bikes, with styling that was inspired by the bodywork on a Buell.

Crane

Crane uses state-of-the-art equipment to manufacture cams, cam kits, ignitions systems and pushrods for Big Twins, and Sportsters, as well as roller-bearing rocker arms for Evolution and Shovelhead engines. Cams are available for every application from touring to blown Fuel. Rocker arms with needle roller bearings are machined from diecast steel and available for Shovelhead and Evolution engines.

Crane
530 Fentress Boulevard
Daytona Beach, FL 32114
(904) 258-6174

C.R. Axtell Company

C.R. Axtell and Mike Libby have been machinists and Harley-Davidson racing engine builders for many years. Much of the work they do is for IMSA, NASCAR, and USAC race cars. Their shop is in Sun Valley, where they manufacture performance products for Evolution street engines including cams, cam kits, pushrods, and valve spring kits with titanium retainers. Their cam kits are complete systems, designed to go right in without any machining.

Mike Libby looks after most of the machining now, with C.R. doing the cylinder head modifications. Their work is available direct only to qualified dealers.

C.R. Axtell Company
10949 Tuxford Street, #17
Sun Valley, CA 91352
(818) 768-5595

Custom Chrome, Inc.

Custom Chrome can provide many parts that could be used in a custom Big Twin or Sportster street bike. RevTech is the high-performance division of CCI. These products include a carburetor, cams, cylinders, cylinder heads, exhaust systems, fork springs, an ignition coil, pistons, valves, and wheels. All of these products are made to fit late model Big Twins with some also available for other bikes.

Carburetors come complete with manifold and air cleaner as well as three interchangeable venturis with 38, 42, and 45mm bores. Cylinder heads are for Evolution Big Twins and come set up for running dual plugs per cylinder. Wheels are cold-forged aluminum, available six designs in 16in, 19in, and 21in diameters. Several custom frames are available, for four-speed and five-speed Big Twins as well as iron Sportsters. And gas tanks include a one-piece, rubber-mounted 3.2gal tank for late Sportsters.

Custom Chrome, Inc.
16100 Jacqueline Court
Morgan Hill, CA 95037
(408) 778-0500—information
(800) 729-3332—orders only
Catalog available

Custom Cycle Engineering Company

CCE has been producing billet aluminum triple clamps since the early seventies. These are offered for Narrow Glide, Mid Glide, and Wide Glide front ends, for use with 35mm, 39mm, or 41mm fork tubes. You can choose between chrome-plated or polished aluminum finishes.

Custom Cycle Engineering Company
629 South Rancho Santa Fe Road, Suite 309
San Marcos, CA 92069
(800) 472-9253
Catalog available

Custom FRP

Dave Hershberger and the staff at Custom FRP manufacture hand-laminated fiberglass fairings for Pro Stock drag bikes.

Custom FRP
1126 Thorton Street
Elkhart, IN 46514
(219) 266-1000—information
(800) 727-6252—orders only
FAX (219) 266-1500
Catalog available

Cycle Fabrications

Cycle Fab is run by Dave Perewitz, who has built some of the finest custom Harley-Davidson street and drag bikes around. Dave and his crew can handle custom frame building, motorcycle construction, paint, and detailing that's as good as it gets.

Cycle Fabrications
909 North Main Street
Brockton, MA 02401
(508) 586-2511

Cycle Performance Products, Inc.

John Basore at Cycle Performance Products has taken the 5in face Auto Meter tach and adapted it for use on Harley-Davidsons with either standard dual-fire or single-fire ignition systems. It has a built-in shift light (also available separately) with a switch on the face for selecting the rpm at which it will come on.

Cycle Performance Products, Inc.
2724 Spring Garden Road
Winston-Salem, NC 27106
(919) 722-1407
Literature available

Cycle Specialists

Cycle Specialists is home to Larry and Steve McBride, who can provide Harley-Davidson drag racers with custom components such as aluminum bodywork, frames, fuel tanks, primary and supercharger belt drives, transmission components that include Top Fuel high gear shafts, billet aluminum triple clamps as well as custom fabrication work in aluminum, steel, and titanium. Frames are usually lay-down style, and are heli-arc-welded from 4130 chromemoly tubing.

Larry McBride is the Top Fuel racer and designer behind Cycle Specialists. His brother Steve is the machinist whose craftsmanship can be found on some outstanding motorcycles—including

The Cycle Performance Products anodized aluminum mounting bracket features a rubber ring for vibration isolation and can also be ordered separately for 5in and 3 3/4in tachs.

This early D&D prototype exhaust, built for Chuck Blackmon's Twin Sports road racer, is a two-into-one system with the collector pipe running underneath the engine. D&D production systems will vary somewhat from the version shown here but should provide increases in power and cornering clearance. *John Dangerfield*

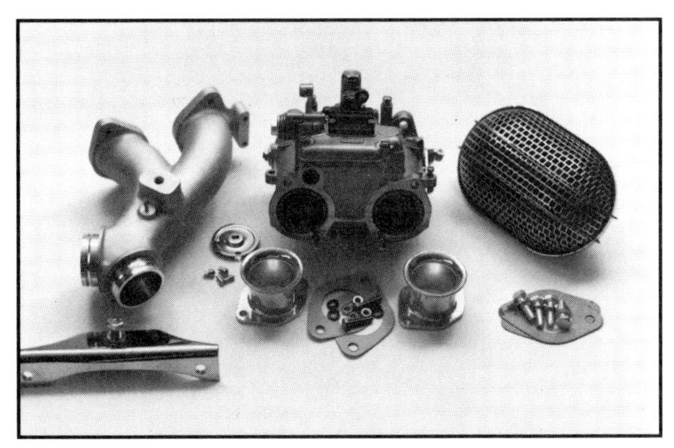

Dell'Ortos are available from Rivera Engineering in two versions: the 40mm Dual Throat shown here; and the single-throat Pumper which comes in a 38mm or 40mm venturi.

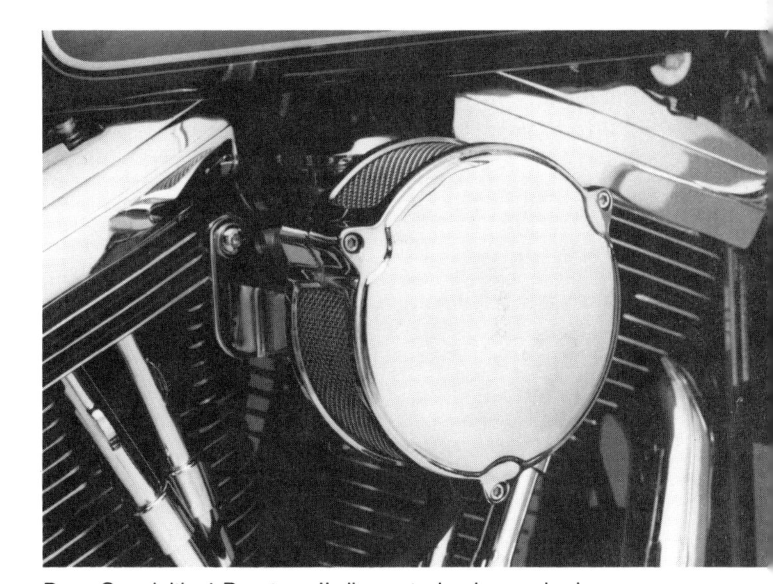

Drag Specialties' Dragtron II die-cast aluminum air cleaners are offered in chrome for CV carburetors and in chrome or polished aluminum for Bendix and Keihin carburetors.

Larry's, which has turned a quarter-mile ET of 6.49 at 218mph.

Cycle Specialists
9922 Jefferson Avenue
Newport News, VA 23605
(804) 599-5236
FAX (804) 599-7840

Damon's Motorcycle Creations

Rich Perez and the staff at Damon's make custom exhaust systems for all current Harley-Davidsons, and an adjustable rear shock link for Softail models. Damon's also offers its own special 7gal Big Twin gas tanks. Complete motorcycle construction, restoration, and superb custom paint are also available at Damon's.

Damon's Motorcycle Creations
547 Apollo, Unit C
Brea, CA 92621
(714) 990-1166

Daniel's Certified Welding, Inc.

In addition to building custom frames and complete street and strip motorcycles to order, Andy Daniel can provide street and strip engine and transmission work. Cylinder head modifications that include dual plug conversions are also available, along with engine case repairs. Daniel's campaigns its own supercharged Top Fuel Harley-Davidson drag bike.

Daniel's Certified Welding, Inc.
Route 1, Box 76
Freeman, VA 23856
(804) 848-4911

Darcy Racing Specialties

Phil Darcy builds dynamometers and also specializes in Harley-Davidson Sportster and XR-750 engines for racing on dirt tracks and road courses. Dynamometers use a chain-driven water brake with no rollers. Phil has also built a sophisticated, computerized flow bench that features data acquisition for good repeatability. The flow bench and his dyno are just part of the complete machine shop that is used for expert cylinder head modifications and whatever else is needed. Phil's work is found on bikes raced by three-time national champion Jay Springsteen in AMA Camel Pro dirt-track, and by Mike Hale in the AMA Twin Sports road racing class.

Darcy Racing Specialties
2524 Weaver Street, Suite 106
Fort Worth, TX 76117
(817) 834-7223

Dave Mackie Engineering

Dave Mackie provides cylinder head modification work for Rivera Engineering as well as any Harley-Davidson owners. His services include porting, valve jobs, or complete reworking that consists of a valve job, porting, contouring, polished intake and exhaust chambers, surfacing, finishing, and assembly. Dave will also look after dual-plug conversions, surfacing, and counterboring for big-bore barrels as well as general racing engine development work.

Dave's heads have proven their excellence on record-setting bikes that include the *Easyriders* streamliner and Bob Taft's "Rat's Whole Place" Top Gas drag bike.

Dave Mackie Engineering
2126 Knoll Drive, Unit D
Ventura, CA 93003
(805) 658-6969
FAX (805) 658-6973

DC Company

Darrell Collier at DC Company manufactures a line of lightweight fiberglass components for racing, including widened replica FXRS (and other) fenders, XLCR and FXRS dummy gas tanks for drag racing, XLCR fairings, XLCR seat housings, and fairings for XR-750 road racers and the XLCR.

One of his more impressive engineering projects was the construction of his Pro Stock Sportster drag bike. It uses a Kosman frame and has lots of tricks including Kawasaki five-speed transmission innards and two front cylinder heads. He has also built one of the quickest stock-appearing FXRS drag bikes in the country. DC also distributes Pro Street Chassis Works frames for five-speed Big Twins (described in their own section).

DC Company
P.O. Box 460
Loomis, CA 95650-0460
(916) 652-4751
Literature available

D&D Performance Enterprises

David Rash manufactures exhaust systems for many motorcycles, most of which are sport bikes. D&D also builds pipes for the Evolution Sportster that are among the most popular in Twin Sports racing. All D&D exhaust systems are designed with the goal of providing real power gains, being thoroughly tested on the dyno before being released. They are hand-built by a perfectionist, and are available in ceramic coated or black finishes.

D&D Performance Enterprises
6360 Airport Freeway, Suite 300
Fort Worth, TX 76117
(817) 834-8961—information
(800) 843-8961—orders only

Delkron Manufacturing, Inc.

Alan Mahan and the crew at Delkron manufacture engine cases for Big Twin engines along with dry sump plates, oil pump bodies, tools, and triple clamps.

These cases are permanent mold 356-T6 aluminum castings. They are available in several versions for your choice of ignition style and bore size. Careful design, CNC machining, workmanship, and inspection guarantee

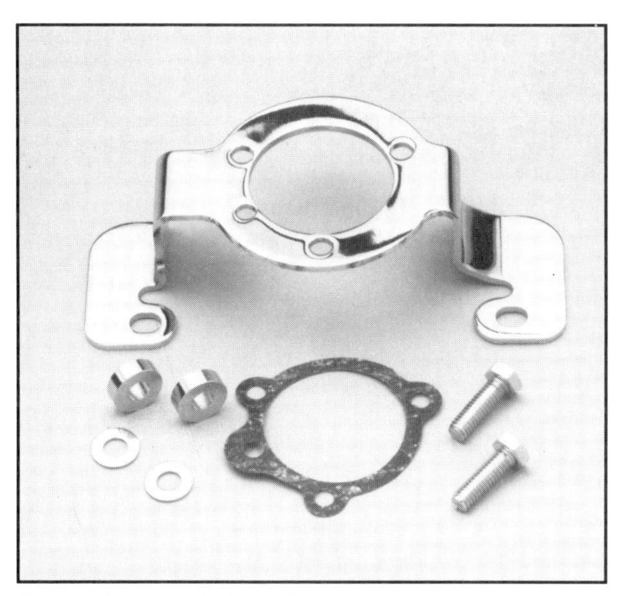

Six versions of this Drag Specialties' air cleaner bracket are available to provide additional support for Dragtron II and other air cleaners. This one mounts to the cylinder heads on 1967 and 1987 Sportsters.

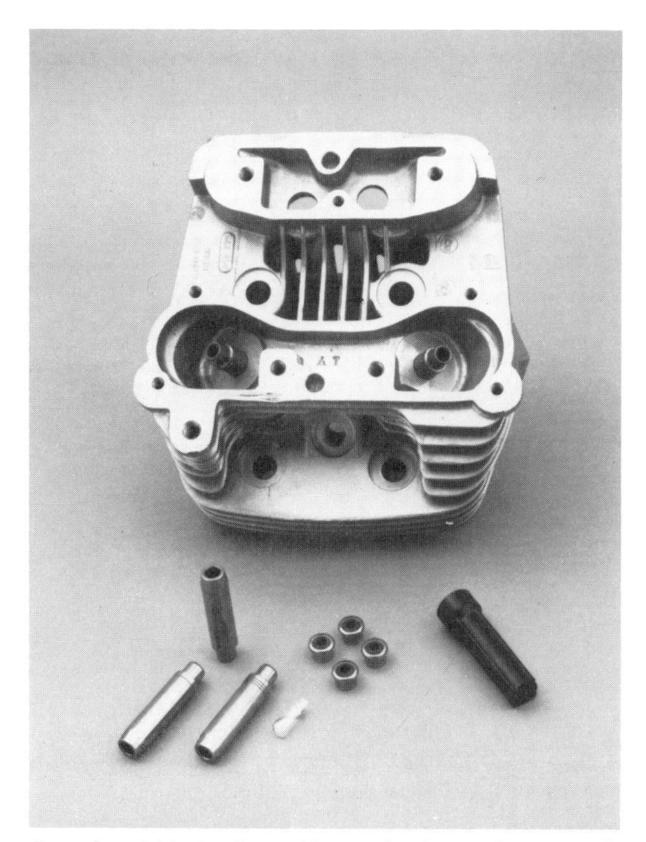

Drag Specialties' valve guides and valve seals are available for Big Twins and Sportsters.

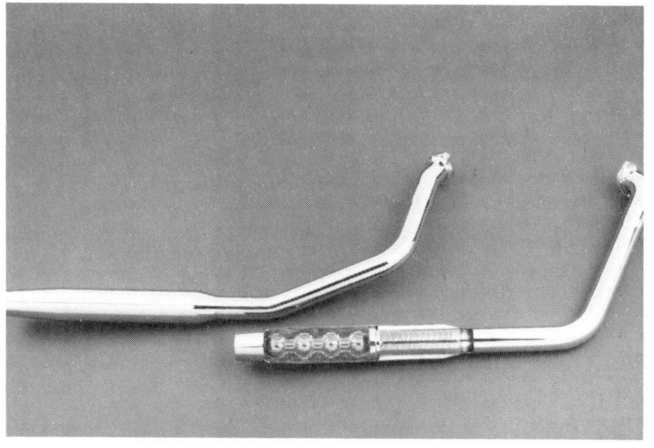

Drag Specialties' Python II exhaust systems are available to fit 1984-and-later FXRs, Softails, and (shown here) 1986-and-up Sportsters.

Dunlop K591F Elite SP front tires can be supplied in two compounds, as 16-, 17-, 18-, and 19-inch belted or radial designs.

component locations being accurate to within .001". The pads areas for the cylinders are substantially increased over stock. Oil passages have been changed to do away with weak spots near the cylinder barrel spigots and the lifter blocks. All threads are standard S.A.E. and are rolled rather than tapped for accuracy and smooth surface finish.

In addition to the standard cast aluminum cases, Delkron also hand-builds billet four-cam Big Twin racing cases in street and strip versions, machined from solid 6061-T6 aluminum plate. No area of either case half has a wall thickness of less than .400". They can be supplied ready to accept your choice of barrels, or complete with an S&S bottom end and barrels installed. These cases are only available on a special-order basis. The customer should be prepared to specify the deck height, cylinder spigot diameter, and flywheel diameter. Machining starts after Delkron receives this information and your deposit.

Dry sump plates are also 356-T6 aluminum castings. Supplied with screws and a gasket, they allow you to reduce the power loss caused by oil slapping against the flywheels.

Oil pump bodies are CNC-machined from 6061-T6 aluminum. They are a replacement for the stock 1968-and-later pump bodies (with the pre-1980 cases requiring oil relief holes to be drilled). Tools include torque plates, intended to minimize distortion during and after boring. Machined from 4130 chromemoly and precision ground to a flatness of within .0005in, they are drilled and tapped to be used on Evolution and Shovelhead cylinders. Triple clamps are machined from billet 6061-T6 aluminum. Designed to replace the stock triple clamps on 1988-and-up Narrow Glide forks, they are supplied in a polished finish, complete with a replacement steel stem.

Other billet aluminum components are available, including front brake caliper mounts for late Narrow Glide forks, as well as fender struts and swing arm pivots for FXRs.

Delkron Manufacturing, Inc.
2430 Manning Street
Sacramento, CA 95815
(916) 921-9703
Catalog available

Del West Engineering, Inc.

Del machines lightweight titanium valves, collars, and retainers for all Harley-Davidson racing engines including the XR-750. These parts are made using CNC machining and billet titanium bar stock. The valve stems are treated with a unique plasma coating to improve durability.

Del West Engineering, Inc.
24711 Avenue Rockefeller
Valencia, CA 91355
(805) 295-5700

Dell'Orto

Dell'Orto carburetors have provided a popular performance upgrade on Harley-Davidsons for many years. Rivera Engineering are the North American experts for installing Dell'Orto carburetors on Harley-Davidsons. They have been using them for many years and have found the 40mm Dual Throat to be the finest carburetor of its kind.

Rivera developed their own cast aluminum intake manifolds for Panheads, Shovelheads, and Evolution Big Twins to fit bikes with small or large tanks as well as iron Sportsters. Also available from Rivera are two styles of air cleaners, polished cast aluminum velocity stacks, complete rebuild kits, throttles, and cables.

Rivera also offers its own high-performance kits for Evolution Big Twins that include the Dell'Orto carburetor along with Rivera's own manifold, cam, pushrods, and your choice of drag pipes or a SuperTrapp exhaust system.

Rivera Engineering
6416 South Western Avenue
Whittier, CA 90606
(310) 692-8944
FAX (310) 699-3943

Denver's

Denver's builds four styles of custom frames to accept your choice of any Big Twin or Sportster engine and transmission, with belt or chain final drive. Their standard rigid frames are available with a choice of straight-leg or wishbone downtubes. Trike, swing arm, and "Soft Tail" frames are also available.

All of Denver's frames are manufactured from 1010 mild steel tubing, with the top tube and seat tube being .220in-wall 1018 mild steel tubing. Engine mounts are made from .5in steel plate. Front end geometry is specified by the customer on all of Denver's frames. Denver's also builds its own axles, gas tanks, oil tanks, springer front ends, seats, and chain guards for its frames. It also offers hubs, laced wheels, polishing, and plating.

Denver's
1575 West Rialto Avenue
San Bernardino, CA 92410
(714) 381-2422
Flyer and price list available

Departure Bike Works

Run by Lee Clemens, Departure offers performance engine and transmission modifications, custom machining, welding, and fabrication as well as bead blasting. Departure campaigns a Big Twin drag bike and also sponsors the annual custom motorcycle show in Virginia.

Departure Bike Works
3091-3093 Hull Street
Richmond, VA 23224
(804) 231-0244—information
(800) 292-0244—orders only

Digger Enterprise

Digger is run by "Cadillac" John Thellin, a journeyman tool and die maker whose specialty is manufacturing custom flywheels along with crank pins, cylinders, engine cases, rods, and transmission cases. Cadillac also builds complete engines, custom frames, and secondary oil pumps, and can provide all kinds of machining and fabrication work for street and strip.

The Digger engines can be built with a maximum of a 5 1/2in bore and a 6in stroke. This works out to 285ci or 4672cc—big enough for a Texan. Cadillac feels strongly that the weight of the flywheel in a Harley-Davidson engine goes a long way toward determining its performance, whether it's for drag racing or touring. Digger flywheels can be supplied in weights up to 36 1/4lb for bullet-nose engines and 38lb for Panheads. Cadillac installed a set of Panhead flywheels in a Sportster over ten years ago and the bike is still going strong.

Digger Enterprise
10501 Kittreal
Houston, TX 77034
(713) 941-3984

Diversified Product Development

Matt Showalter at Diversified manufactures the Roto-Glide RG-II oil pump for Big Twins, hydraulic clutch kits for Big Twins and Sportsters, and end doors for five-speed Big Twins.

The Roto-Glide RG-II oil pump for Big Twins was designed by Matt Showalter of Baltimore. The RG-II uses the same technology used by the Harley-Davidson factory on their Sportster oil pumps since 1977. The system uses needle roller bearings and pair of steel rotor gears mounted on centers that are eccentric to each other, with the inner rotor having one less tooth than the outer. Oil pressure regulation is adjustable, and the pump body is CNC-machined from aluminum billet. Its modular design allows the RG-II to be configured in a variety of choices including a single input and single return; a single input and dual returns; and a single input and dual returns with an extra feed for a turbocharger or other use.

Hydra-Shift hydraulic clutch systems are available for four-speed and five-speed Big Twin transmissions as well as four-speed Evolution Sportsters. The five-speed version is CNC-machined aluminum billet; the four-speed version is a CNC-machined 356 aluminum casting; and the four-speed Evolution Sportster version fits inside the stock primary cover with no machining necessary. Diversified's Bullet Bore master cylinder is provided with all three of these kits and is also available separately.

Reinforced end doors for five-speed Big Twin transmissions were developed from an idea by the people at Departure Bike Works in Virginia. Compatible with both early and late end covers, they are CNC-machined from billet aluminum and provide greatly improved strength.

Diversified Product
Development
1399 Ramsay Street
Baltimore, MD 21223
(301) 644-1557
FAX (301) 234-0585
Catalog available

Don's Speed & Custom

Don's Speed & Custom is run by Don Hotop, who has built some great-looking street bikes. Don and resident master machinist Sieg Wieler fabricate custom gas tanks and aluminum air dams, primary covers, supercharger drives, and triple clamps. They can also provide complete motorcycle construction as well as performance engine and transmission modifications. Their workmanship is superb.

Don's Speed & Custom
2613 Avenue L
Fort Madison, IA 52627
(319) 372-6216

Don Tilley

Don Tilley is a Harley-Davidson racing engine builder who can provide performance engine and transmission modifications and tuning, custom fabrication and machining, as well as complete racing motorcycle construction.

The legendary road racer Lucifer's Hammer was campaigned out of Tilley Harley-Davidson. Gene Church (from Statesville, North Carolina) rode the bike to AMA Battle of the Twins championships in 1984, 1985, and 1986. Lucifer's Hammer is being restored and will be placed in the Harley-Davidson factory's museum.

Don works out of his shop, Tilley Harley-Davidson, which is located about forty miles north of Charlotte, North Carolina, in the heart of stock car racing country. And that's how Don got started in racing. He was the 1963 Hickory Motor Speedway track champion and went on to race in NASCAR Grand National (now Winston Cup), Modified and Sportsman races in 1964. Don entered the Daytona 500 in 1965.

Don is the builder, tuner, and crew chief for Scott Zampach in the Twin Sports racing series. Together they won the Twin Sports national championships in 1991 and 1992, winning seven of the ten races in the 1992 series. Don loves it when those California boys tell him, "for someone who talks so slow, you sure go fast."

Don Tilley
Tilley Harley-Davidson, Inc.
Route 216, Box 263
U.S. Highway 70 West
Statesville, NC 28677
(704) 872-3838

Dragon Precision Machining

Dragon Precision Machining is run by Mel Bernstein, who manufactures big-bore kits for Shovelhead engines. They are available with bore sizes of 3.625in (3 5/8in) or 3.6875in (3 11/16in). Mel is a machinist who can repair and fabricate most any Harley-Davidson component, including custom frames for street or strip. Instructional videotapes for engine building and cylinder head modifications are also available.

Dragon Precision Machining
1200 Dragon Man Drive
Colorado Springs, CO 80929
(719) 683-2800
FAX (719) 683-3868
Catalog available

Drag Specialties

Drag Specialties is a manufacturer and distributor of a line of accessories, performance parts, and tools exclusively for Harley-Davidsons, including air cleaners, exhaust systems, pistons, valve guides, and valve seals.

Python exhaust systems are available for most Shovelhead and Evolution Big Twins as well as 1957-1981, 1982-1985, and 1986-and-later Sportsters. In 1992, Python II systems, which use different baffles for improved top-end performance, were introduced. All Python systems use Drag Specialties' patented Anti-Reversionary cone. Each header pipe is expanded and fitted with an investment-cast flange which accepts the A.R. cone. The cone is designed to "suppress the reversion waves which are most disruptive at lower rpm ranges." Pistons are cast, in 8:1 compression for Shovelheads and Panheads, in standard bore to .070in oversize.

Drag Specialties
P.O. Box 9336
Minneapolis, MN 55440-9336
(612) 942-7890—information
(800) 222-3400—orders only
FAX (612) 942-7891
Catalog available

Dave Rowe Performance Products

Dave Rowe produces starters for Sportsters and a variety of CNC-machined billet aluminum components that includes derby and inspection covers. On a special-order basis he can also fabricate custom gas tanks and oil tanks and provide complete motorcycles based around the frames his father Marc builds. Starters are designed to provide improved greater torque, and fit 1981-and-later Sportsters.

Dave Rowe Performance Products
148 Batchelder Road
Seabrook, NH 03874
(603) 474-7278
FAX (603) 474-9114

D&S Performance

D&S manufactures its own Billet Plus cylinder heads, which are strictly for four-cam Big Twin and Sportster racing engines. These heads are CNC-machined from billet 6061-T6 aluminum and feature 2 1/8in intake valves. Intake ports are completely different from stock heads, running straight in from the right side of each head. Billet Plus heads are supplied complete with aluminum roller-bearing rockers, titanium retainers, and cast aluminum valve covers with integral upper engine mounts.

D&S Performance
2184 Rice Avenue
Lake City, PA 16423
(814) 774-2591

Dunlop Tire Corporation

Dunlop has a comprehensive line of motorcycle tires, including models designed especially for Harley-Davidson street bikes in the standard 16in, 19in, and 21in sizes as well as tires specifically designed for road racing.

The D402 Touring Elite II front MT90HB 16 is 25.3in in diameter, 5.4in wide, and is for 5.00/5.10 rim widths. The D402 Touring Elite II tubed front MH90 21 is 27.1in in diameter, 3.3in wide, and is for 2.50/2.75 rim widths. The D402 Touring Elite II rear MT90HB 16 is 25.7in in diameter, 3.3in wide, and is for 2.50/2.75 rim widths.

Dunlop Tire Corporation
P.O. Box 1109
Buffalo, NY 14240-1109
(716) 879-8258
Catalogs available

Dunlop Tires Canada, Ltd.
260 Hanlan Road
Woodbridge, Ontario
Canada L4L 3P6
(416) 851-6784

Dynatech

Dynatech manufactures the Dyna ignition components that are available for most Harley-Davidsons and include batteries, coils, electronic ignition systems, and two styles of rev limiters.

Batteries are intended for racing and are sold without a warranty. They are military-style, sealed, lead-acid units that are sold in six-volt sections weighing 3.5lb. Each six-volt section is 4in high, 2in wide, and 5 1/4in wide. Coils are rated at 35,000V and come in several versions, based on 6V/1.5Ω (red), 12V/3Ω (green) and 12V/5Ω (black).

Dyna "S" ignition systems come in two versions: the single-fire, which is compatible with single-plug or dual-plug heads; and the standard Dyna "S". Both systems maintain the factory advance curve by utilizing a magnetic rotor with the stock spark advancer and are claimed to change less the three degree all the way up to 12,000rpm.

The Dyna 2000 ignition system is available in single-fire

Dunlop K591R Elite SP rear tires are available as 15-, 16-, 17-, and 18-inch belted or radial styles.

The Dynojet has become the dyno of choice for mobile dynamometer trucks and well-equipped motorcycle shops.

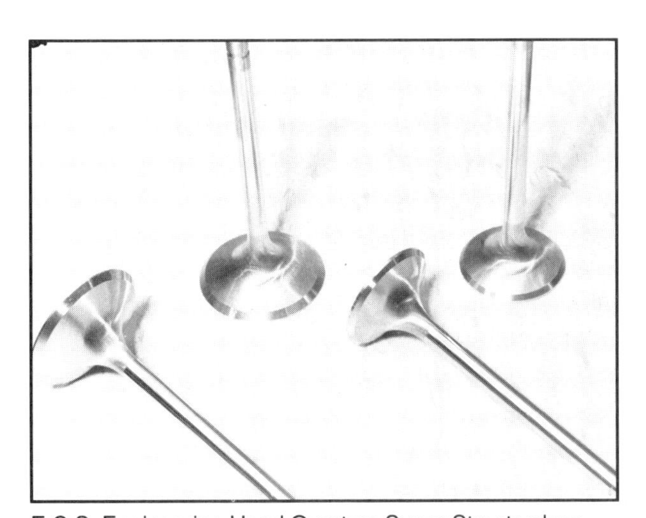

E.C.S. Engineering Head Quarters Super Street valves.

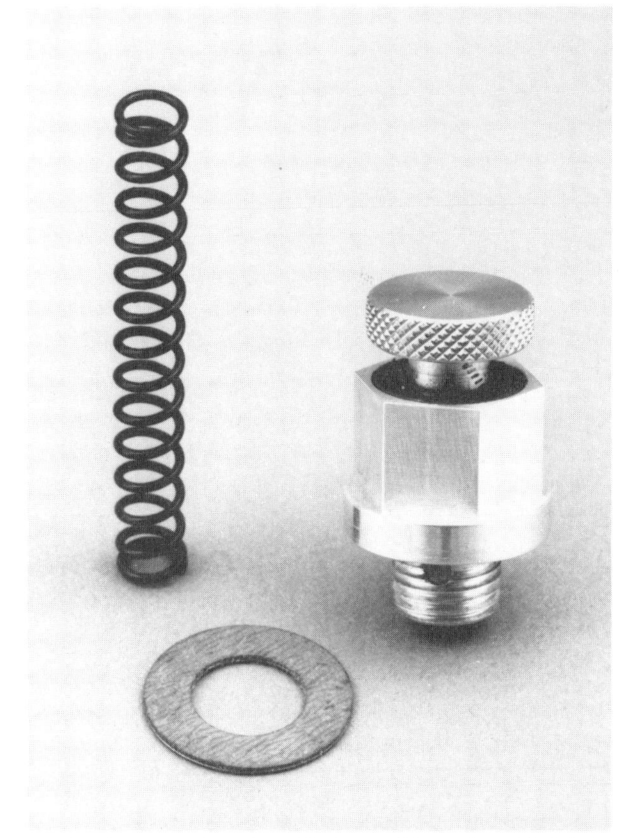

E.R.T. Products' Pro-Just Kit lets a rider adjust his bike's oil pressure.

E.C.S. Engineering Head Quarters valve spring kit.

and dual-fire versions, and features include a programmable advance curve that provides the opportunity to select from several factory-set curves with a DIP switch (with custom-calibrated curves available for racers); a four-position DIP switch to control the point the built-in rev limiter kicks in (in 250rpm increments from 5,000 to 8,750rpm); and a digital dwell control that measures the charging of the coil it is connected to and adjusts the dwell period according to that coil's particular need. The Dyna 4000 Pro ignition system features a built-in single- or two-stage rev limiter. It can be used with single-fire and dual-fire engines.

The Dyna RPM Limiter is compatible with any inductive electronic ignition. Your engine's maximum speed can be set anywhere from 6,000rpm up to 13,000rpm. Upon reaching the speed you have set it for, the spark going to one or both (your choice) of the ignition coils will be shut off until the engine speed drops below the limiter's maximum rpm setting. The Dyna rev limiter is designed to have no other effect on an engine's performance other than cutting at the speed it has been set for. Dyna also offers a Two-Stage RPM Limiter that provides two selectable rpm limits, with the additional one being set lower for launching a drag bike. Accuracy is claimed to be within 40rpm of the speed selected on the unit's switch for the lower limit and within 100rpm for the upper limit.

Ignition boosters allow those using points systems to do away with condensers. This booster is intended to provide the coil with precisely controlled energy. Other Dyna products include advance units, battery chargers, coil mounts, two types of spark plug wires, and tach adapters.

Dynatech
810 North Cummings Road
Covina, CA 91724
(818) 967-3786

Dynojet Research

Dynojet manufactures motorcycle dynamometers and jetting kits for Keihin carburetors.

Dynojet dynamometers measure rear-wheel horsepower versus rpm. A computer program called Race Routine allows users to run the bike through the gears as you would on the track. Time to distance, time to speed, and differences in dyno runs can be stored and compared. Readings of actual or corrected horsepower relative to mph or rpm are stored in the computer's memory and can be easily printed out as detailed graphs. The Dynojet motorcycle dyno will handle up to 500hp.

Jetting kits are available for all 1989-1993 Harley-Davidsons with accelerator pumps and for 1988 Sportsters without accelerator pumps. These kits solve the problems of sealed idle jets and adjusting screws, while the stock, fixed fuel needle is replaced with a Dynojet needle with five settings. These kits transform the Keihin carburetor, allowing it to reach its potential. The twist drill needed to enlarge the breather hole in the slide is included along with complete instructions.

Dynojet Research
200 Arden Drive
Belgrade, MT 59714
(406) 388-4993—information
(800) 992-4993—orders only
FAX (406) 388-4721
Literature available

Eagle

Eagle makes 35,000-volt ignition coils which are designed to replace the stock Harley-Davidson coils. Three 12-volt versions are available: for points ignitions; for 1980-1984 electronic ignitions and for 1985-and later electronic ignitions. A six-volt, 1.3Ω coil for dual-plug engines is also offered.

Rivera Engineering distributes Eagle coils, and should be contacted for further information.

Rivera Engineering
6416 South Western Avenue
Whittier, CA 90606
(310) 692-8944
FAX (310) 699-3943

Eagle Engineering

Jim Ulasich, Mike Roland, and the rest of the staff at Eagle Engineering specialize in performance modifications for Harley-Davidsons for the street and strip. Complete engines from mild to wild can be built for any application. Fabrication and machining services are also available. Mike's drag bike is campaigned out of this shop.

Eagle Engineering
1837 East Lake Street
Minneapolis, MN 55407
(612) 729-2599

EBC Brakes

EBC brake pads are available for all current Harley-Davidson disc brakes. Kevlar is used in their construction, with the goal of providing progressive braking power without noise. Kevlar also provides improved brake feel and minimal disc abrasion.

EBC has tested its pads in West Germany at the world's only institution that has established a severe brake performance test for both high-speed and wet-weather braking performance. EBC pads are manufactured in the United Kingdom and Holland, and they are distributed in the United States by Hy-Tech Motorcycle Components.

Freeman Automotive (UK), Ltd.
Motorcycle Component Division
Units B-H, Barker Buildings,
Countess Road
Spencer Bridge, Northampton
United Kingdom NN5 7EA
Phone: 0604-583344
FAX: 0604-583744

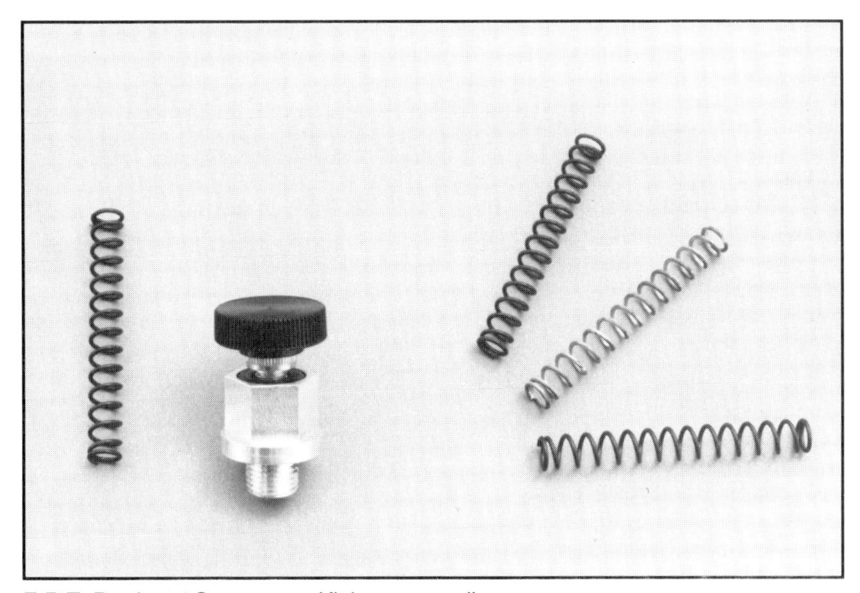

E.R.T. Products' Superpump Kit increases oil pressure.

Perhaps the world's most popular brake pads for road racing, Ferodo pads are available for all disc-brake Harley-Davidsons.

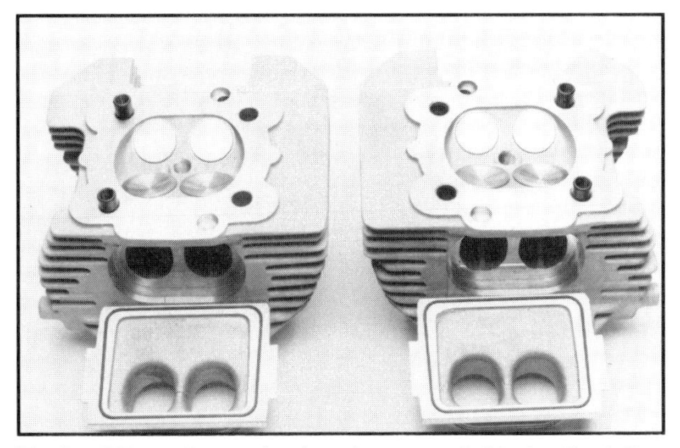

Feuling/Rivera four-valve heads are available for Evolution Big Twin and Sportster engines.

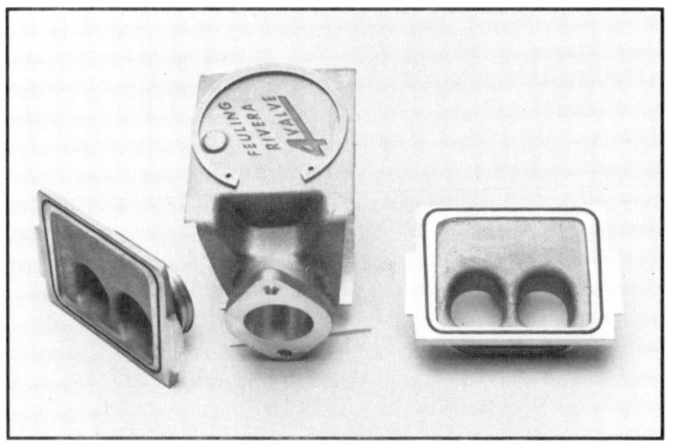

Feuling/Rivera heads are supplied with a unique, O-ring-sealed intake manifold.

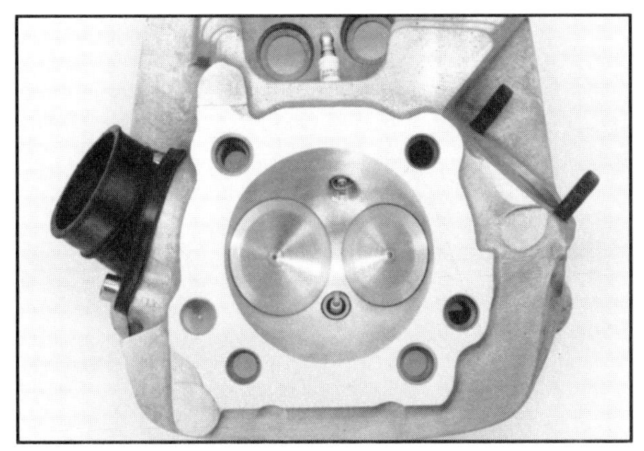

With fresh combustion chambers, valves, seats, completely revised ports and a double-plug conversion, this Flo Dynamics head is all ready for the big dance.

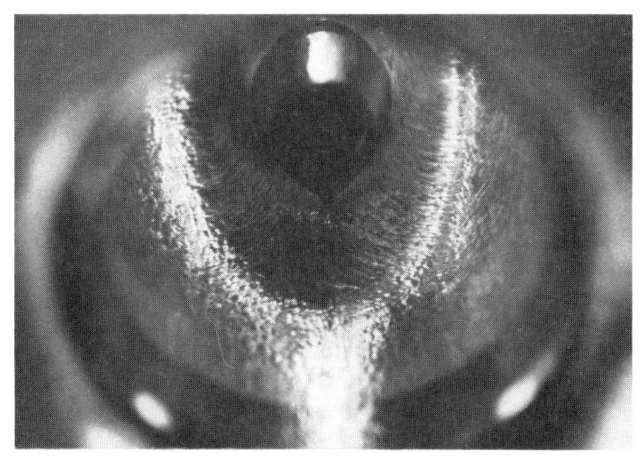

A look at the unique tooled finish Flo Dynamics developed with carbide cutter manufacturer R&R Specialties. It looks wild, and it works.

Hy-Tech Motorcycle Components
12860 Bradley Avenue
Sylmar, CA 91342
(818) 362-5534

E.C.S. Engineering

Since 1970, Earl Calhoun at E.C.S. has specialized in Harley-Davidson performance engine modifications for drag racing and street bikes. Earl can provide complete cylinder head modifications, custom fabricating, machining, and heli-arc welding. Custom frames will be made to order starting in late 1993. E.C.S. is also the American distributor for all products made by and for Head Quarters in Ontario.

E.C.S. Engineering
220 South Columbia Street
Gastonia, NC 28054
(704) 861-0596—orders
(704) 861-1226—tech
FAX (704) 861-1226

Head Quarters
P.O. Box 119
Komoka, Ontario
Canada N0L 1R0
(519) 657-8532
FAX (519) 657-3333

Ed Heil

Harley-Davidson drag racing specialist Ed Heil specializes in custom-building drag bike frames and swing arms. He also provides aluminum and steel fabrication and welding services to racers.

Ed Heil
10428 Long Street
Oak Lawn, IL 60453
(708) 422-8188

E.R.T. Products

E.R.T. Products manufactures the Superpump Kit, which increases oil pressure. The kit fits all Big Twins with aluminum-bodied oil pumps. These are supplied with three color-coded springs which provide varying oil pressure ranges: blue is 20psi; yellow is 24psi, and red is 28psi. E.R.T. also manufactures the Pro-Just Kit. Its adjustable pressure relief cap lets you make fine adjustments in oil pressure. The Pro-Just uses valves machined from stainless steel and 6061-T6 aluminum, with models available for 1965-1984 and 1985-and-up.

E.R.T. Products
P.O. Box 31
234 West Summit Street
Delphi, IN 46923-0031
(317) 564-3946—information
(800) 245-5067—orders only
FAX (317) 564-2296

Fantasy Motorcycles

Steve Frisbee specializes in Harley-Davidson drag bikes. He builds cylinder barrels, cylinder heads and frames to order and also handles custom fabrication.

Fantasy Motorcycles
1510 Hubbard Street
Sumner, WA 98590
(206) 863-5445

Fast Company

Fast Company is operated by John McLeod, who specializes in high-performance Harley-Davidson cylinder head modifications. Racing engine building, fabrication, and welding are also available.

In 1992, the Fast Company staff turned a stock FXR into the A/Production record holder at Bonneville, backing up their 153mph pass with one at 152, beating the old record by over 20mph.

Fast Company
835 Seventh Avenue
Kirkland, WA 98033
(206) 828-4130

Ferodo, Ltd.

Ferodo brake pads are a popular improvement for Harley-Davidsons, available for every Harley-Davidson that was originally equipped with disc brakes, as well as for aftermarket motorcycle brake calipers made by Brembo, Grimeca, I.S.R., Lockheed and Spondon. Performance Research Organization in California is the American distributor for Ferodo pads, which have been made in the U. K. since 1897.

Ferodo, Ltd.
Chapel-en-le-Frith, Stockport
United Kingdom SK12 6JP
Phone 0298-812520
FAX 0298-812600

Performance Research Organization
1194 Shetland Way
El Dorado Hills, CA 95630
(916) 933-4166—information
(800) 443-9863—orders only
FAX (916) 933-402
Catalog available

Feuling/Rivera

Feuling/Rivera four-valve cylinder heads are available for Evolution Big Twin and Sportster engines. Designed by Jim Feuling, these heads come complete with all valve gear, an intake manifold, polished aluminum rocker covers, and an exhaust system.

Feuling/Rivera heads are available in four basic states of tune, with the mildest Stage I heads good for perhaps an extra 35hp. A stock Big Twin engine with Feuling/Rivera Stage I heads and valve gear has turned 9,500rpm and lived to tell about it, an accomplishment in itself. They come complete with gaskets, bolts, pushrods, mounting brackets, plugs, plug wires, and a VHS videotape. These heads and components are distributed exclusively by Rivera Engineering.

Rivera Engineering
6416 South Western Avenue
Whittier, CA 90606
(310) 692-8944
FAX (310) 699-3943

Florida Caliper brake calipers and brake discs.

Florida Caliper's stainless steel valves.

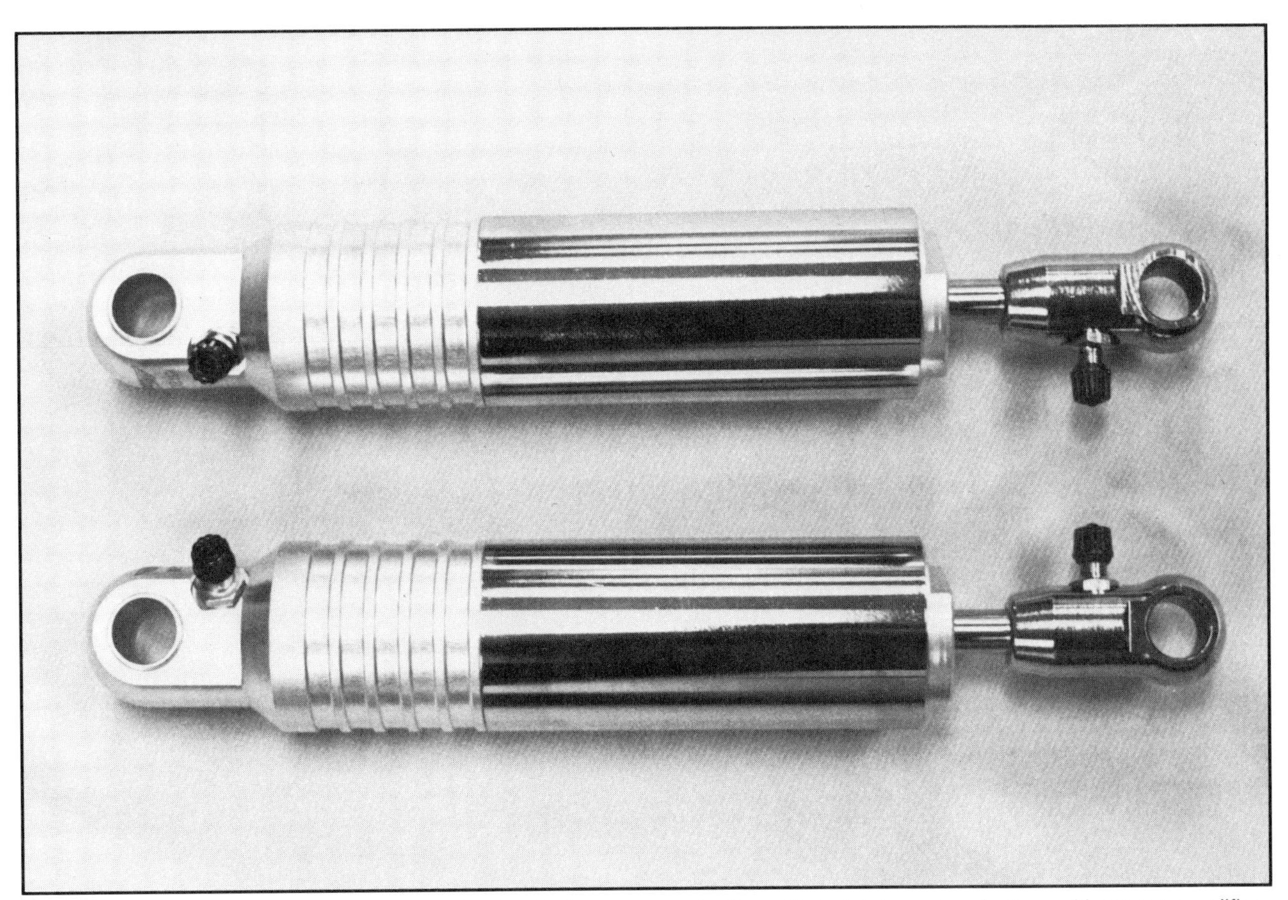

The Fournales Pan-Cruise suspension units for Softails use the olepneumatic principle found on all of their models. Beautifully finished, they bolt on without any modification to provide an adjustable ride height.

The Twin Sports bike (foreground) campaigned by Harley-Davidson of Citrus Heights from northern California is one of the many road racers using Fox suspension components. *AMA*

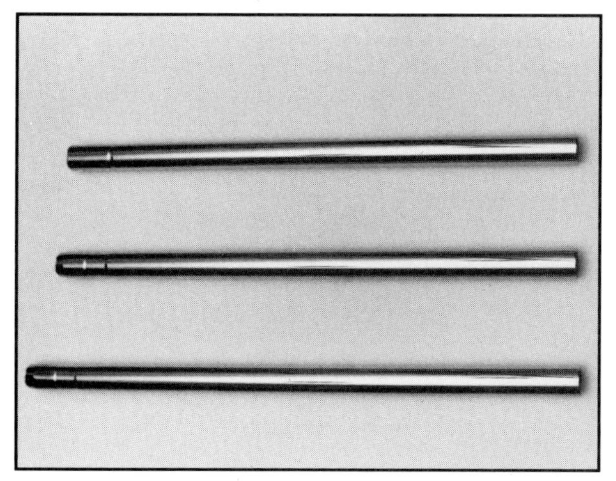

Frank's fork tubes and related products are all guaranteed to fit.

The GMA Model F four-piston caliper uses four 1 1/4in pistons.

Finch's Custom Cycles, Inc.

Ron Finch is a master craftsman who has been building amazing custom Harley-Davidsons professionally since 1965. He can fabricate virtually anything needed for street and drag bikes.

Finch's Custom Cycles, Inc.
4480 Joslyn Road at Brown Road
Auburn Hills, MI 48326
(313) 391-0200

Flo Dynamics

Flo Dynamics is headed by Perry Kime, who specializes in high-performance Harley-Davidson cylinder head modifications and also manufactures ignition components.

The Flo Dynamics Super Port Flow modification provides a considerable increase in flow characteristics. After being reshaped, the ports are given a special tooled finish to double the atomization of incoming fuel. With a two-week turnaround time, the complete Flo Dynamics head treatment with porting, finishing, new valves and seats, and a double-plug conversion has resulted in cylinder head temperature dropping by 20percent with horsepower improved by over 25percent at 5,500rpm. Other cylinder head mods include new exhaust flanges and top end oiler kits for Panheads and Shovelheads in addition to dual-plug conversions for all models. Wiring kits for dual-plug ignition applications are also available for Big Twins made since 1936 and all Sportsters.

Flo Dynamics
1150 Pike Lane, #2
Oceano, CA 93445
(805) 481-6300
FAX (805) 481-6341
Literature available

Florida Caliper Manufacturers, Inc.

Florida Caliper manufactures a line of brake calipers and discs for Big Twins and Sportsters. They also have their own line of stainless steel rocker arms and valves. Rocker arms can be supplied in a choice of several ratios and feature needle bearings.

Florida Caliper Manufacturers, Inc.
1450 S.W. Tenth Street
Delray Beach, FL 33444
(407) 734-0994—information
(800) 327-1166—orders only
FAX (407) 265-1859

Forcella Italia / Ceriani

Formerly known as Ceriani, the classic Forcella Italia forks are built by Enrico Ceriani and imported from Italy by Steve Storz in California.

Forcella Italia forks are made in conventional as well as upside-down styles. They are available as forks only, or as a complete front end ready to bolt onto any late model Big Twin or Sportster, ready to accept stock Harley-Davidson fenders and disc brakes. Steve manufactures his own triple clamps out of billet aluminum. They come in two widths, for standard "mid glide" and Wide Glide applications. Both versions accept stock or Performance Machine calipers and are usually for dual-disc systems, with single-disc front ends also available.

Storz Performance
239 Olive Street
Ventura, CA 93001
(805) 641-9540
Catalog available

Fournales Suspension

Jean Pierre Fournales builds these unusual looking shocks you've seen on some custom Harley-Davidsons. All Fournales suspension units are olepneumatic, and most are available in a choice of lengths. One of the nice things about their narrow design is that you won't have any clearance problems that sometimes occur with wider aftermarket shocks which can interfere with final drive belts and belt guards. The manufacturer claims these suspension units will never bottom out. Fournales suspension components are also available for race cars, street cars, off-road vehicles, medical equipment, and aircraft.

Fournales Suspension
502 South Post Oak Lane, #205
Houston, TX 77056
(713) 850-1524
FAX (713) 850-0708
Literature available

Fox Factory, Inc.

Fox specializes in racing motorcycle shock absorbers. They build a variety of designs including models with aluminum bodies and remote reservoirs for compressed nitrogen.

Fox Factory, Inc.
3641 Charter Park Drive
San Jose, CA 95136
(408) 269-9200

Frame Oddities

Frame Oddities is run by Jamie Morocco and George Masavage. They build custom frames and engines for drag racing and street bikes, and also look after any custom fabrication. Their engines go all the way up to Top Fuel, and they will work on any Harley-Davidson motorcycles.

Their frames are all built to order to meet your needs. Many of them are lay-down frames for drag bikes built from chromemoly tubing, but Jamie says the trend towards Pro Street Harley-Davidsons has been strong of late. Frame Oddities has machining and fabrication services available. Jamie also builds fuel injector pump drive systems (described under Morocco Racing). George and Jamie are active in drag racing, running under four sanctioning bodies with several Harley-Davidsons, including a Top Fuel bike.

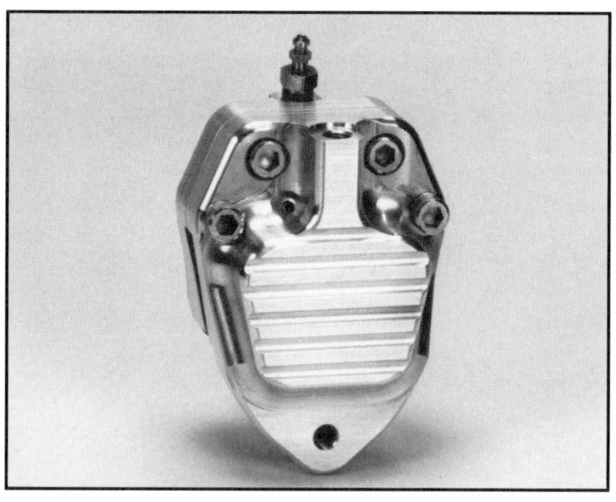

The lightweight GMA Model B dual-piston caliper uses a pair of 1 5/8in pistons.

This GMA rear brake kit is made especially for Big Twins from 1973 to 1984.

The clean, understated elegance of the Goodman makes it an extremely appealing piece. One of the reasons this bike looks the way it does is because it wasn't designed by a 70-year-old Republican.

Goodyear is the world leader in producing drag slicks. Gary "Tator" Gilmore campaigns this bike out of his shop, The Chrome Horse in Spencer, IA, which runs a 15in Goodyear race car rear tire along with an 18in Goodyear Eagle Dragway Special on the front.

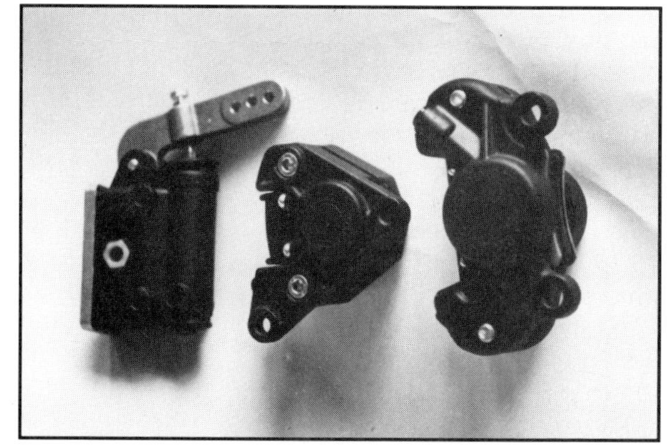

A Grimeca rear master cylinder beside dual-piston rear and front calipers. *Cosmopolitan Motors*

Frame Oddities
13001 Abbey Road
North Royalton, OH 44133
(216) 582-0240

Frank's Maintenance and Engineering, Inc.

Frank's makes a complete line of custom and stock replacement fork tubes for Harley-Davidsons. They are centerless-ground from seamless high-carbon steel and can be supplied in any length. Frank's can also supply fork boots and braces as well as custom kickstands, brake hoses, and speedometer cables in any length you need.

Frank's Maintenance and
Engineering, Inc.
945 Pitner Avenue
Evanston, IL 60202
(708) 869-6792

Fred's Speed & Sport

Fred's Speed & Sport is run by Fred Cuba, who builds custom Harley-Davidson frames to order and complete bikes for street and strip.

Fred's Speed & Sport
847 South Burlington Avenue
Hastings, NE 68901-6912
(402) 462-4436

Frentubo

Frentubo is an Italian manufacturer of Kevlar brake lines. While they are not available as ready-to-install kits for Harley-Davidsons, their American distributor can supply them in lengths of 21in to 42in, or in custom-built sets that can be terminated in your choice of the standard banjo fittings or with 10mm threaded ends.

Frentubo Kevlar lines are notable in that they reportedly will not expand at pressures of up to 8,000psi. In comparison, conventional braided stainless lines typically begin expanding at around 6,300psi.

Frentubo lines are distributed by Fast by Ferracci, which is run by Eraldo Ferracci, who specializes in performance parts and services for Ducati racing and street bikes. Some of the finest Ducati roadracers ever built have rolled out of his shop, including the eight-valve Ducatis that Doug Polen won the FIM World Superbike championships on in 1991 and 1992.

Fast by Ferracci
1641 Easton Road
Willow Grove, PA 19090
(215) 657-1276

Fuel Injection Engineering

Stuart Hilborn and the crew at Fuel Injection Engineering can set you up with a Hilborn mechanical fuel injection system for your Harley-Davidson drag bike. The customer has to supply the pump drive and manifold.

Fuel Injection Engineering
25891 Crown Valley Parkway
Laguna Niguel, CA 92677-1498
(714) 582-1170

Full Blast Engineering

Veteran drag racer Leo Hess runs a shop specializing in fabrication, mechanical work and nitrous injection system installation for Harley-Davidson street and drag bikes.

Full Blast Engineering
3204 South Walts
Sioux Falls, SD 57105
(605) 332-2659

Gardner-Wescott Company

Gardner-Wescott in Michigan specializes in chrome-plated stock replacement fasteners for all Harley-Davidsons. These products are only sold through their dealer and distributor network, and they have requested that their contact information not be printed.

Gas-O-Line

Gas-O-Line has built some of the quickest and most beautiful Harley-Davidson drag bikes in France. This shop can provide street and strip engine building and complete motorcycle construction.

Gas-O-Line
19 Rue de la Trinouille
7110 Chalon-Sur-Saive,
France
Phone: 011-33-8593-1283

G&C Racing

G&C is home to Carl Patrick, whose specialty is fabricating components for XR-750 dirt-track racers. Carl can help with construction, engine modifications, parts, and restoration.

G&C Racing
7220 North Dixie Drive
Dayton, OH 45414
(513) 878-0061

GMA Engineering, Inc.

GMA Engineering is run by Bill Gardner, who manufactures a line of brake calipers, master cylinders, and triple clamps exclusively for Harley-Davidsons. All GMA products are nicely finished and clear-anodized for lasting appearance.

Calipers are available in several versions, including the Model A and the more compact Model B, each with a pair of 1 5/8in pistons; and the Model F, with four 1 1/4in pistons. All GMA calipers feature centerless-ground pistons and organic brake pads.

Complete caliper and mount kits can be supplied for the front of all 1984-and-later narrow and wide hydraulic forks (with mirror-imaged brackets used to allow two of these kits to be used on dual-disc forks); Paughco and 1988-and-up factory springer front ends; 1977-1983 dual-disc models; and 1974-1977 FX and Sportster forks. Rear caliper and mount kits are offered for FXRs from 1982-up; Big Twins from 1973-1980, and 1981-1984; Softails from 1984-1986 and 1987-up; and all factory and aftermarket rigid frames that use a 10in disc.

Master cylinders can be sup-

Harley-Davidson factory rider and three-time AMA Camel Pro Grand National series champion Jay Springsteen has ridden Harley-Davidson XR-750s to forty National race wins. Harley-Davidson motorcycles continue to dominate this class. *Bartels' Performance Products*

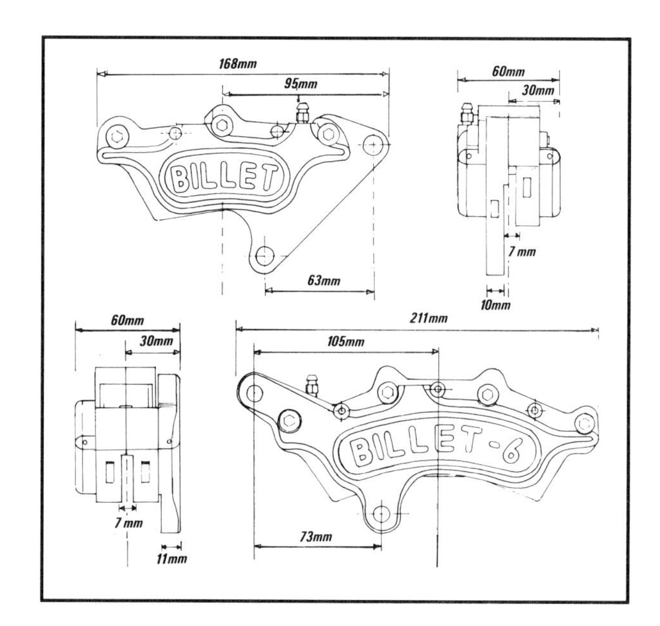

Two of the many different mounting styles for Harrison Engineering billet aluminum calipers are shown in their four-piston (upper) and six-piston configurations.

plied for applications that include the 1973-1979 FX; 1980-1982 FLH and FX; and 1958-1979 FLH. GMA master cylinders use a 5/8in piston. Brake pads, replacement parts, and rebuild kits are available for all GMA calipers and master cylinders. Their triple clamps are designed to be direct replacements for the stock Narrow Glide or Wide Glide triple clamps, and are available complete with a steel steering stem and an aluminum headlight bracket.

GMA Engineering, Inc.
2808 Q Street
Omaha, NE 68107
(402) 734-6141
FAX (402) 734-1574
Catalog available

Goodman Engineering, Ltd.

Simon Goodman and the staff at Goodman Engineering in the U. K. build some interesting chassis for Evolution Sportster engines. Named the Goodman Harley-Davidson Special and styled like the classic British cafe racers, they are available as a bare frame and swing arm (for early or late versions of the Evolution Sportster engine), as a rolling chassis, or complete with a new XLH-1200 engine and five-speed transmission.

In addition to the frame and swing arm, Goodman manufactures its own aluminum castings, exhaust systems, gas and oil tanks, side panels, seats, triple clamps, and wiring harnesses. The Goodman HDS has ten vibration-isolating engine mounts that go a long way to smoothing things out. When coupled with the 5.2gal steel gas tank and the stable-but-responsive handling, the result is a Sportster that does just fine on the highway.

The frame and swing arm are built from Reynolds 531 tubing. The frame's design was inspired by the Norton Featherbed frame. The main frame tubes are 1.25in diameter, with an oval-tubed swing arm. Steering is much more responsive than any stock Harley-Davidson street bike, with a 26-degree head angle and 3.2in of trail providing a much lighter feel. The seat, triple clamps, clip-ons, and rearsets are all handmade. Koni shocks, Marzocchi M1R forks, Tecnomagnesio 18in wheels and Brembo brakes are used, and the complete package weighs in at around 450lb.

Complete machine shop and engine modification services are available to finish off the bike just the way you'd like. The HDS 1200 is available ready to ride with a new 1200 engine and your choice of paint and powder coating. The high parts quality and low production volume put the Goodman HDS in the same price range as some exclusive superbikes like the Buell, the Ducati 851, and the Moto Guzzi Daytona 1000. Of all of these, the Goodman is sure to be the rarest. Simon Goodman is the former managing director for BSA whose grandfather founded another classic British motorcycle company—Velocette.

A feature on the Goodman HDS appeared in the March 1992 issue of *Cycle World* magazine.

Goodman Engineering, Ltd.
Westwood, Buckle Street,
Honeybourne
Evesham, Worcestire
United Kingdom WR11 5QQ
Phone: 011-44-386-832090
FAX: 011-44-386-831614

Goodyear Racing Tire Division

In addition to completely dominating the NASCAR Winston Cup and IndyCar tire market, Goodyear's Racing Tire Division produces some of the world's most popular tires for motorcycle dirt-track and drag racing.

Like much of the equipment in here, these products are strictly for racing. They are sold without any warranty.

The "G3 DT II Eagle Dirt Track Special" front and rear tires are available in the following sizes:

27.0 x 7.0 x 19—for 2.75in rims; 26.8in outside diameter; 7.0in tread width; 5.1in section width; 11.0lb.

27.5 x 7.5 x 19—for 3.50in rims; 27.7in outside diameter; 7.5in tread width; 5.7in section width; 12.0lb.

The "Eagle Dragway Special" front slick is available in the following size:

23.5 x 4.5 x 18—for 2.5in rims; 23.3in outside diameter; 4.3in tread width; 3.3in section width; 5.0lb.

"Eagle Dragway Special" rear slicks are available in the following sizes:

25.0 x 7.0 x 18—for 5.0in rims; 24.9in outside diameter; 7.1in tread width; 6.1in section width; 9.0lb.

25.0 x 8.5 x 18—for 6.0in rims; 25.2in outside diameter; 8.3in tread width; 7.7in section width; 9.5lb.

26.0 x 9.0 x 18—for 7-9in rims; 26.1in outside diameter; 8.7in tread width; 10.0" section width; 14.0lb.

28.0 x 10.0 x 18—for 8-10in rims; 27.7in outside diameter; 9.8in tread width; 11.8in section width; 15.5lb.

Goodyear Racing Tire Division
Goodyear Tire & Rubber Company
1144 East Market Street
Akron, OH 44316-0001
(216) 796-4580
FAX (216) 796-1386
Brochure available; specify Eagle Racing Tire Prices & Engineering Data

Graham's Speed & Custom

Graham Duffy manufactures a variety of machined aluminum components for late Big Twins that includes a hydraulic clutch, triple clamps, and fork braces for Wide Glide forks, four-piston brake calipers and mounts, final drive sprockets, and chain drive conversions.

Graham's Speed & Custom
Barn Close, Langage Industrial Estate
Plympton, Plymouth
United Kingdom PL7 5HQ
Phone: 011-44-752-346575
FAX: 011-44-752-346576

Grimeca

Grimeca disc brakes are popular for all kinds of custom and racing bikes. Installing them on Harley-Davidsons generally calls for some machining unless you are using Marzocchi or other forks they are designed to bolt onto. Grimeca makes some nice four-piston calipers as well as the more common dual-piston versions.

Dual-piston calipers are available in left- and right-side versions for front or rear. They feature die-cast aluminum bodies and use hard-anodized alloy pistons and Ferodo brake pads. Part of their popularity is based on their light weight: 14 ounces for the models that use 30mm pistons, and 30 ounces for the 38mm piston versions. Four-piston calipers share all of the same features as the dual-piston versions but for the four 22mm pistons.

Cosmopolitan Motors is the North American distributor for Grimeca brakes.

Bassano-Grimeca S.p.a.
Via Remigia, 42
40068 S. Lazzaro di Savena (BO), Italy
Phone: 051-625-51-95
FAX: 051-625-63-21

Cosmopolitan Motors, Inc.
301 Jacksonville Road
Hatboro, PA 19040
(215) 672-9100—information
(800) 523-2522—orders only

Gustafsson Plastics

Gustafsson manufactures windshields for Harley-Davidson XLCR cafe racers and XRTT vintage roadracers.

Gustafsson Plastics
P.O. Box 3567
Saint Augustine, FL 32085-3567
(904) 824-3443
FAX (904) 471-4897

Hahn Racecraft

Hahn builds turbochargers and injection systems which, with some engineering and machining work, have been installed on some Big Twin racing engines. This isn't a bolt-on kit and is best left for an expert. Hahn equipment has been used on some serious and successful drag bikes, some of which have been based on Harley-Davidson engines.

Originally a manufacturer of ignition components and machined parts, Bill Hahn Sr. built a turbocharged alcohol-burning Kawasaki in 1981 which set four IDBA records. Bill Hahn Jr. has been piloting the Brad Foote Gear Works Big Twin drag bike.

Hahn Racecraft
110 Kirkland Center, Unit J
Oswego, IL 60543
(708) 851-5444

Hank Scott Racing

A former AMA Grand National racer, Hank Scott now looks after racing cylinder head modifications and engine building in his shop just north of Charlotte, North Carolina. Complete XR-750 dirt-track racers can also be built to order.

Hank Scott Racing
119 Tradewind Lane
Concord, NC 28025
(704) 784-8992

Hannan's Machine Shop

Paul and Jim Hannan specialize in Harley-Davidson cylinder head modifications, custom fabrication and machining for racers and street bikes. Hannan's shop may not be well known, but it is known throughout the industry as a group of talented innovators.

Hannan's Machine Shop
21050 Mission Boulevard
Hayward, CA 94541
(510) 581-5315

Harley-Davidson Motor Company

The Harley-Davidson factory's Racing Department builds limited quantities of the XR-750 Grand National engines for dirt-track racing. The current versions can be special-ordered through Harley-Davidson dealers along with SuperTrapp exhaust systems and other components.

Harley-Davidson's Screamin' Eagle line of components for Big Twins and Sportsters are described in their own section of the directory. Other accessories that are available through Harley-Davidson dealers include oil cooler kits and tachometer kits for all late-model bikes and slightly wider 3.25gal gas tanks for 1982-and-up Sportsters.

Harley-Davidson
Motor Company
P.O. Box 653
3700 West Juneau Avenue
Milwaukee, WI 53201-0653
(414) 342-4680

Harrison Engineering

Ken Harrison has a shop right across the street from the Brands Hatch racetrack. He manufactures brake calipers that bolt onto Harley-Davidsons. These calipers are CNC-machined from billet 6083-T6 aluminum, and are available in four-piston and six-piston versions that will bolt right on to all late model Big Twins and Sportsters.

The six-piston versions of these calipers are about as serious as you can get for a motorcycle. One magazine test rider borrowed one of Ken's test bikes and loved the brakes—but another magazine staffer grabbed a

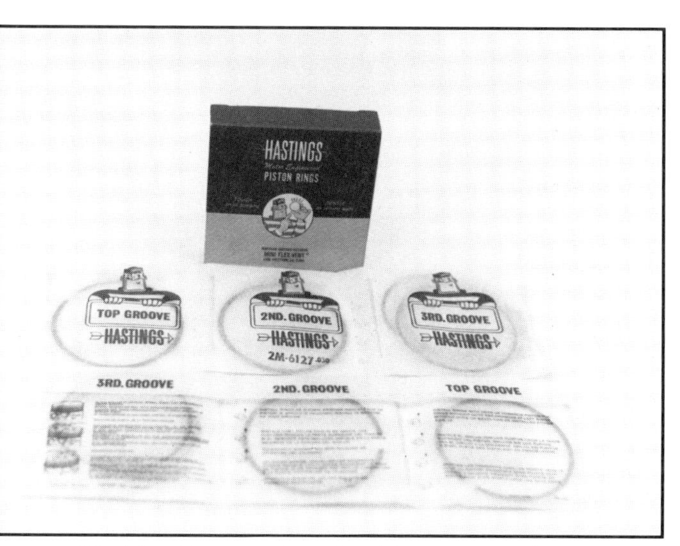

All of the Hastings rings listed here are stocked and distributed by Rivera Engineering. *Rivera Engineering*

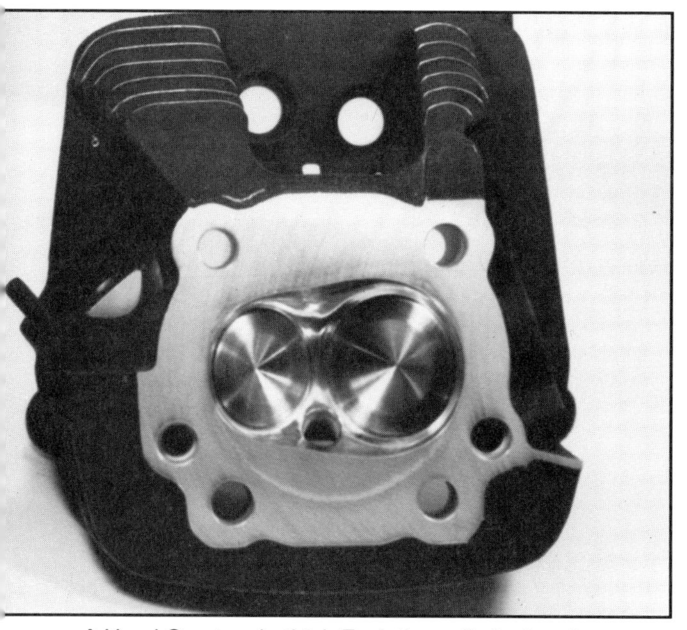

A Head Quarters bathtub Evolution cylinder head.

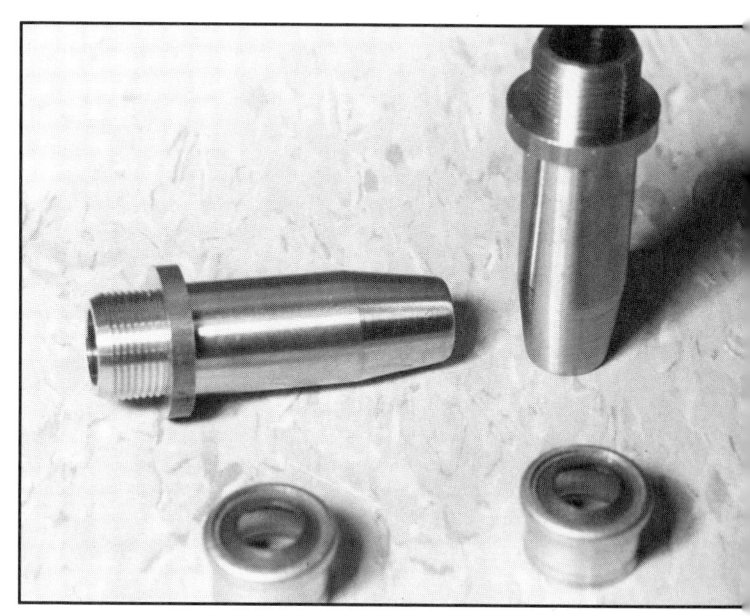

Head Quarters offers these manganese bronze valve guides for Shovelheads with a .376in bore which is intended to be finish-machined by the engine builder.

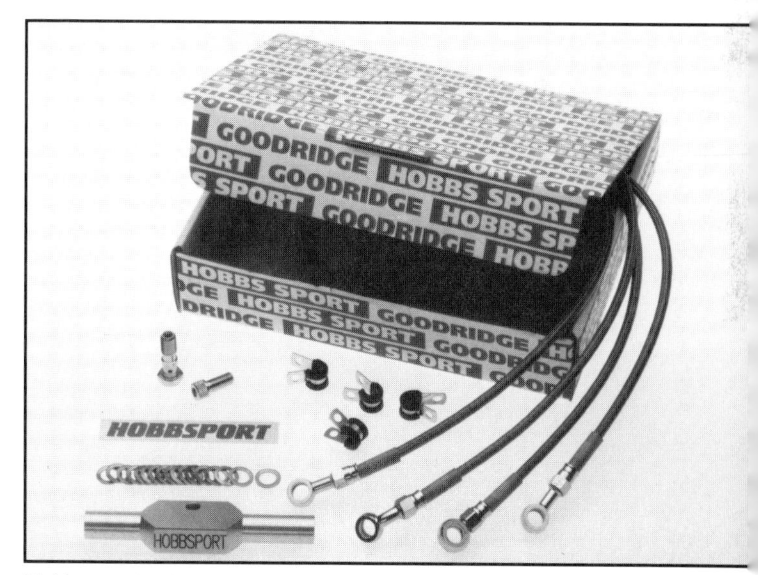

Hobbsport brake line kits are designed to bolt on, fit, and work.

Bob George and Andy Hanson were the two main builders of the Bonneville streamliner that was sponsored by Jammer Cycle Products. It used two 91ci Shovelhead engines running on a mixture of nitro and alcohol. In 1978 they set a two-way average record of 276mph with it, after a one-way qualifying pass at 294. *Bob George, R&R Cycle*

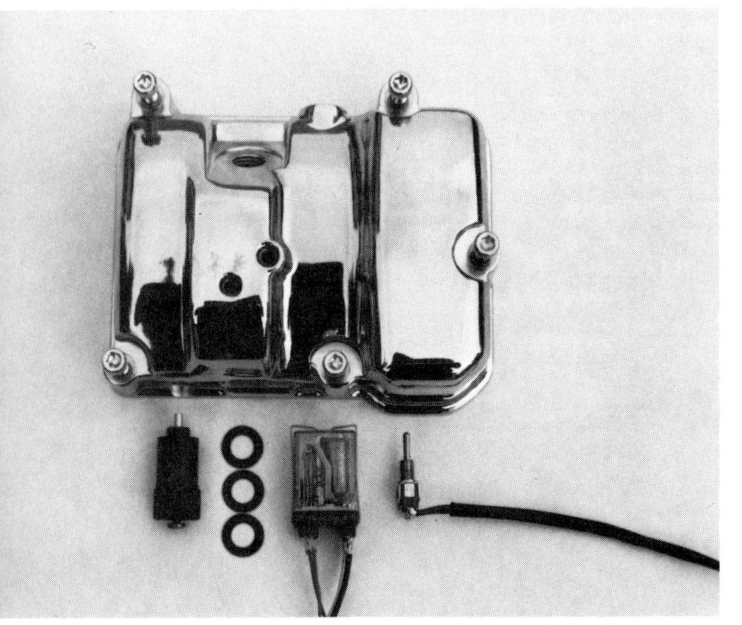

Holeshot's five-speed Big Twin Power Shifter kits cut the power to the ignition coils at the touch of a button, taking the load off the powertrain and allowing instant upshifts without using the clutch.

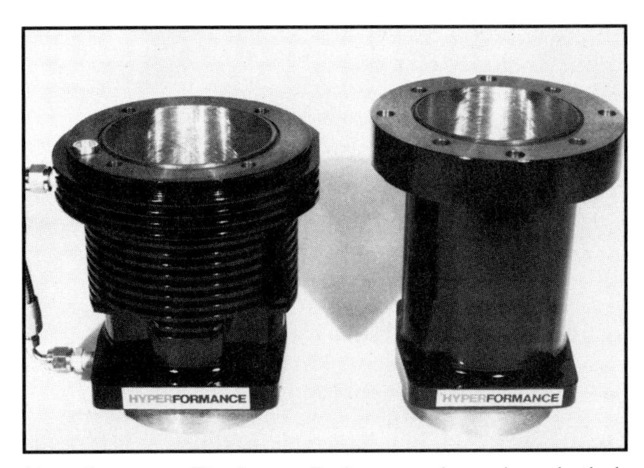

Hyperformance Big Jugs cylinders are shown here in their street (left) and strip (right) versions.

big handful of front brake at 100mph and scared himself silly when his body weight was transferred forward so suddenly. The lesson here is that all things being equal, six-piston calipers will require less lever effort than what we're used to. Harrison calipers accept small Brembo-style brake pads. These calipers are nicely made and reasonably priced.

Harrison Engineering
Unit 35, Blue Chalet Industrial Park
London Road (A20),
West Kingsdown
Sevenoaks, Kent
United Kingdom TN15 6BT
Phone: 011-44-47485-4247
FAX: 011-44-47485-4270

Hastings

Hastings piston rings are manufactured for Harley-Davidson engines in the following sizes:

Big Twins, 1983 and later—standard, .005in, .010in, .020in and .030in.

Big Twins, 1978-1983—standard, .010in, .020in and .030in.

Big Twins, 1948-1980, standard, .010in, .020in, .030in, .040in, .050in, .060in and .070in.

Sportsters, 1986 and later 883—standard, .010in, .020in and .030in.

Sportsters, 1986 and 1987 1100—standard, .010in, .020in and .030in.

Sportsters, 1972-1985 1000—standard, .010in, .020in, .030in, .040in, .050in, .060in and .070in.

Sportsters, 1957-1971 900—standard, .010in, .020in, .030in, .040in, .050in, .060in and .070in.

XR-1000—.010in, .020in, .030in, .040in and .060in.

Moly filled top rings are found on all sets (except for the 900 Sportster top rings, which are cast). The second rings feature a reverse torsional taper face. The three-piece oil rings are designed to be easy to install.

Rivera Engineering
6416 South Western Avenue
Whittier, CA 90606
(310) 692-8944
FAX (310) 699-3943

HDI Systems

Compatible with virtually all Harley-Davidson engines, HDI SWASER ignition systems include a high-energy coil, a set of spark plug wires, and a pair of spark plug boots. This is a "hard discharge ignition" system that makes use of a "pulse forming network." "SWASER" stands for "shock wave amplification through stimulated energy release."

HDI Systems
7424 Second Street
Albuquerque, NM 87017
(505) 345-1527
FAX (505) 344-4105

H-D Performance Specialists

Tom Kelly and the staff at H-D Performance Specialists offer engine modifications for all Harley-Davidsons, including XR-750s. The shop is equipped with a dyno and complete fabricating and machining facilities. They can also provide custom frames on a special-order basis. Engine services include supercharger and turbocharger installations as well as building competitive race bikes for drags or dirt-track racing. Tom has been building Harley-Davidson alcohol, fuel, and gas engines for over thirty years.

H-D Performance Specialists
10395 68th Street
North Pinellas Park, FL 34666
(813) 545-8299
FAX (813) 447-8201

Head Quarters

Head Quarters is run by Doug, Bud, Jo, and Jaime Coffey along with Jim Brooks and Cari Jarvis. They provide expert cylinder head services and offer a line of cams and pistons and a variety of valvetrain components that include adjustable chrome-moly pushrods, valve guides, keepers, seals, seats, shims, springs, and spring collars. Head Quarters also has complete machine shop and service facilities for repairs and component fabrication, including custom intake manifolds.

They have designed cams (which Crane manufactures) for Evolution and Shovelhead Big Twins with ported cylinder heads. Thunder Stick cams with up to .600in lift are available for Evolution engines and up to .535in lift for Shovelheads. Pistons are available in standard and oversizes for Panheads, Shovelheads, Evolution Big Twins, and iron Sportsters. Head Quarters uses a Sunnen VGS 20 head machine that has been modified for working on Harley-Davidson heads which allows them to install valve seats and do valve jobs perfectly concentric to the valve guide bore.

E.C.S. Engineering is the company's American distributor.

Head Quarters
P.O. Box 119
Komoka, Ontario
Canada N0L 1R0
(519) 657-8532
FAX (519) 657-3333

E.C.S. Engineering
220 South Columbia Street
Gastonia, NC 28054
(704) 861-0596—orders
(704) 861-1226—tech
FAX (704) 861-1226

Heavy Duty Cycles, Ltd.

Donny Petersen and a friend founded Heavy Duty Cycles in the early seventies, specializing in engine and transmission modifications and repairs for Harley-Davidson street and drag bikes. You may have seen some of Donny's technical articles in some of the Harley-oriented magazines. He is a firm believer that for the street, performance gains should

Hyperformance Megaheads can be supplied for use with valve diameters up to over 2 1/2in and bore sizes from 4in to 5 1/8in.

hyPerTek Dominator wheels can be supplied with aluminum or magnesium rims, center sections and hubs.

Black Diamond stainless steel valves are one-piece with Stellite tips and are impregnated by a special process for superior wear and corrosion resistance. Also shown here are Hytech guides, seals, seats and springs.

be made without sacrificing reliability. Years of research and experimentation have resulted in a good understanding of which components and combinations work.

Heavy Duty Cycles, Ltd.
2230 Kingston Road
Toronto, Ontario
Canada M1N 1T9
(416) 265-1765

H.E.S. Performance Products

Andy Hanson at H.E.S. offers a variety of solutions for performance-oriented Big Twin and Sportster riders, including clutch pressure plates for Shovelheads, coil kits, engine case inserts for repairing broken Big Twin cases, gaskets, intake manifold adapter rings for Shovelheads and iron Sportsters, intake manifolds for all Evolution engines, pinion shaft bushings for 1936-1972 Big Twins, open primary drive covers for Big Twins with belt primary drives and electric starters, rocker arm shims for Shovelheads, and offset 21-, 22- and 24-tooth sprockets. Andy also provides a variety of custom machining and heli-arc welding services for Big Twin and Sportster owners, including cylinder boring, engine balancing, double-plug cylinder head conversions, and complete street and strip engine building and transmission modifications.

H.E.S. Performance Products
P.O. Box 66294
Los Angeles, CA 90066-6294
(310) 397-3195
Catalog available

Hobbsport, Ltd.

Paul Hobbs at Hobbsport manufactures braided stainless brake line kits for every current Harley-Davidson model that are complete right down to the brake light switch blocks and all of the required hardware. Kits for bikes with dual front discs include an anodized aluminum junction block machined from billet which replaces the stock steel part. Hobbsport components are made from stainless steel, aluminum and chrome-plated steel. Universal oil line kits are also available.

Hobbsport, Ltd.
4D Brent Mill Industrial Estate
South Brent, Devon
United Kingdom TQ10 9YT
Phone: (0364) 73956
FAX: (0364) 73957

Hog Heaven

Run by Werner Hinzmann, Hog Heaven is a large shop in Germany specializing in high-performance modifications for Harley-Davidsons. While they aren't a manufacturer of performance parts, they have built and maintain a number of serious drag bikes and also stock a good supply of speed equipment.

Hog Heaven
Castroper Strasse
203 D—4350
Recklinghausen, Germany
Phone: 011-49-2361-44445

Holeshot Performance

Dale Walker at Holeshot Performance manufactures cam degreeing kits, electric Power Shifter kits, and work stands for Big Twins and Sportsters.

Cam degreeing kits include a dial indicator with a 1in travel and a 3in extension, a degree wheel, and a 17-minute instructional videotape. Power Shifter kits are available for five-speed Big Twin transmissions. They are a bolt-on for 1988 and earlier bikes, while the 1989-1993 models call for a transmission cover modification. The Power Shifter allows riders to power-shift (without using the clutch) at the touch of a button that mounts on the handlebar. A rev limiter is built-in to help keep your engine from becoming "improperly disassembled".

Stands can be used in the shop or in the pits. Made in the popular lever style, these stands are chrome-plated and are designed to fit all conventional (as opposed to single-sided) swing arms. Dale was the 1991 Dragbike! USA Pro Street champion, having ridden his turbocharged and nitrous-injected 1394cc Suzuki in a Kosman chassis to a best time of 8.22 seconds at 171mph. He also sells his own motorcycle drag racing videotapes and operates a motorcycle drag racing school.

Holeshot Performance
311 Chestnut Street
Santa Cruz, CA 95060
(408) 427-3625 or (408) 427-0299
Catalog available

House of Horsepower, Inc.

House of Horsepower, Inc. is run by Greg Richards, who manufactures performance barrels and cases for Big Twins, including Evolution, Shovelhead, Panhead, and Knucklehead engines. Greg also repairs damaged Harley-Davidson engine cases.

House of Horsepower, Inc.
9164 Davidson Way
Lafayette, CO 80026
(303) 665-2827

Howell's, Inc.

Howell's is run by Phil and Pat Howell. All fabricating associated with building a Harley-Davidson street or drag bike can be handled in-house, including custom frames. They have a complete machine shop as well as heli-arc and a flow bench. Phil builds and repairs Harley-Davidson engines, transmissions, and frames for street and strip. An electric oil pump called The Pump II is available for serious drag racing use.

Phil and Pat campaign a Pro Stock Sportster drag bike in AMRA events and have won several Nationals.

Howell's, Inc.
232 South Federal
Denver, CO 80219
(303) 922-2419

Hunt Magneto

Joe Hunt has been building magnetos for race engines since the early days of hot rodding. Hunt magnetos were the first produced for Harley-Davidsons and have been used on all kinds of race cars and motorcycles. They are available for all Big Twins, iron Sportsters, and the flathead WL 45. Hunt can provide repair and rebuilding services for most magnetos, including the Fairbanks Morse magnetos that were original equipment on XR-750s.

Hunt Magneto
11336-A Sunco Drive
Rancho Cordova, CA 95742
(916) 635-5387

Hyperformance

Randy Torgeson opened Hyperformance in 1983 as a full-service machine shop specializing in services for Harley-Davidson enthusiasts. Randy credits his dedication to excellence to a long and rewarding apprenticeship with his mentors, Doc Dytch and Shorty Axtell.

Hyperformance manufactures cylinder heads, cylinders, pistons, and rocker arms for Big Twins. They can also provide expert cylinder head modifications for all Harley-Davidsons from Evolutions all the way back to Knuckleheads.

Big Jugs ductile iron cylinders are available for most Big Twin engines, in two versions. The drag racing barrels have no fins, while the street barrels are finned and include provision for running external oil lines. Bore sizes up to 3 13/16in for the street and up to 4 7/16in for the strip can be supplied, for any combination of engine case and cylinder head. All of these barrels are cast from 80-60-03 ductile iron which is heat treated to 90,000psi and machined for uniform wall thickness. Their own custom-machined and fitted Hytech pistons are recommended for the ideal combination.

Billet aluminum Megaheads are used on the engine produced by (and described under) Michael Düx Industries. Hyperformance Rock n' Rollers rocker arms have roller tips and provide a 1.72:1 ratio. They are available for all Evolution cylinder heads. Hyperformance also offers custom cylinder head modifications, including aluminum welding and repair, combustion chamber machining, resurfacing and bead blasting. They have precision guide plates, fixtures, and related tooling that allows them to accurately weld and machine valve guide holes, valve spring pockets, and spark plug holes, as well as intake and exhaust flanges—all to the correct factory geometry.

Hyperformance
5152A N.E. Twelfth Avenue
Pleasant Hill, IA 50317
(515) 266-6381
FAX (515) 263-8006

hyPerTek, Inc.

Dave Himebauch at hyPerTek builds lightweight modular wheels to fit any current or vintage Harley-Davidson. These wheels feature spun aluminum or magnesium rims and distinctive triangular magnesium center sections. Modular (and laced) wheels offer the advantage of having replaceable rims, to allow repair or changing sizes without having to buy a complete new wheel.

When Dave tried in 1987 to buy a set of aftermarket wheels for his road racer, he found the wheels available were expensive, expensive to fit, easily made obsolete by changes in tire technology, and often difficult or impossible to use on more than one model of bike.

In 1988 he designed a wheel that would address all of these shortcomings while remaining light and having low aerodynamic drag. The result is the hyPerTek Dominator wheels, which feature spun aluminum or magnesium rims along with CNC-machined magnesium three-spoke center sections and hubs. All components are clear-coated after polishing. The modular design allows the use of different tires by changing rims. Changing hubs allows a wheel to be run on a different bike. Dominator wheels are available in 3.5in, 4.25in, 5.25in, 5.5in, and 6.0in widths in 17in diameter; and in 2.5in, 4.25in, 5.75in, or 6.25in widths in 18in diameter.

hyPerTek, Inc.
1463 Acadia Street
Simi Valley, CA 93063
(805) 583-2447

International Engineering Industries, Inc.

International Engineering manufactures a line of products for drag racing including air shifters, barrels, aluminum oil tanks, swing arms, throttles, transmission mounts, triple clamps, and spun aluminum wheels. IEI can also supply complete rolling chassis for Big Twin and Sportster drag bikes.

Barrels are machined from 4130 chrome-moly bar stock and can be supplied with bores from 3 5/8in to 3 13/16in. Swing arms are made from chrome-moly tubing in a choice of 4, 6, or 8in over the stock length. Throttles have a 7/8in bore and require only one-fifth of a turn to open fully. Transmission mount plates are aluminum, fully machined to save weight. They accept all four-speed Big Twin transmissions from 1936.

International Engineering
 Industries, Inc.
9020 South Odell
Bridgeview, IL 60455
(708) 598-7799
Catalog available

Iskenderian Racing Cams

Ed Iskenderian pioneered "Isky" cams and valvetrain components, which have been known to the race car crowd for more than three decades. Isky now produces valve spring assemblies for all Evolution Big Twin engines. These kits are compatible with cams having as much as .600in of lift and include keepers, seats, and shims, with a choice of steel or titanium retainers.

Iskenderian Racing Cams
16020 South Broadway
Gardena, CA 90247-9990
(213) 770-0930
FAX (310) 515-5730
Literature available

I.S.R.

I.S.R. in Sweden manufactures disc brakes and complete brake kits for late-model Harley-Davidsons in addition to their steering damper. The high end of the line of I.S.R. calipers has a one-piece body machined from billet aluminum, six 28mm pistons, and six separate Ferodo brake pads. With the pads, they weigh in at 30 ounces. Full-floating discs are available in 13in and 11 1/2in.

Steering dampers can be supplied with a stroke of 100mm or 120mm. Both versions provide a choice of 27 damping adjustments. The American distributor for I.S.R. is Slater Brothers.

Slater Brothers
P.O. Box 1
Mica, WA 99023-0001
(509) 924-5131
FAX (509) 928-0918

Jack Hagemann, Jr.

Jack is a master fabricator whose specialty is hand-formed aluminum gas tanks and bodywork. If you've seen a recent Harley-Davidson XR-750 Grand National race bike, chances are it had a Hagemann gas tank on it. Jack will custom-build an aluminum tank for your particular need, whether it's a bigger tank for your Sportster or a one-piece 5gal tank for an FXR or a road racer. These tanks can be fitted with conventional or aircraft filler caps.

Jack, Jr., began forming sheet aluminum components in 1965, following in the footsteps of Jack Sr., the master of this art. Jack Jr. inherited his father's talent for hand-forming sheet aluminum. In the mid-seventies Jack started building gas tanks for XR-750 flat-trackers and TT bikes. Initially considered a luxury, they soon became necessary because the high-octane fuel being used was dissolving fiberglass tanks. Requests for oil tanks for the Harley-Davidson racing bikes came soon after, followed by seats, fenders, and fairings. Jack also built several custom tanks for roadracers and for street and competition vintage bikes.

Jack now concentrates on fabricating XR-750 gas tanks and oil tanks for about ninety-percent of the American racing teams and privateers. Many of the "XR-883" custom Sportsters (described under Storz Performance) are running Hagemann gas tanks.

Bernie Willett, a talented Australian fabricator, met and worked with Jack in the early eighties. They collaborated on the fabrication of about 130 gas tanks for XR-750s. Jack doesn't advertise because he is already busy enough. In fact, the number below is unlisted. He will be happy to help you with a special project, but his shop is one of the many small shops in this book that just doesn't have the time to deal with a lot of casual inquiries. Hagemann ain't snarly, but there's only one of him.

Jack Hagemann, Jr.
7380 Croy Road
Morgan Hill, CA 95037
(408) 779-4898

Bernie Willett
Eltham, Victoria
Australia
Phone: 03-437-0232

Jacobs Electronics

Jacobs manufactures ignition systems and components for Harley-Davidsons. The complete "Energy Team" ignition system is comprised of the Energy Pak electronic module, a Twin Tower Ultra Coil, metal-core ignition wires, instructions, and tuning tips. Jacobs makes some impressive claims for the performance of their Energy Team systems, including their systems' "delivering over 400 percent more spark energy than any other ignition system."

Jacobs Electronics
500 North Baird Street
Midland, TX 79701
(915) 685-3345—information
(800) 627-8800—orders only
Catalog available

Jagg

Jagg manufactures oil coolers suitable for racing and street use Their current model has six internal oil passages. The tanks on the coolers have machined aluminum fins and provide a great amount of cooling area for the unit's size—Jagg claims it's three times the cooling area of its closest competitor. Four oil cooler models are available, to fit 1965-and-later Big Twins as well as 1957-and-later Sportsters. Every Jagg cooler is pressure tested to 200psi. Their literature points out that every 20-degree (F) reduction in operating temperature doubles the life of the oil, with a related effect on engine components.

Jagger Sales
24 South Clayton Street
Centerburg, OH 43011
(614) 625-6228
FAX (614) 625-6113
Literature available

The Hagemann one-off aluminum tank on this custom Shovelhead makes the bike stand out.

Right, Jagg uses Uralite mounts to isolate vibration, and mounts them on the left downtube so as not to block the airflow to the front cylinder as some other designs do.

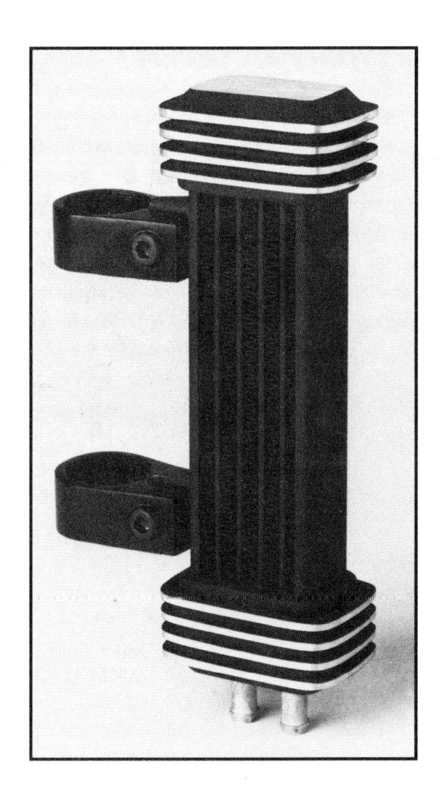

The heart of the Jacobs Energy Team system is the Energy Pak module, which "automatically measures the electrical resistance of each spark; then by adjusting that spark, meets each cylinder's individual demands, guaranteeing 100 percent fuel burn".

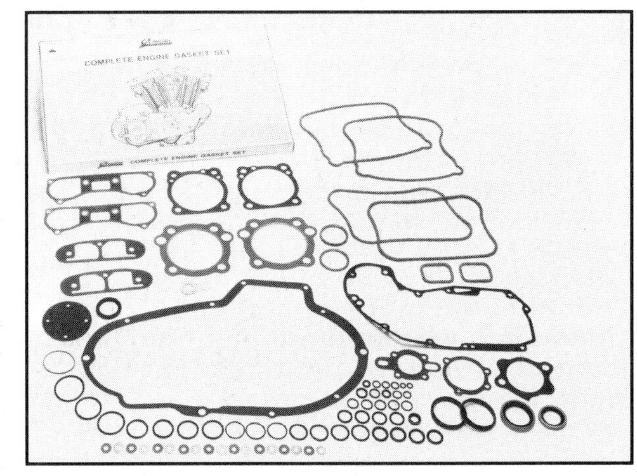

Here is a complete Sportster gasket set from James Gaskets. Gaskets are also available for Evolution Big Twins with big-bore kits. *Ralph Foster, Pro Product Photography*

James Gaskets, Inc.

James Clark's company manufactures gaskets, oil seals, and O-rings exclusively for Harley-Davidson motorcycles. All of these products are available for Evolution, Shovelhead, Panhead, and Knucklehead Big Twins, Evolution and iron Sportsters, and all 80in, 74in, 61in, and 45in flatheads.

James Gaskets, Inc.
P.O. Box 5297
Modesto, CA 95352-5297
(209) 578-3599—orders and inquiries
(800) 523-7843—orders outside California
(800) 523-6195—orders in California
FAX (209) 529-8678

James Haithcock

Drag racer James Haithcock's machine shop produces the cylinder heads he designed for his own Top Fuel Harley drag bike. They are machined from 6061-T6 billet aluminum and feature unique combustion chambers, 1.950in intake runners, 2.125in intake valves, 1.95in exhaust valves, and D-shaped exhaust ports.

James Haithcock
4000 New Hope Road
Raleigh, NC 27604
(919) 876-5883
FAX (919) 878-9205

Jan's Cycle Gaskets

Jan Van de Vaarst and the staff at Jan's have a complete line of gaskets, available individually and in sets, for Harley-Davidson Big Twins and Sportsters. Their products include Teflon-lined head gaskets and exhaust gaskets for Shovelheads. The selection of gaskets is huge, with each gasket available in a choice of several 100 percent asbestos-free, American-made materials. Jan's products are manufactured in the United States.

Jan's Cycle Gaskets
P.O. Box 5790
Somerset, NJ 08875-5790
(908) 613-4494
FAX (908) 613-4593

JayBrake

JayBrake manufactures CNC-machined disc brake calipers, caliper brackets, levers, and master cylinders for Harley-Davidsons. Brake calipers are available in two-piston and four-piston versions. The two-piston calipers use a pair of steel 1.25in pistons. The four-piston versions are made in two styles with the difference being the mounting ears. Caliper brackets are available in twenty-five different versions, including anodized aluminum or chrome-plated steel for 10in or 11.5in discs and a variety of frame styles. Master cylinders are CNC-machined from solid aluminum. Front master cylinder and lever assemblies have a 5/8in bore, and matching clutch levers are available.

JayBrake
P.O. Box 1551
145 North Fourth Street
Lewiston, NY 14092-1551
(716) 754-9092

Jaynes Electric

After working in the automotive electrical business since 1972, Allen Jaynes now also manufactures alternators that are designed to be direct replacements for the stock Harley-Davidson generators.

Jaynes Electric
9060 Sunset Boulevard West
Pleasant Grove, CA 95668
(916) 991-1999

JFZ Engineered Products

JFZ makes disc brake calipers that can be installed on racing or street Harley-Davidsons with some fabrication. Larger versions of their brakes are popular on the NASCAR Winston Cup stock car racing circuit and on Top Fuel cars.

JFZ Engineered Products
440 East Easy Street #3
Simi Valley, CA 93065
(805) 581-3674
FAX (805) 581-3601

Jim's Aero Glide Racing, Ltd.

Jim Mantle produces spun aluminum racing wheels designed to bolt right onto Big Twins and Sportsters. They are normally supplied with cast and machined aluminum hubs; billet aluminum hubs are also available. The side plates are spun from .188in marine grade aluminum plate. These wheels have stainless steel bolts and valve stems, a rolled-in safety bead, and a finely brushed finish.

The standard sizes for Jim's rear wheels are (measurements in inches) 15x5, 16x3, 16x4, 16x5, and 18x4. Front wheels are offered in 16x3, 16x4, and 19x2.5. Other sizes can be supplied if at least ten wheels are ordered to offset the cost of tooling up for a new size.

Jim's Aero Glide Racing, Ltd.
8086 Alexander Road
Delta, British Columbia
Canada V4G 1C6
(604) 946-3993
FAX (604) 946-6665
Literature available

Jim's Machining

Jim Thiessen and the staff at Jim's Machining have been making high-performance components and specialized tools for Big Twin and Sportster engines since 1967. Jim's components include bearing races, bushings, cam bushings, countershafts, crank pins, crank pin nuts, distributor shaft bushings, engine case races, idler gear shafts, kick starter shafts and bushings, lifters and guides, mainshafts, oil pump bushings and shafts, pinion shafts and bushings, rocker arm shafts, and sprocket shafts.

Vintage racing parts include crank pins for WR-TT models

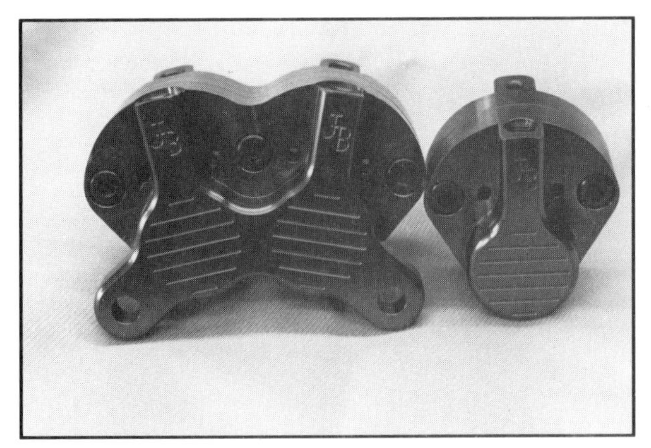

JayBrake offers a variety of styles of calipers.

Typical weights for Jim's wheels are 16lb for 16in and 18lb for 19in.

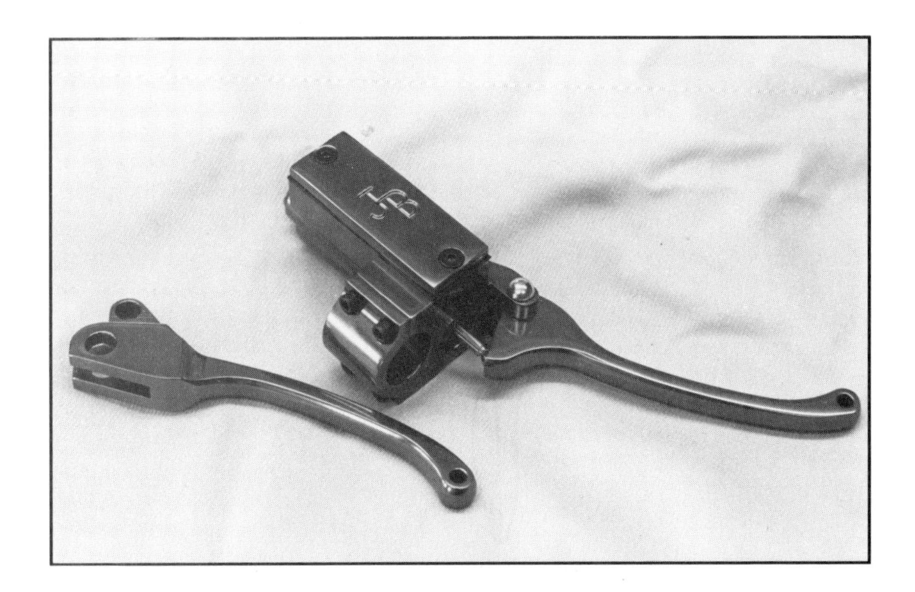

JayBrake has levers of all kinds.

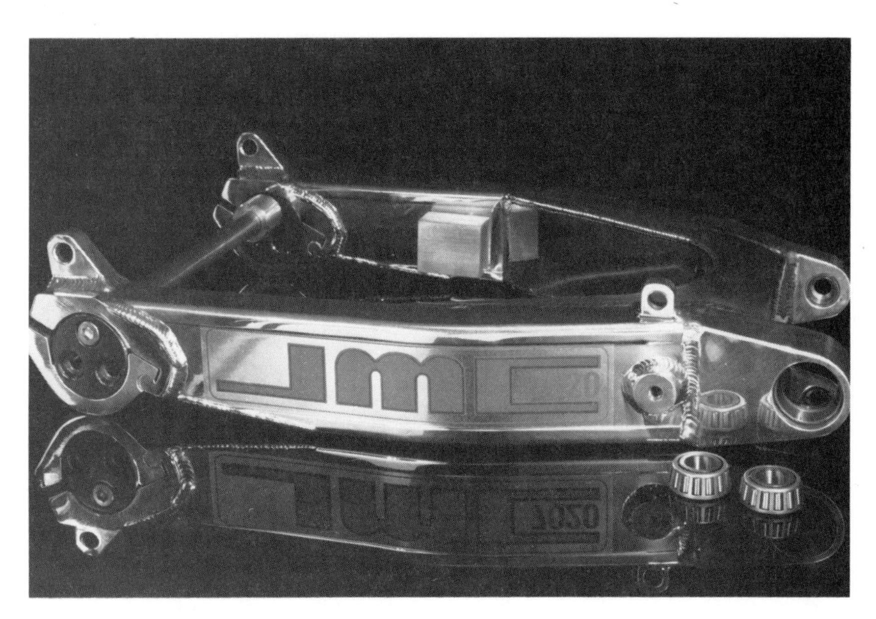

This aluminum swing arm for Evolution Sportsters shows the trick JMC eccentric rear axle adjusters.

and 1915-1929 Big Twins, and sprocket shafts and two versions of pinion gear shafts for WR and KR models. They make over thirty-two different tools for Harley-Davidsons, including clutch hub pullers for Big Twins from 1936 and up, connecting rod race tools to support the rod while the races are removed and replaced, lifter roller tools, pinion gear pullers, stands for Big Twin and Sportster engines, and wheel bearing race tools.

Jim's Machining
531 Dawson Drive
Camarillo, CA 93010
(805) 482-6913
FAX (805) 482-7422

JMC

John McCarten at JMC fabricates components for roadracing and manufactures aluminum swing arms for all swing arm Harley-Davidsons including Shovelheads and Evolution Sportsters. Made from 7020 aluminum, all of their swing arms have the patented JMC rear axle quick-release system for quick wheel changes. Another feature that comes from their roadracing background is their eccentric axle adjusters, which give you the option of making fine adjustments to the height of the back end for cornering clearance, or for slightly altering steering geometry.

JMC aluminum swing arms are complete kits designed to bolt on. They include a high-tensile steel axle, aluminum axle spacers, and new tapered roller bearings for the swing arm pivot. They are available with a standard satin finish or fully polished.

JMC
1 Lodge Works, Birchill Road
Kirkby, Merseyside
United Kingdom L33 7TD
Phone: 011-44-51-546-0604
FAX: 011-44-51-546-9613

Johnstone Products

Gordon Johnstone manufactures performance cams and intake manifolds for Big Twin and Sportster engines. Cams can be ordered for virtually any Big Twin or Sportster. Manifolds are available to fit all Evolution engines and are compatible with Mikuni and S&S carburetors. They are CNC-machined from solid aluminum and put an end to leakage problems.

Johnstone Products
P.O. Box 1715
Ormond Beach, FL 32175-1715
(904) 673-4714
Literature available

Jørn "Høvding" Jacobsen's MC-rep.

Jørn Jacobsen is a Swedish drag racer whose shop provides engine modification services for Harley-Davidson engines as well as fabrication and machining work. I heard about Jørn in a Swedish publication called *Norsk Biker Magazine*. Unfortunately I don't understand a word of Swedish, so from looking at the article about him and his bike I can only tell you this: his bike is a Top Fuel Evolution Big Twin based on a set of Delkron cases, a Bentec transmission, a Red Shift cam, and a Nungesser Engineering slipper clutch; sitting in a Nungesser Engineering chassis. He feeds it 96percent nitro, and, like many of the most interesting people I've met in my life, he has the eyes of a wild man.

Jørn "Høvding" Jacobsen's MC-rep.
2634 Fåvang, Sweden
Phone: 062-82-870
FAX: 062-82-170

JRT Cycle Performance

JRT is run by Teddy Grabowski, who specializes in high-performance engine building for Big Twin and Sportster drag bikes.

JRT Cycle Performance
2462 North Jerusalem Road
North Bellmore, NY 11710
(516) 785-6440

JW Racing

Jim Whitaker is a Twin Sports roadracer who makes clip-on handlebars, rearsets, and steering damper mounts for Sportster roadracers.

Clip-on bars are designed for the 39mm Sportster forks (other sizes available, too). Their exceptionally rugged fork tube clamps are machined from billet aluminum (as opposed to the more common castings). They are modular in construction, providing racers with the ability to replace any damaged parts without having to buy a new set or disassemble the forks. The 11 1/2in handlebar tubes are machined from .120in-wall aluminum tubing and angle downward at six degrees.

Rearsets are machined from 6061-T6 aluminum and are fully polished. They can be supplied in two basic styles. One retains the stock shift pattern, while the GP style inverts it (one up, four down) as most of them do. The GP style versions accept a Suzuki GSX-R clevis and footpegs; while the Standard (non-inverted shift pattern) rearsets are designed for stock footpegs. Steering damper mounts are machined and welded from aluminum and bolt directly to the front cylinder head.

JW Racing
9 Pondview Drive
Auburn, NH 03032
(603) 483-5458

Karata Enterprises

Jim Longo at Karata produces belt drive kits for Big Twins and Sportsters and makes a magneto for Big Twins. The Karata magneto was a joint venture between Karata and Vertex.

This right-side view of the JW Racing rearsets shows the relocated footpeg, brake lever and master cylinder. *Jim Whitaker*

These JW Racing rearsets do not change the stock Sportster's shift pattern and accept the stock footpegs. *Jim Whitaker*

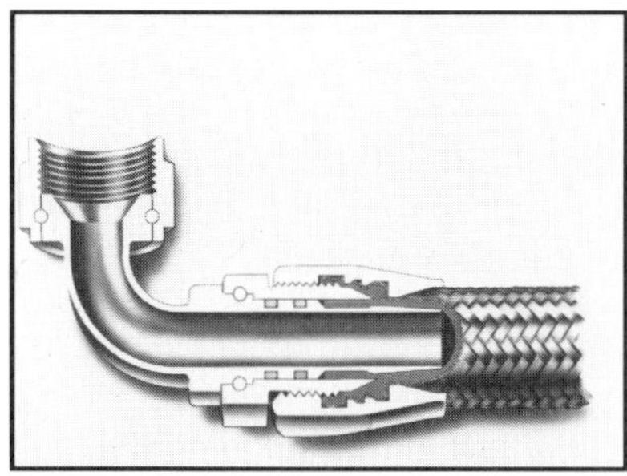

This cutaway view shows the unique construction of the Keith Black Dual Seal adjustable hose ends, which are available in several angles.

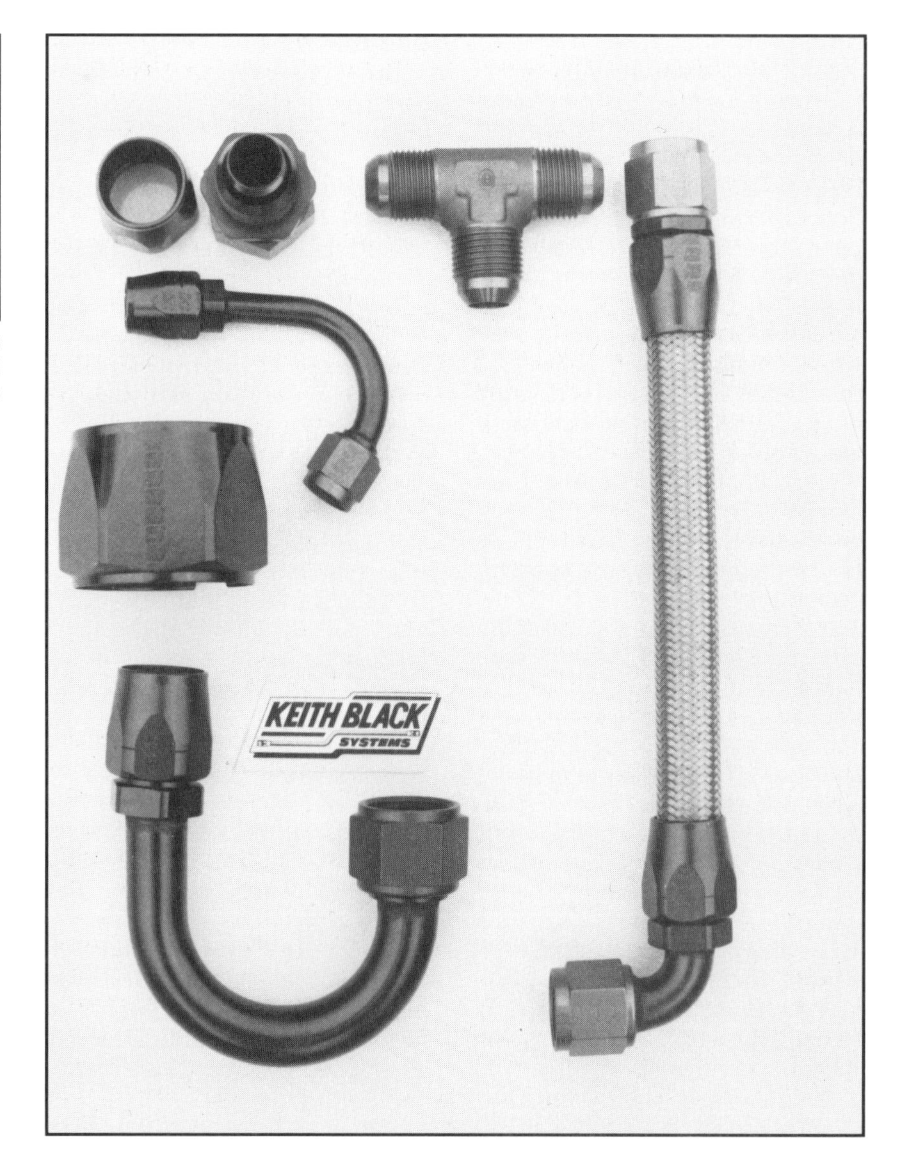

Keith Black stainless steel braided hose has an operating temperature range of -40° F to +300° F, and comes in several inside diameters. A good selection of Keith Black hose and fittings are available for a wide variety of applications.

Karata Enterprises
3 River Road
Conshocken, PA 19428
(215) 825-2070

Kateley Performance Products

Gordon Kateley manufactures cams, pushrods, valve springs, and pistons for Big Twin and Sportster engines. Several years ago Gordon built an outstanding Pro Stock FXRS drag bike for competition and to develop new products.

Kateley Performance Products
P.O. Box 25271
Anaheim, CA 92852-5271
(714) 534-0564 (6:00 pm—9:00 pm only)

Keith Black Systems, Inc.

In 1990, the legendary Top Fuel and Blown Alcohol automotive drag racing engine builder Keith Black began manufacturing a variety of brake lines and related hardware. These products are intended for use on automotive, marine, and motorcycle applications and are the lines of choice for many NASCAR Winston Cup racing teams. One of the interesting features of the Keith Black lines is the patented Dual Seal adjustable hose ends, which use a pair of O-rings to provide adjustability and positive sealing. Open-end hose end wrenches are designed to be used with Keith Black hose ends. Double-ended wrenches are made in #3 and 4, #6 and 8, #10 and 12, and #16 and 20.

Keith Black Systems, Inc.
5630 Imperial Highway
South Gate, CA 90280
(310) 861-4765
FAX (310) 861-5503
Catalog available

Keith Peterson

Keith specializes in Harley-Davidson fabrication and machining. His products include custom frames and wheels. After riding a rigid frame Big Twin for years, Keith injured his back in an accident. He then designed a frame that combined the soft ride of a swing arm frame with the look of a rigid. Wheels are spun aluminum, similar in appearance to those made by Jim's Aero Glide Racing.

Keith Peterson
Slatthog 340 36
Moheda, Sweden

Ken Maely Enterprises

This is the man who builds the plates for the bottom of the boot on practically every winning flat-track and speedway racer's left foot. This is his specialty, and he's been at it since 1950. You send him your left boot and specify flat-track or speedway racing. Ken also offers disc brakes, an ignition kill switch, and can provide frame straightening and welding services for dirt-track racers.

Ken and his truck are fixtures at dirt-track races, where he works out of the van to hard-face the riders' boot plates. Nobody does it better, and for that matter, no one else specializes in offering these services. He's like the dirt-track racing community's town blacksmith.

Ken Maely Enterprises
8580 Bedford Motorway
Corona, CA 91719
(714) 277-8989
Price list available

Pat Kennedy's Custom Motorcycles

Pat Kennedy and Brook Bryant have scratch-built some of the cleanest custom Harley-Davidsons around. Their products include disc brake kits using I.S.R. calipers and cast aluminum rocker boxes for Shovelheads. They also offer engine building, machining, and fabrication for all high-performance Harley-Davidsons, including building custom exhaust systems, frames, and wheels. Most of their work is done on street bikes, but they have fabricated a number of Big Twin and Sportster drag bikes.

Pat Kennedy's Custom Motorcycles
905 East Fremont Street, P.O. Box 670
Tombstone, AZ 85638-0670
(800) 331-9903
FAX (602) 457-2239
Catalog available

KF Engineering

Mark, Ray, and Austin Fageol manufacture four models of superchargers for a variety of applications, some have been used on Harley-Davidsons, with the largest models intended for racing engines. Their four sizes are rated at 33.5, 48.3, 63.2, and 70.6ci per revolution. These superchargers feature a pair of three-lobe rotors, spinning on ball bearings. The supercharger housings are extruded from 6061 aluminum to provide the accuracy required for maintaining close internal clearances. The end plates are cast from 356 aluminum which, along with the housing, is hard-anodized for durability after machining.

KF Engineering
1255 Hayden Lane
El Cajon, CA 92021
(619) 447-1092
Literature available

Kinsler Fuel Injection, Inc.

Kinsler can supply a complete fuel injection system for any Harley-Davidson street or race bike. Their products include throttle body fuel injection manifolds, bypass valves, fuel filters, jets, nozzles, and shut-off valves. They also offer fuel injection services that include barrel valve spool custom grinding, calibration, flow testing, jet matching, rebuilding, and repair.

Kinsler's fuel injection system for Harley-Davidsons is available with a variety of throttle bore sizes. These systems fea-

Kennedy custom frames are heli-arc-welded from chrome-moly tubing to your specs for length, steering head angle, stretch, engine, drive system, and transmission. They can be built to accept rear tire widths up to 10in. Reproductions of Panhead and Shovelhead frames are also available. The bike shown here isn't a race bike, but it shows you Kennedy's superb craftsmanship.

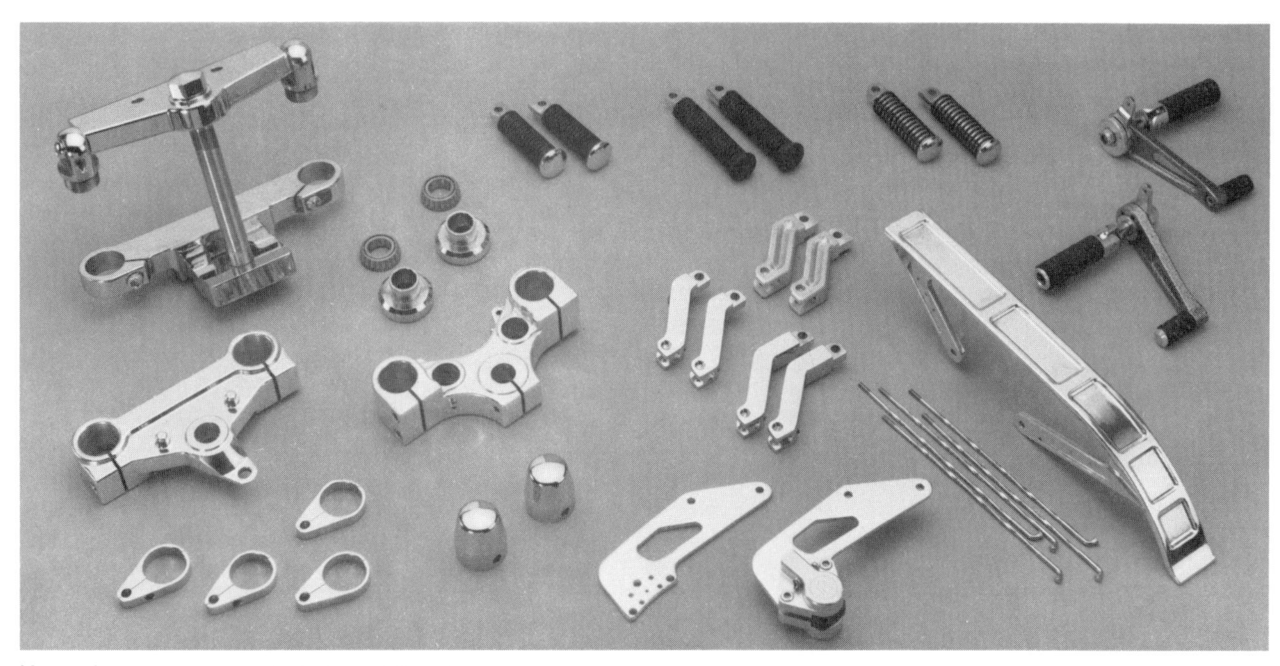

Kennedy's custom parts includes a billet aluminum belt final drive guard produced by BW Billets.

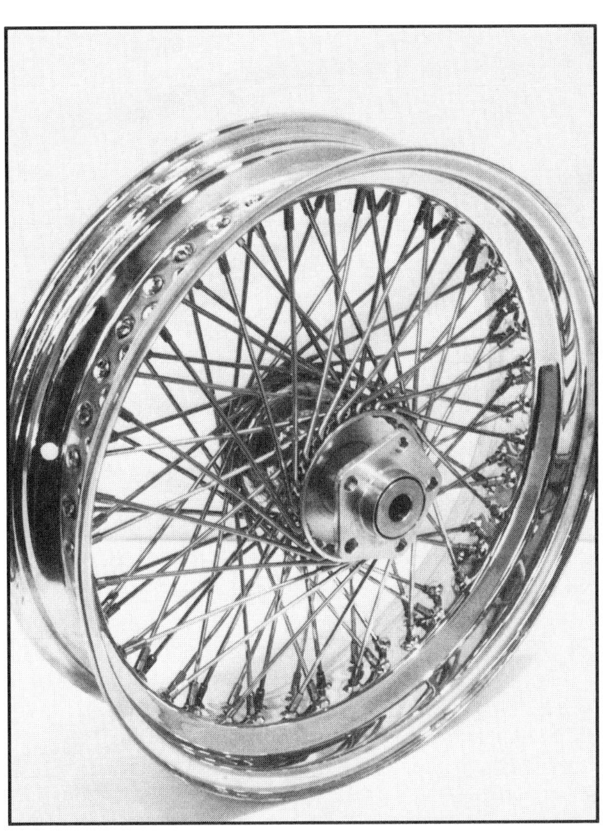

Kennedy's resident wheel lacing expert Brook Bryant builds custom laced wheels, using machined and polished stainless steel hubs.

This Kinsler throttle body fuel injection manifold is shown with the optional safety shut-off valve and constant-flow barrel valve.

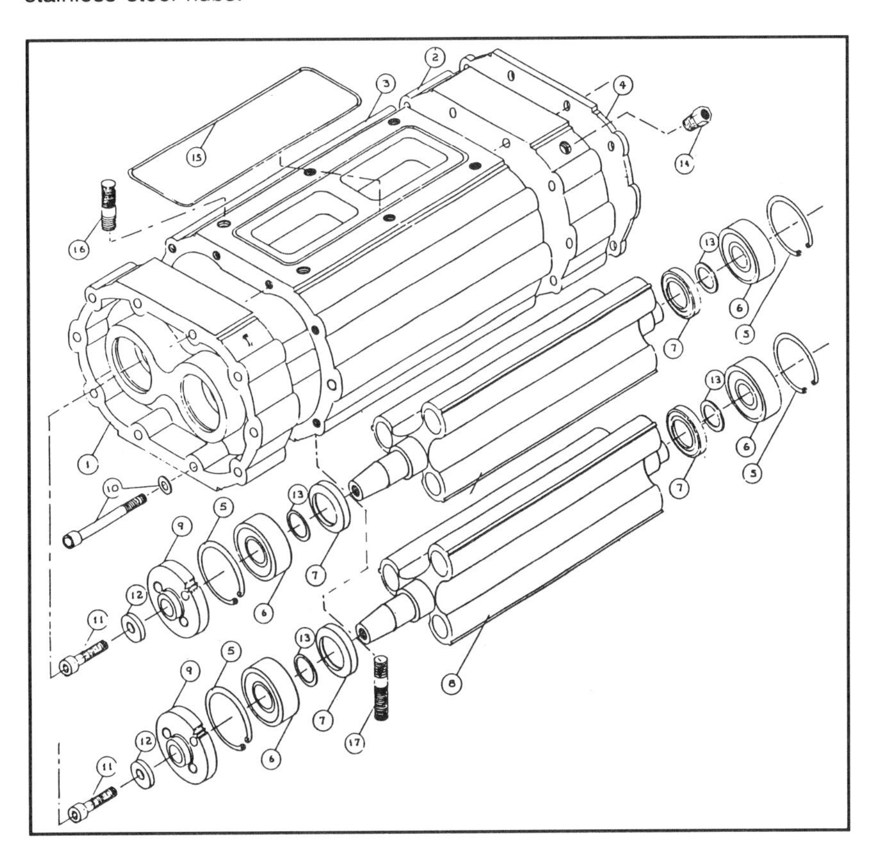

An exploded view of a KF Engineering supercharger. All four models are essentially the same, varying in length and displacement.

ture bronze throttle shaft bushings, a housing machined from billet aluminum with an O-ring seal on the manifold mating surface, and a spun aluminum ram tube with a removable adapter. They can be supplied with an optional safety shut-off valve and constant-flow barrel valve.

The Kinsler catalog is also a handbook filled with useful information such as detailed plumbing schematics, troubleshooting charts, and explanations of complete fuel injection systems from the fuel tank to bypass valves.

Kinsler Fuel Injection, Inc.
1834 Thunderbird
Troy, MI 48084
(313) 362-1145
FAX (313) 362-1032
Catalog available

K&N Engineering

In business more than thirty years, K&N manufactures a line of high-performance air filters, filter elements, jetting kits, and brake pads for Harley-Davidsons.

Custom air filters are available for Bendix, Keihin, early four-bolt Linkert, Mikuni, and S&S carburetors. K&N Filtercharger replacement air filter elements are available for most models, including the XR-1000 and the Harley-Davidson Eagle Iron and teardrop S&S air cleaners. K&N brake pads are completely asbestos-free and are claimed not to squeak or squeal. They are available for Big Twins from 1937 and up and for all Sportsters.

Dirt-track filters for the XR-750 are made to fit the Mikuni 36mm and 38mm carburetors. Oval versions come in various lengths, as do the newer D-shaped oval versions with longer necks. Dynojet Stage 1 recalibration kits come in two versions, one for models with 40mm CV carburetors, and one for models with 40mm CV carburetors with accelerator pumps. K&N also supplies its own air filter oil and sealing grease as well as filter cleaner and degreaser. It's worth noting that K&N makes some nice drag bars (as well as other styles of 1in bars) for Harley-Davidsons. Like all K&N products, they are designed and manufactured in America.

K&N Engineering
561 Iowa Avenue
Riverside, CA 92502
(714) 684-9762—technical
(800) 858-3333—orders only
FAX (714) 684-0716
Catalog available; specify motorcycle catalog

Knight Racing Frames

Terry Knight produces frames and swing arms for Harley-Davidson XR-750 Grand National dirt-track racers using chrome-moly tubing. Terry will also custom-build chrome-moly street or drag bike frames for any engine. Knight Racing produced the frames for the last batch of XR-750 Grand National race bikes that were sold complete by the Harley-Davidson factory.

Knight Racing Frames
2707 Mount Baker Highway
Deming, WA 98226
(206) 592-2838

Koenig Engineering

Koenig makes brake discs and mounts, forks, frames, triple clamps, and modular wheels for drag bikes. The 29lb Koenig F-16 frame is heli-arc welded from 4130 chrome-moly tubing. It has a fuel tank built into the top tube, and can be supplied in your choice of 65- to 90in wheelbase, ready to accept most motorcycle engines.

Koenig Engineering
298 N.W. 48th Place
Des Moines, IA 50313
(515) 244-1410
Catalog available

Koni America, Inc.

Koni manufactures a line of shock absorbers with black springs for fit most late-model Harley-Davidsons. Arlen Ness also has his own line of chrome-plated Koni shocks that were designed for 1982-and-up FXRs and 1979-and-up Sportsters. They are available in several lengths.

Koni America, Inc.
8085 Production Avenue
Florence, KY 41042
(606) 727-5000
FAX (606) 727-5001

Kosman Specialties, Inc.

If you follow motorcycle racing, chances are you've already seen Kosman's products. Sandy Kosman has been around Harley-Davidson drag and dirt-track racing since the seventies.

Kosman Specialties manufactures all kinds of specialized equipment for drag racing and dirt-track racing, including chrome-moly frames for drag bikes with any Harley-Davidson engines, drag racing forks, traditional laced or lightweight modular wheels, engine mounts, triple clamps, drilled or solid stainless steel axles, wheelie bars, and aluminum sprockets. They can fabricate or supply just about anything your drag bike chassis is likely to need, or build complete rolling chassis for drag racing or street riding. Goodyear drag slicks and Dunlop front tires are stocked, and a tire skimming service is available. Kosman can modify your existing frame for drag racing, by giving it a new head tube and reinforcement or by building a new top half that includes a beefier top tube that also contains the fuel tank.

The basic Kosman Stage 1 frame can be supplied with Big Twin or Sportster engine mounts. Any extras can be supplied, including assorted brackets and an aluminum fuel tank. A Kosman rolling chassis in-

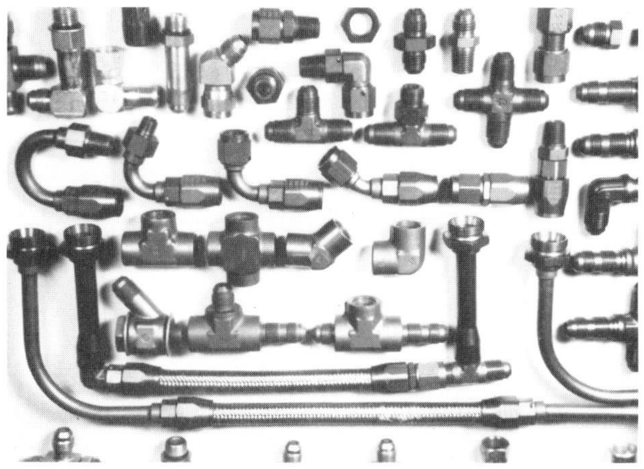

Plumbing components available from Kinsler stock include filters, flapper check valves, fuel shut-off valves, and tank vents.

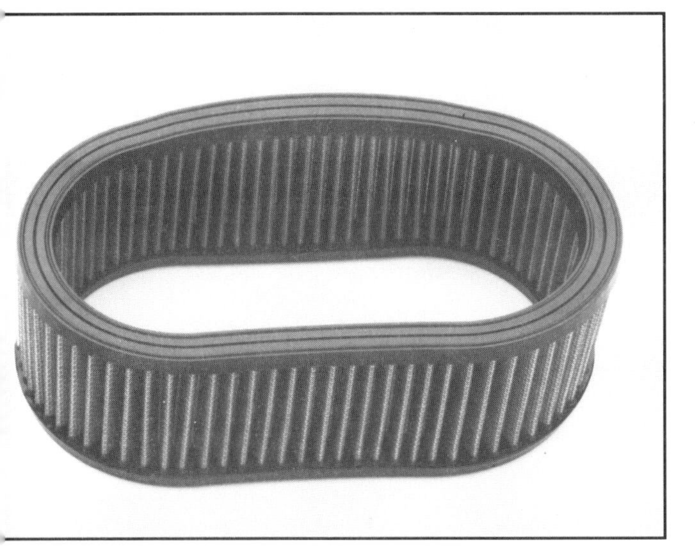

This K&N Filtercharger air filter element is a replacement for the standard oval air cleaner. The oval air cleaners are commonly used with the popular S&S air cleaner.

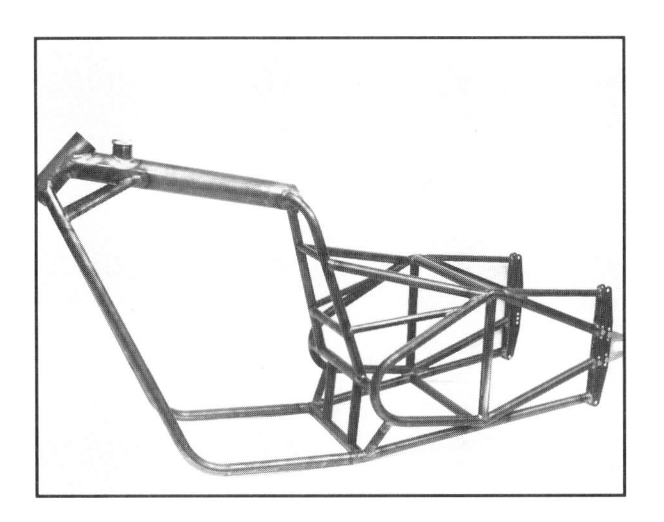

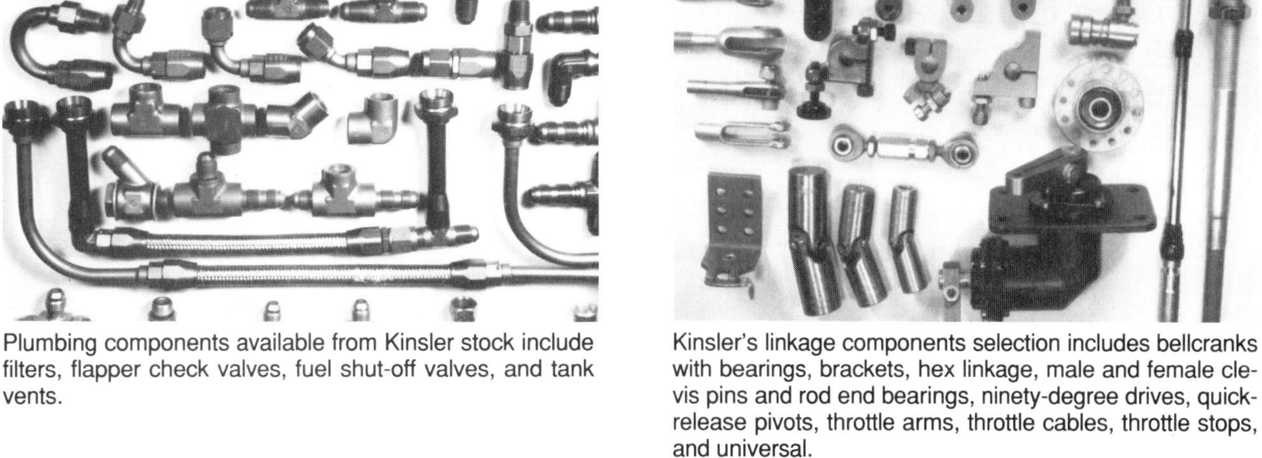

Kinsler's linkage components selection includes bellcranks with bearings, brackets, hex linkage, male and female clevis pins and rod end bearings, ninety-degree drives, quick-release pivots, throttle arms, throttle cables, throttle stops, and universal.

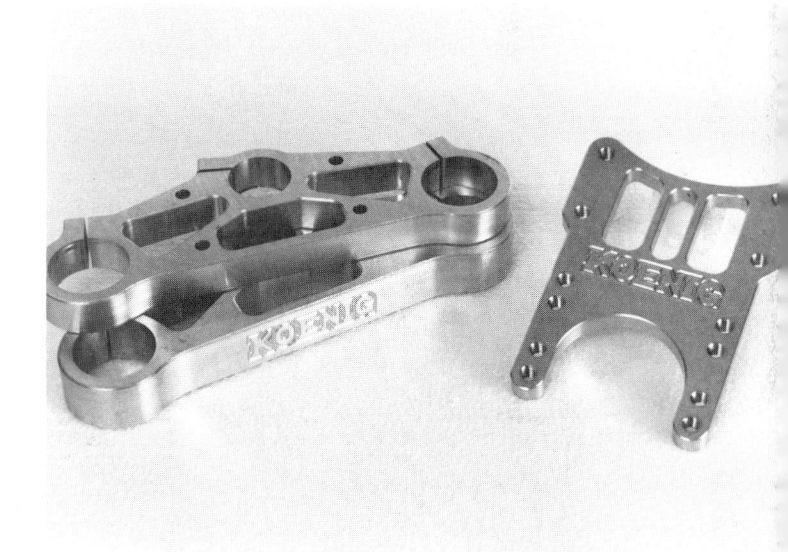

Koenig's triple clamps are CNC-machined from billet aluminum and accept 7/8in handlebars and your choice of steer tube. The handlebar plate provides adjustable handlebar reach.

The Koenig F-16 frame features vertical adjustment in the rear axle mounts to provide minimal ground clearance with 26- to 29in rear tires.

Koenig's modular aluminum rear wheels can be supplied in 1in increments from 4in to 10in wide, with or without polished billet aluminum spools.

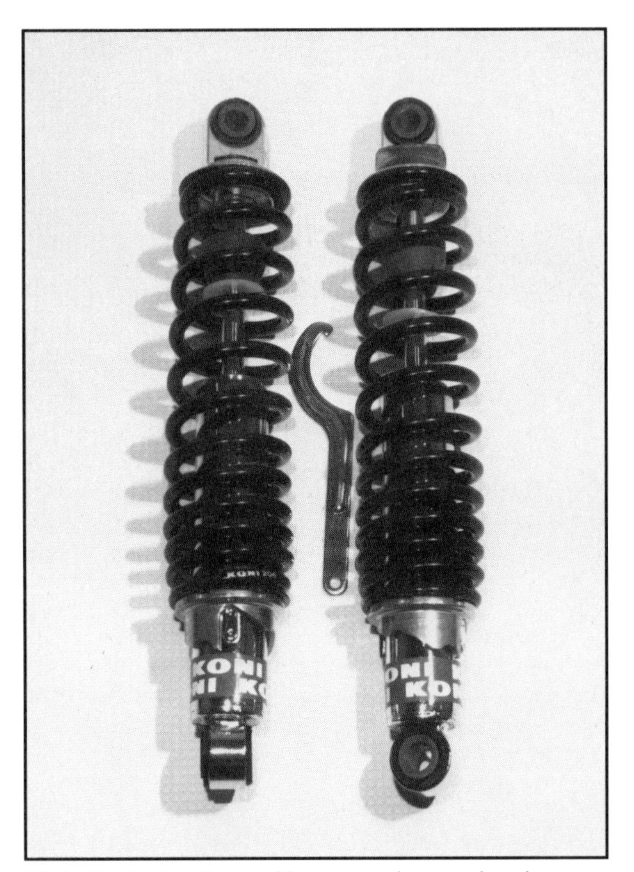

Koni shock absorbers with progressive-rated springs are available to fit most late-model Harley-Davidsons.

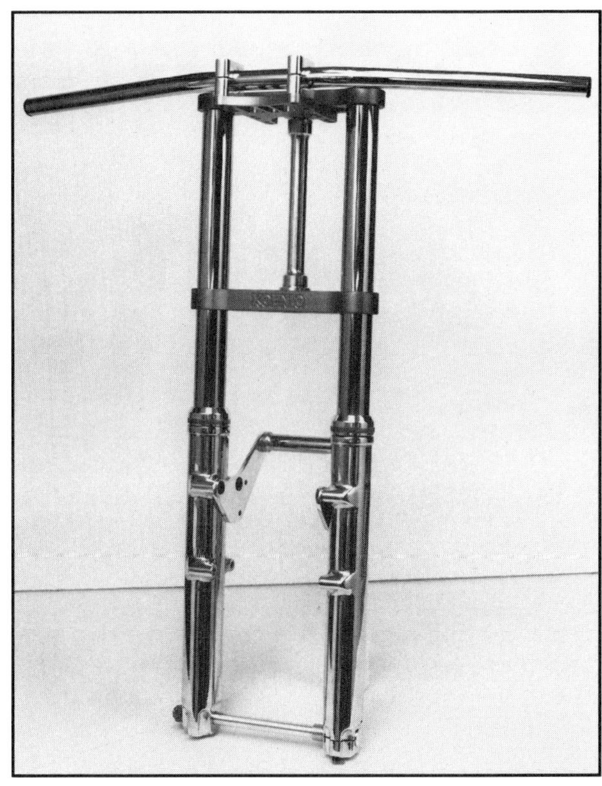

The Koenig Drag Fork is built from scratch for drag racing and weighs in at 14.7lb. They can also provide titanium fasteners to bring the weight down even further.

This Sportster drag bike is a typical project for Kosman. Except for the engine and tires, everything you see was designed and built in their shop. What you can't see is the quality of the welds and the rest of the workmanship—it's first-rate.

cludes their own forks, an aluminum fork brace, aluminum triple clamps, stainless steel drag bars, stainless steel axles, custom fuel and oil tanks, an aluminum sprocket, footpegs and brake discs, along with Grimeca brake calipers.

In early 1992, Kosman started producing a lightweight high-performance street chassis for the Evolution Sportster. The goal was to produce something Sportster owners could put together, without needing machining or welding, to end up with a lighter and stiffer package. The frames are available as a complete rolling chassis with your choice of components, including a hand-built Jack Hagemann aluminum gas tank, or as a bare frame and swing arm. Either way features heli-arc-welded chrome-moly tubing, with the top tube serving as the oil tank and battery mounts above the transmission. The stock suspension components can be used, although a project of this caliber usually makes use of aftermarket suspension components and brakes.

Kosman has also began building Pro Stock frames with a single rear shock to help the chassis launch off the starting line.

Kosman Specialties, Inc.
55 Oak Street
San Francisco, CA 94102
(415) 861-4262
Catalog available; specify drag racing or dirt-track

KüryAkyn U.S.A.

KüryAkyn offers their Hypercharger air cleaner, which is designed to improve airflow. The Hypercharger is styled along the lines of an automotive fuel injector intake, complete with opening butterflies.

KüryAkyn U.S.A.
P.O. Box 37
Stillwater, MN 55082-0037
(715) 386-2916

Larson Machine

Jack Larson at Larson Machine produces frames and transmissions for Big Twin drag bikes. Frames are heli-arc-welded from 4130 chrome-moly tubing, designed for Pro Gas or Pro Stock racing. They accept up to a 9in tire and can be supplied complete with aerodynamic fiberglass bodywork. Complete five-speed automatic transmissions are available as well as relatively economical automatic transmission conversions for the stock five-speed transmissions. Larson automatic transmissions have been tested since 1988 and have proven reliable.

Larson Machine
P.O. Box 693
Belton, MO 64012-0693
Phone or FAX (816) 322-1007

Lectron Fuel Systems & Don Vesco Racing

Used for drag racing, road racing and Bonneville, Lectron carburetors use a single, tapered metering rod to meter the fuel so the carburetor has no nozzles or jets. Lectron carburetors are manufactured in Texas by Lectron Fuel Systems, and Don Vesco Racing in California distributes them and provides research and the technical support. These carbs are also available through Sputhe Engineering and Pingel Enterprise, Inc.

Don Vesco Racing is one of the world's few race shops to make racing on the Bonneville salt flats its main focus. Don first ran a bike at Bonneville in 1957. In addition to running a number of serious streamliners (including an Unlimited), Vesco did much of the construction on the Harley-Davidson factory's new streamliner, which is powered by a pair of Evolution Big Twins, running S&S carburetors and nitro.

Don Vesco Racing
28011 Front Street
Temecula, CA 92390
(714) 676-2099

Lectron Fuel Systems
West Highway 84
McGregor, TX 76657
(817) 848-4044

Leineweber Enterprises

Veteran Harley-Davidson racer Jim Leineweber manufactures a complete line of performance cams, pushrods, and valve spring kits exclusively for Harley-Davidson engines. Leineweber cams are available for applications ranging from loaded touring and sidecar grinds to nitro.

Leineweber valve spring kits are available in double or triple spring versions for all Evolution engines and Shovelheads. These kits have black oxide steel bottom collars and can be provided with your choice of aluminum or titanium top collars.

Leineweber Enterprises
P.O. Box 335
Yucca Valley, CA 92286-0335
(619) 364-4432
Catalog available

Lightning Bolt Company

Chris Bloomfield at Lightning Bolt specializes in manufacturing stainless steel fasteners exclusively for Harley-Davidsons. In addition to regular nuts and bolts, Lightning offers socket head cap screws ("Allen bolts"), countersunk socket screws, button head screws, acorn nuts, nylon locking nuts, cylinder head bolts, primary cover screws, various other specialized fasteners, and complete engine bolt kits.

Lightning Bolt Company
P.O. Box 69
Rochester, Kent
United Kingdom
Phone or FAX 011-44-634-271276
Price list available; mention bike's year and model

Another Kosman Sportster drag bike, with a slightly different frame style and mounts. Kosman supplies the glass components, too. You could have it on the track by the weekend if you thrashed.

This Kosman lay-down Stage 1 frame is all chrome-moly and heavily triangulated for rigidity. Add bucks and shake vigorously. Repeat if necessary.

Jack Larson and his drag bike at the Texas Motorplex. *J & J Photo*

Lineaweaver Racing

Dale Lineaweaver has been working on Harley-Davidson race bikes since 1971 and is a former AMA dirt-track racer who specializes in XR-750 Grand National components. In his shop which includes a dyno and machine tools he builds and tunes racing engines and also fabricates specialized components. Dale's own XR-750 is a street-legal play bike that features his own kickstart conversion.

Lineaweaver Racing
951 Saint Andrews Drive
El Sobrante, CA 94803
(510) 223-9052

Los Angeles Sleeve Company

Los Angeles Sleeve manufactures big-bore kits and cylinder sleeves for Harley-Davidsons. This is where the Harley-Davidson factory has the sleeves for XR-750 cylinders manufactured and installed.

Los Angeles Sleeve Company
8311 Chetle Street
Santa Fe Springs, CA 90670
(310) 945-7578
FAX (310) 698-7029

M.A.C. Products

M.A.C. manufactures a complete line of street and strip exhaust systems for Big Twins and Sportsters.

M.A.C. Products
1410 West Gaylord Street
Long Beach, CA 90813
(310) 436-5462—information
(800) 367-4486—US orders
(800) 423-5501—California orders
Catalog available

Mac Thrasher

Mac is a veteran Top Fuel Harley-Davidson racer who can provide consultation services for other drag racers.

Mac Thrasher
P.O. Box 1312
Laurel, MD 20725-1312
(301) 604-3670

Magura

Magura is an Italian manufacturer, specializing in hand controls for 7/8in handlebars. Their brake levers, clutch levers, and throttles have been popular for decades on all kinds of motorcycles. Many Harley-Davidson drag racers and road racers change their 1in handlebars and controls over to the industry-standard 7/8in so they can use Magura controls.

The American distributor for Magura is Magura U.S.A. Corporation in Illinois.

Magura U.S.A. Corporation
2 Union Drive
Olney, IL 62450
(618) 395-2200—information
(800) 448-3816—orders only

Majestic Turbo

Kevin Draper at Majestic Turbo specializes in Harley-Davidson turbocharger systems. The staff at Majestic has considerable drag racing experience and can provide complete turbocharger systems, components, and technical help.

Majestic Turbo
815 Jefferson
Waco, TX 76701
(817) 757-3759

Manley Performance Products

Manley has a line of tools, valve guides, valve springs, and valves for most Harley-Davidson engines.

Tools include a cylinder leakdown tester with a pair of gauges and air plugs; a piston ring end gapping tool; a safety wire bolt drilling fixture; spring seat tools in Big Twin and Sportster versions, with pilots also available; a TDC indicator with a 14mm thread; a thickness gauge set which ranges from .001in to .035in in half-thousandths increments for checking valve clearance; and valve train checking springs, which have a light tension, a .750in bore and a height of 3.25in free and .650in fully compressed.

Valve guides are bronze or cast iron, in standard or oversize for all Big Twin and Sportster engines. Valve spring kits work on Sportsters, Evolution Big Twins, and Shovelheads. Versions for mild cams are furnished with steel collars, with titanium collars used for cams with high lifts up to .600in. Valves are stainless and come in standard intake and exhaust diameters for all post-1948 engines. Shovelhead valve stems with a chrome plating or a black nitrite coating are available. Intake valves are available in standard diameters and 1.940in Evolution and 2in Shovelhead versions.

Manley Performance Products
1960 Swarthmore Avenue
Lakewood, NJ 08701
(908) 905-3366
FAX (908) 905-3010
Catalog available; specify Harley-Davidson catalog

Marchesini

Marchesini builds die-cast magnesium racing wheels that can be adapted to fit Harley-Davidsons. They are available in a variety of sizes, mostly intended for road racing. Marchesini wheels are distributed in the US by Slater Brothers.

Marchesini S.R.L.
Via Copernico #33
36034 Malo (VI)
Italy
Phone or FAX
011-39-445-606-442

Slater Brothers
P.O. Box 1
Mica, WA 99023-0001
(509) 924-5131
FAX (509) 928-0918

The Larson Machine frame and fiberglass bodywork.
Jackie Rae

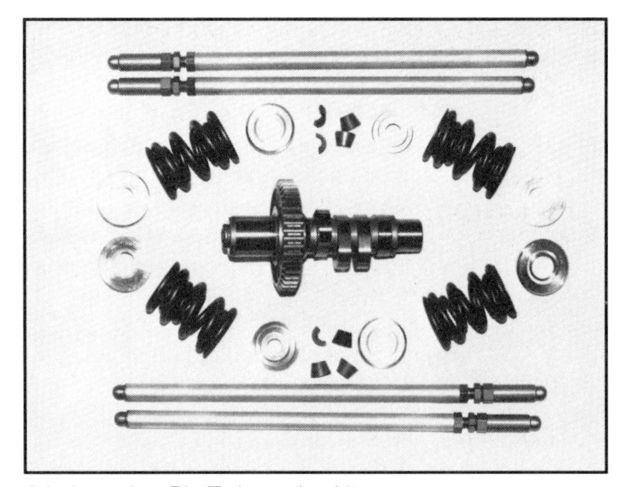

A Leineweber Big Twin engine kit.

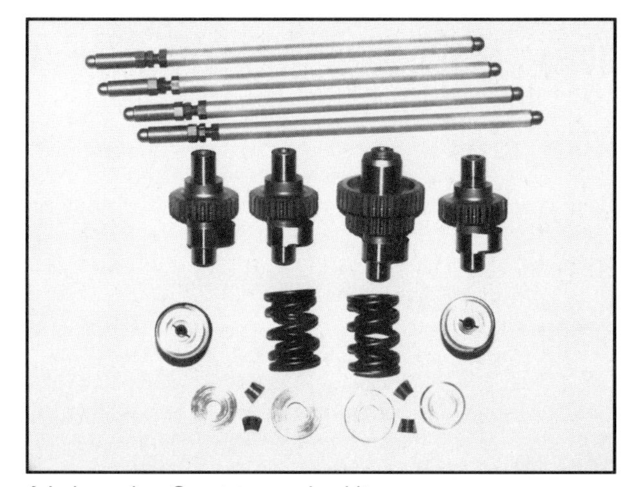

A Leineweber Sportster engine kit.

In the sixties Jim Leineweber was a very successful drag racer, building and riding the quickest and fastest Harley-Davidsons in the world to over 170mph.

Lightning Bolt can supply the most complete range of stainless steel fasteners available for Harley-Davidsons.

These cylinder head bolts are an example of Lightning Bolt's products.

Marzocchi

Along with shock absorbers, Marzocchi manufactures some of the most popular forks in the world. They aren't available specifically for Harley-Davidsons but they can be installed with aftermarket triple clamps and some axle modifications. You will find both models of Marzocchi forks on current motorcycles made by Ducati and other manufacturers.

The Italian-made Marzocchi M1R 41.7mm forks are available with or without triple clamps and come set up for dual front discs. The compression damping and rebound on these forks are each handled exclusively by one fork leg to reduce hydraulic friction. These forks won't bolt right on like the Forcella Italia (Ceriani) forks that Storz Performance has adapted to Harley-Davidsons, but it's not too big a job for a good machinist. Kosman is among the manufacturers of billet aluminum triple clamps and other components for fitting Marzocchi forks. Otherwise you may have to machine front brake mounts and adapt the front axle and spacers.

The Marzocchi USD (upside-down) forks are among the finest front ends available, and they come without triple clamps, which are manufactured by Kosman. The Marzocchi USD represents a lower-cost alternative to the Dutch-made WP Racing upside-down fork. Marzocchi shock absorbers come in several models, including the Strada, for most bikes with twin rear shocks. The Strada shocks have completely separate gas and oil systems to avoid fading, four-position rebound damping, a five-step preload adjuster, and a lifetime limited warranty.

All Marzocchi products are distributed in North America by Cosmopolitan Motors.

Marzocchi S.p.a.
40069 Lavino di Zola Predosa (BO)
Via Grazia, 2
Italy
(051) 75-86-39
FAX (051) 75-88-57

Cosmopolitan Motors, Inc.
301 Jacksonville Road
Hatboro, PA 19040
(215) 672-9100—information
(800) 523-2522—orders only

Master Performance Racing

Jim and Phyllis McClure distribute the Schumaker Racing four-cam Big Twin engine cases and connecting rods made by Jim Schumaker at Schumaker Racing in Ohio. Jim has complete machine shop facilities and provides Harley-Davidson race engine building services from engineering to balancing to construction. The Schumaker cases are available on a special-order basis, with numerous options available.

Jim holds Harley-Davidson class world records for a 4.702 ET in the eighth-mile and a 7.315 ET in the quarter-mile. The McClures are among the most successful racing teams; Jim won twenty-one Top Fuel races in a row in 1990 and 1991, and won 31 of 45 races.

Master Performance Racing
3707 Rochambeau Drive
Williamsburg, VA 23185
(804) 566-0544
FAX (804) 566-8172

MB Products

Mike Bernstein at MB Products offers air cleaners and oil coolers for Big Twin and Sportster engines, along with Mike's Short Shocks. The air cleaners use a 6in S&S element and are claimed to flow more air than any other air cleaner. Mike's Short Shocks are available for 1958-and-later Big Twins as well as 1952-and-later Sportsters. They can be supplied outright or on an exchange basis.

MB Products
8025 Aerostar
Falcon, CO 80831
(719) 683-3838—information
(800) 852-5545—orders only
FAX (719) 683-3838

MC Advantages

Steve Campbell and the staff at MC Advantages manufacture the Power Arc single-fire ignition system for Big Twin and Sportster engines. It provides four-step programmable advance, advance status indicators, an adjustable rev limiter, a static timing indicator, a vacuum retard input, and will drive a 2Ω coil.

An inverted trigger plate is also available, which allows owners of early Big Twin engines with flat cam covers to use the Power Arc single-fire ignition system in a distributor like the one made by Weird Engineering (described under that heading).

MC Advantages
P.O. Box 22225
Des Moines, IA 50325-2225
(515) 255-9031—information
(800) 726-9620—orders only
Literature available

MC Fabrications

MC Fabrications is run by Monte Mathias and Torch. They can provide all you need to build a custom or drag bike, custom-built chrome-moly frames to head modifications. Their shop races a Top Fuel bike in AMRA events.

MC Fabrications
714 Broadway
Rockford, IL 61104
(815) 964-5260
Brochure available

MC Tuning

Located in Trondheim, Norway, MC Tuning is a shop that specializes in custom laced wheels for Harley-Davidsons. They build them from 21in right

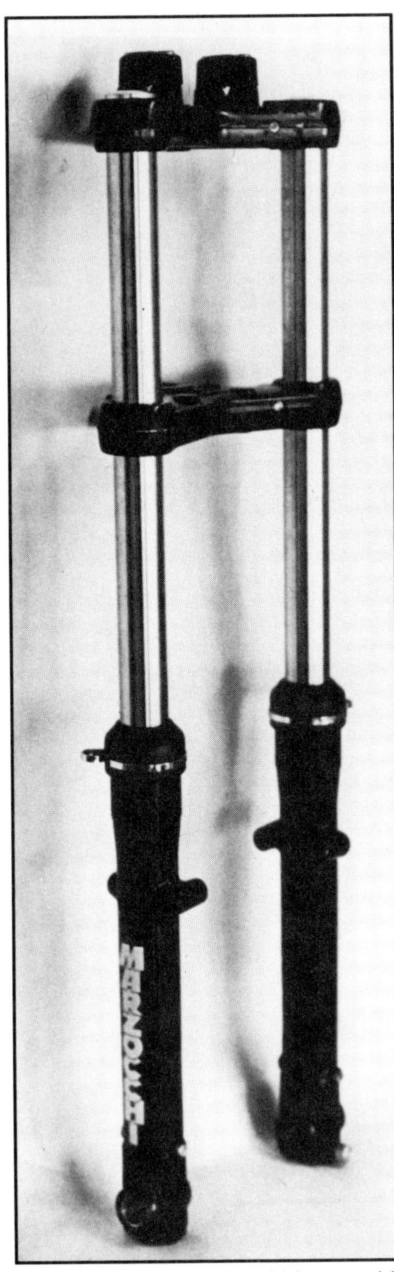

The Marzocchi M1R could be considered the classic race fork, combining fine performance with great appearance.

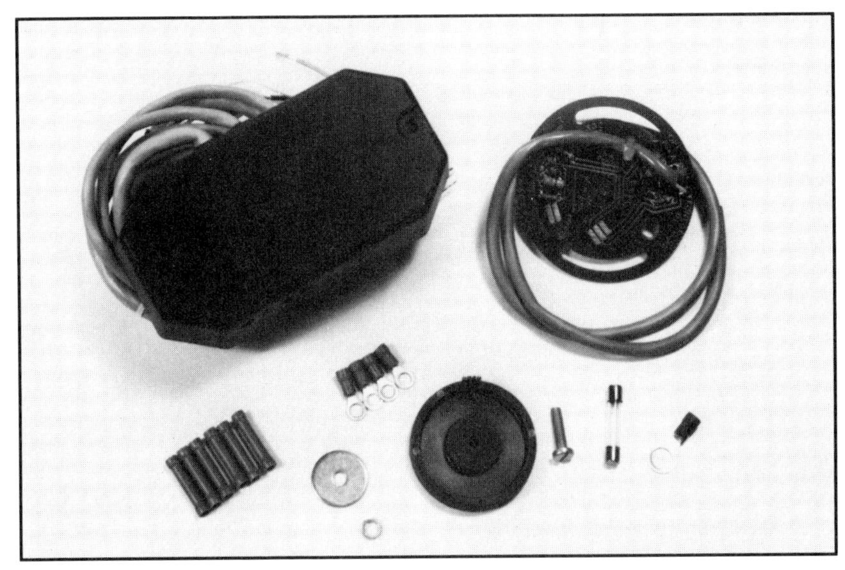

MC Advantages' Power Arc single-fire ignition systems include an electronic ignition module (left), rotor (center), trigger plate (right), and hardware.

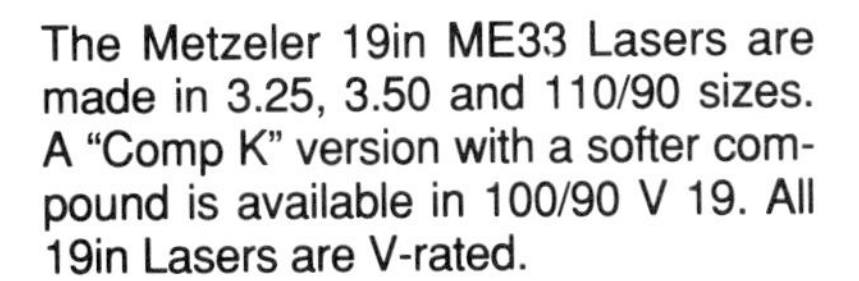

The Metzeler 19in ME33 Lasers are made in 3.25, 3.50 and 110/90 sizes. A "Comp K" version with a softer compound is available in 100/90 V 19. All 19in Lasers are V-rated.

Metzeler's ML2 Marathon front tires are available in 130/90 H 16, 120/80 H 17, 120/90 HB 18 and 130/70 HB 18.

Metzeler's ML2 Marathon rear tires are available in 140/80 HB 15, 150/90 HB 15, 140/90 HB 16 and 160/80 HB 16.

Michael Düx stainless steel hubs are shown at three stages of their production. Laced wheels using these hubs are also available, built completely from stainless steel components.

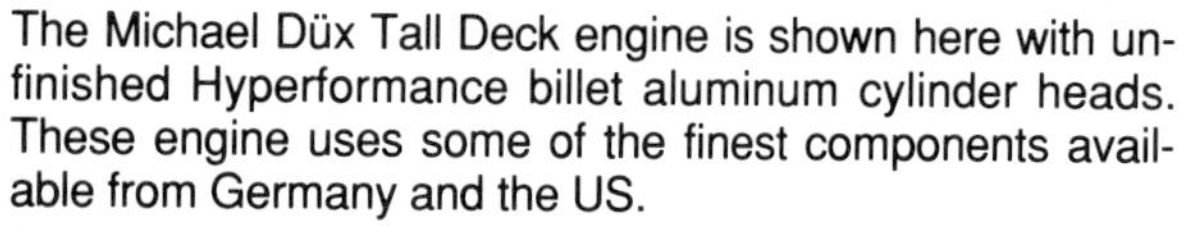
The Michael Düx Tall Deck engine is shown here with unfinished Hyperformance billet aluminum cylinder heads. These engine uses some of the finest components available from Germany and the US.

down to 14in, with up to 80 spokes. MC Tuning can provide all of the services that go along with wheel building and repairing, including drilling, lacing, truing, and glass-beading.

MC Tuning
Sorgenfrivn. 14
7031 Trondheim, Norway
Phone 07-94-51-32
FAX 07-94-03-33

Mega-Performance

Mega-Performance manufactures cast aluminum four-valve cylinder heads for Evolution Big Twins. They are said to provide a substantial increase in horsepower and torque when used with the stock cam, lifters, and pistons. Valve sizes are 1.340in intake and 1.180in exhaust. Stock pistons provide a 9.5:1 compression ratio. An intake manifold for an S&S or Mikuni carburetor is supplied along with 1.39:1-ratio needle bearing rocker arms and Crane adjustable pushrods. These heads are supplied with exhaust flanges and transition pipes that are to be used in building the exhaust system. Complete exhaust systems and custom intake manifolds are also available.

Mega-Performance heads are distributed by Rivera Engineering.

Rivera Engineering
6416 South Western Avenue
Whittier, CA 90606
(310) 692-8944
FAX (310) 699-3943

Mega-Performance
891 Taschereau Boulevard
Lonqueil, Quebec
Canada J4K 2X2
(514) 463-2166
FAX (514) 463-2005

Mert Lawwill Racing

A real legend of the motorcycle racing world, Mert Lawwill was a Harley-Davidson factory rider for 13 years. His smooth, fluid style helped him qualify his XR-750 on the pole regularly, and in 1969 he won the AMA championship.

Mert now devotes most of his time to the suspension systems he is designing and building for mountain bikes, but he can provide engine building services and consultation for XR-750 racers. Although he no longer stocks XR-750 parts, he can supply components on a special-order basis.

Mert Lawwill Racing
148 Rockhill Drive
Tiburon, CA 94920
(415) 435-0782

Metzeler Motorcycle Tire

Metzeler manufactures at least seventeen styles of tires for street riding, touring and road racing. Several of them are available to fit most models of Harley-Davidsons. The ME33 Laser remains a popular front tire for all three applications. It's available in two profiles, two speed ratings, and a wide variety of sizes. Specialized touring tires from Metzeler include the durable ME88 Marathon and the ML2 Marathon front tires, and the ME88 Marathon MBS and ML2 Marathon rear tires.

Metzeler Motorcycle Tire
4520 107th Street S.W.
Mukilteo, WA 98275
(206) 348-4000
FAX (206) 353-6760
Brochure available

Michael Düx Industries

Mike Düx (pronounced "Duke") manufactures complete high-performance engines and stainless steel hubs for Harley-Davidsons. Michael Düx Industries is a wholesaler only, selling to motorcycle dealers, custom bike shops and engine builders worldwide.

Designed to fit stock frames from 1936 and later, the "Tall Deck Big Block" engine uses a 5.06in bore combined with a stock 3.5in stroke for a displacement of 140ci, just over 2.3 liters. Valves are titanium for light weight—2.55in intake and 2in exhaust. Billet aluminum cylinder heads are manufactured by Randy Torgeson at Hyperformance in Iowa, whose expertise was put to use with the combustion chamber design, port flow, and valvetrain geometry.

The Tall Deck engine, introduced at the Cologne, Germany, motorcycle show in September 1992, is available with or without cooling fins on the barrels, in kit form or ready to rock.

Michael Düx Industries
Bei der Johanneskirche 20
D-2000 Hamburg 50, Germany
Phone 011-49-40-434037
Phone 011-49-40-4390263
FAX 011-49-40-436652

Michelin Tire Corporation

Michelin tires for the street and racing are available for all Harley-Davidsons. Road racing slicks are available in several sizes and compounds. Michelin racing tires are distributed in the Southeastern US by Walt Schaefer Cycle Supply in Alabama.

Michelin Italiana S.p.a.
Corso Sempione, 66
20154 Milano, Italy
Phone 02-38821

Michelin Tire Corporation
P.O. Box 19001
Greenville, SC 29602-9001
(803) 458-6053

Walt Schaefer Cycle Supply
Route 3, Box 231
Altoona, AL 35952
(205) 538-5906

Mickey Thompson Enterprises

If you're going to try something really wild out on the Bonneville salt flats, you might want some Mickey Thompson tires for your bike. They are the only new tires you can buy for running over 300mph.

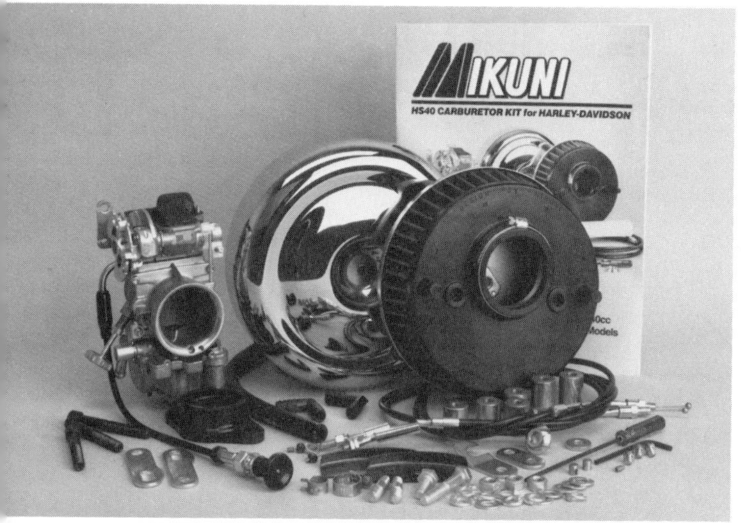

Here's the Mikuni HS40-6-K kit for all Evolution engines.

Here's the Mikuni HS40-7-K kit for Shovelheads and iron Sportsters.

Sam Evans (left), Robbie Miley (center), and Wayne Miller (right) of Miller Racing set several AHDRA records in 1992.

This shot shows the Miller Racing one-piece exhaust pipe barrier shields.

Mickey Thompson made an immeasurable contribution to the racing world. Among many other accomplishments he is credited with designing the first "wide oval" tire, and was the first to build a race car so streamlined that the tech inspectors forced him to change it. Mickey was also the first to pilot a piston-powered car to over 400mph. His son Danny is now a successful racer himself.

Mickey Thompson Enterprises
P.O. Box 227
Cuyahoga Falls, OH 44222-0227
(216) 928-9092

Mike's Frame Shop

Mike Geokan specializes in building custom Big Twin and Sportster frames for race bikes and the street. Mike has fabricated and repaired hundreds of frames. He can build any design, including sit-up, lay-down, rigid, or swing arm, and they're made from chrome-moly, mild steel, or aluminum. Mike's most popular design is the Competition frame, which has carried him at over 180mph at the Bonneville salt flats with Evolution Big Twin power.

Mike's Frame Shop
1716 Allumbaugh
Boise, ID 83704
(208) 323-8134

Mike's Precision Machine Shop

In addition to machining and fabrication, Mike Raque specializes in expert repair and reinforcement for all Big Twin and Sportster engine and transmission cases.

Mike's Precision Machine Shop
4588 "M" East Second Street
Benicia, CA 94510
(707) 747-1711

Mikuni

Mikuni manufactures the popular HS40 40mm smoothbore carburetor, which is the basis for two of their complete carburetor kits for Harley-Davidsons. Also available is the HSR42 42mm carburetor for highly modified engines.

The 40mm HS40-6-K kits are for all Evolution Big Twins and Sportsters, and the HS40-7-K kit is made especially for 1970-1984 Shovelheads and 1971-1985 iron Sportsters. Shovelhead kits include an intake manifold, and both kits come with an air cleaner with a K&N filter. Mikuni points out that these carburetors must be used with a push-pull throttle assembly and include one in their kit for the earlier models that came without one.

The 42mm HSR42 carburetors will flow twenty-percent more air than the 40mm version, and they have needle roller bearings for the flat throttle slide (which allow a lighter return spring). The HSR42 is available for all Evolution engines and for Shovelheads. At press time, a Sportster version was also being considered, but unless you have a big, highly-modified engine, you're likely to be best off with the 40mm HS40.

Mikuni offers complete rebuild kits with gaskets and O-rings; Barnett Tool & Engineering throttle cables in various lengths; chrome or black air cleaner covers; and other replacement parts for their carburetors and kits.

Motorcycle Carburetor Division
Mikuni American Corporation
8910 Mikuni Avenue
Northridge, CA 91324-3496
(818) 885-1242
FAX (818) 993-7388
Motorcycle carburetor products catalog available

Miller Racing Systems

Wayne Miller started Miller Racing Systems in May 1992 based on the incredible success of his Big Twins crankcase pressure regulator. When this book went to press, Wayne was patenting the regulator, so he couldn't discuss it in technical terms. But we know that the internal resistance from oil and air is bad, and the CPR regulates the pressure in the crankcase to minimize the problem. And it works well enough that the first time out, some of his competitors who had been eliminated protested the system to race officials who found the bike legal.

With the help of the cylinder head expertise from Sam Evans at Sam's Performance Specialties, Robbie Miley and Wayne kicked down the old AHDRA 5.90-second record in the eighth-mile with a 5.57 on gas at Greensboro, South Carolina. Then the duo set another eighth-mile AHDRA record of 125.50mph at the Myrtle Beach, South Carolina, track.

Wayne has been building Harley-Davidson racing engines since the early eighties. He has set at least one new drag racing record every year since 1984, except in 1991, when he only raced twice while building a new bike.

Miller Racing Systems
Route 1, Box 1151-D
Ridgeville, SC 29472
(803) 688-4948

Milmeyer Precision

Joe Kling at Milmeyer Precision manufactures a line of gaskets for most popular Big Twin and Sportster engines.

Milmeyer Precision
18650-E Collier Avenue
Lake Elsinore, CA 92339
(714) 245-9664

Morocco Racing

In addition to providing fabrication work, Jamie Morocco builds engine cases and fuel injector pump drive systems for Harley-Davidson drag bikes. Engine cases are machined from billet aluminum for Big Twins. Unlike most other billet Big Twin cases, these use a single cam instead of four Sportster cams. Morocco Racing is at the same address as Frame Oddities.

Morocco Racing
13001 Abbey Road
North Royalton, OH 44133
(216) 582-5801

Morris Magneto

Morris has added an ignition module to their complete line of magnetos for all Harley-Davidsons, from flatheads to Evolution engines. The ignition module is built into the spark plug wire, and is designed to send a spark only to the live cylinder. Two of these modules can be used on bikes with double-plugged heads.

Aside from the hotter spark, an advantage of a magneto system is that regardless of the electrical system, the bike will still run, even without a battery. The Morris M-5 magneto works on all 1970-and-up Big Twins—electric or kick start, with or without a battery. It produces up to 60,000 volts. Starting is easier through the use of a recoil spring system that winds up when the engine is first turned over—when it fires, the recoil spring drops out centrifugally. Morris has a number of accessories available for the M-5, including electronic tach adapters, kill switch levers, solid-core spark plug wires, and locking caps.

Morris also has magnetos for Big Twins from 1936 to 1969 (MM-74E), for 1971-and-up Sportsters (MM-2), and for flatheads and 1957-1970 Sportsters (MM-3, and MM-3K, an upgrade kit for factory magnetos). Mechanical and electric tach drives and injector pump adapters are also available.

Morris Magneto
103 Washington Street
Morristown, NJ 07960
(201) 540-9171—information
(800) 237-8624—orders only
FAX (201) 605-8910
Literature available

Mother's Harley Shop

Klas Hellgren and Crister Helgesson run Mother's, one of the largest shops in Sweden specializing in high-performance Harley-Davidsons. Some of the quickest Harley-Davidson drag bikes in Europe roll out of Mother's. Besides race engine building they have a complete machine shop and do custom fabrication for street riding and drag racing.

Mother's Harley Shop
Box 194
421 22 Vastra Frolunda, Sweden
Phone 011-46-31-474746
FAX 011-46-31-474708

Motorrad Müller GMBH

Motorrad Müller of Germany manufactures drag bars, machined aluminum triple clamps, and laced rear wheels. Their products are distributed in the US by Pasadena Hot Rods.

Pasadena Hot Rods
2164 East Crary Street
Pasadena, CA 91104
(818) 798-8249
FAX (818) 798-2627

The Motor Shop

Ed "Fast Eddie" Bass and the crew at The Motor Shop do all kinds of work on Harley-Davidson street and drag bikes. They build slipper clutches and custom frames for drag racing, and have a complete machine shop and equipment for balancing, bead blasting, dyno testing, and arc, gas, and heli-arc welding.

Induction systems are a specialty at The Motor Shop, the people who built the first supercharged Evolution engine. They work with gas, alcohol, and nitro systems, carburetors, fuel injectors, nitrous oxide injection systems, and superchargers.

The Motor Shop
6802 North 55th Avenue
Glendale, AZ 85031
(602) 842-4222

Mototech Enterprises

Mototech builds the V-sport performance exhaust system for all Evolution Sportsters. Claimed to weigh 30 percent less than the stock system, it has lightweight carbon fiber composite mufflers that can be repacked. The end caps are machined from 6061-T6 aluminum and the mounting hardware is stainless steel.

Mototech Enterprises
P.O. Box 5156
Fullerton, CA 92635-5156
(714) 526-8477

Mountain Cycle

Mountain Cycle is run by Tony and Colleen Mattioli. A longtime drag racer, Tony makes power heads for slipper clutches and does fabrication and machining for racers.

Mountain Cycle
7447 Wileytown Road
Galway, NY 12850
(518) 882-9863

Mountain Motors

Mike Doenig runs Mountain Motors and offers complete drag bikes, cylinder heads, frames, intake manifolds, roller-bearing rocker arms, wheelie bars, and special-order engine components, all exclusively for Harley-Davidsons. He also does development work, fabrication, engine modifications, and dyno work. A talented and dedicated builder, he has built and raced Harley-Davidson drag bikes since the early seventies.

Mike does not produce cylinder heads, but he has focused on head development and testing for over twenty years. In 1992 he fabricated a pair of trick billet aluminum four-valve heads. The intake tracts are as straight as possible, with a tunnel ram manifold between the heads. (He started with two 30lb blocks of aluminum, and after 300 hours at his Bridgeport vertical milling machine, had the heads and

The Morris M-5 magneto works on all 1970-and-up Big Twins—electric or kick start, with or without a battery.

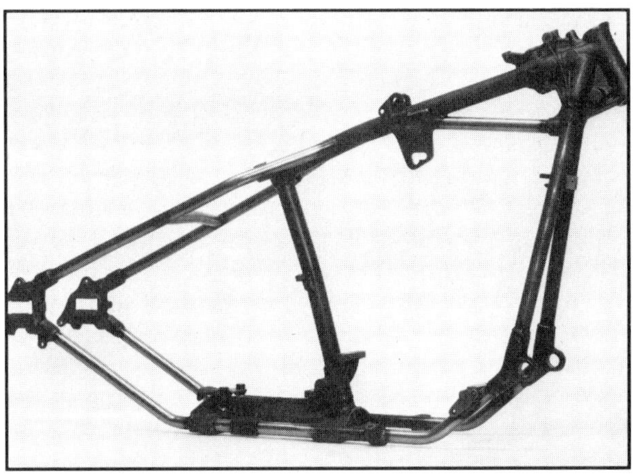

Mother's sells these Swedish-built straight-leg frames to fit any Big Twin engine.

Mountain Motors' Mike Doenig began racing this Sportster in 1977. Shown here at 317lb, the bike is now down to 310lb, with a best run so far of 9.07 seconds at over 147mph. This bike has made over 400 passes and it's never given Mike any handling or mechanical problems.

Mountain Motors' Mike's second Sportster has turned over 147mph in 8.82 seconds with the much-modified Evolution heads shown here. He's headed for the mid-eights with his new billet aluminum four-valve heads.

three garbage bags full of chips.)

Cylinder head services include flow testing, O-ring conversions, valve guide hole welding and machining, valve jobs, and development work and fabrication. Custom-order frames are heliarc welded out of chrome-moly tubing. Beyond drag bikes, Mike can modify, repair, or build street frames from scratch. Rocker arms are done on an exchange basis for Evolution engines. These conversions provide precision needle bearings, with billet rocker arm shafts replacing the stock cast shafts.

Other services include cylinder boring, Sunnen honing, connecting rod rebuilding, dyno work, engine development, engine case repairs, line boring, machining, and thrust washer installation for S&S flywheels.

Mike's upstate New York shop is high on a mountainside with a view overlooking five states. I first heard about Mike Doenig when his low-nine-second Sportster drag bike was featured in a chopper magazine in 1978. All black and sitting low to the ground, it was built around a 96in iron Sportster engine in a Mert Lawwill XR-750 dirt-track frame, with a lengthened swing arm and XR-750 bodywork. When Mike finished putting this bike together he wanted to get the beast dialed in but his shop was some distance from a drag strip so he rolled it out into the street and fired it up. A crowd gathered and most everybody enjoyed the show but someone called the police. When the officer arrived he was so knocked out by Mike's engineering and workmanship he kept the crowd back so Mike could practice his burnouts and launches.

Mountain Motors
Route 23
East Windham, NY 12439
(518) 622-8225

MRE—Murdoch Racing Enterprises

Drag racing specialist MRE is the place to find complete air shifter systems and related parts. They also custom-build transmissions strictly for drag racing. A successful motorcycle drag racer from 1964 through 1980, Mike Murdoch started MRE in 1969. In 1976 he became the first racer to use an air shifter on a drag bike. Later that year, on a drag strip in Florida, Mike was seriously injured when his bike threw him off just before the timing lights—and his sliding body set a new national record. The following year Mike invented an automatic transmission for drag bikes.

In January of 1993, respiratory failure took Mike's life. One of his final wishes was that the business would carry on, and the staff at MRE will continue to move ahead in the world of motorcycle drag racing.

MRE
625 Pinellas Street
Clearwater, FL 34616
(813) 443-5330

MSD Ignition

MSD has a complete line of ignition components for Big Twins and Sportsters, including a popular series of single-fire ignition systems.

MSD Ignition
1490 Henry Brennan Drive
El Paso, TX 79936
(915) 857-5200

M&T Engineering

The System II Atomizer is available from Mike Kaiser at M&T for popular Big Twin and Sportster carburetors. Models are available for Bendix, Keihin, Mikuni, and S&S, the Screamin' Eagle 40mm; and the four-bolt SU carburetors.

M&T Engineering
Route 2, Box 906
Oroville, WA 98844
(509) 486-4000—information
(800) 228-7599—orders only

Nico Bakker

Nico Bakker of Holland is a talented and innovative frame builder. His work is by no means limited to Harley-Davidsons and can be found on numerous road racers powered by a variety of engines. Nico also builds custom frames and does custom fabrication, machining, and welding. A consultant to BMW and Laverda, Nico has been building motorcycle frames since the early seventies. Innovations such as aluminum frames, single-sided swing arms, and rising-rate rear suspension systems were all seen first on motorcycles he designed and built.

One of his recent projects was producing a limited run of Bakker QCS1000 superbikes. The QCS is powered by Yamaha FZR1000 engine sitting in an aluminum frame. One of the more interesting features is his unique, scissors-link front end, pivoting on needle bearings.

Nico Bakker Frames BV
Donkerweg 1
1704 DV Heerhugowaard
Netherlands
Phone 011-31-2207-4642

NitroCycle

NitroCycle specializes in Harley-Davidson drag bikes. Bob Spina and John Jordan have been racing since the seventies, and look after Big Twin and Sportster engine and transmission modifications along with custom fabrication and machining.

Bob Spina has ridden his Northern Thunder Top Fuel bike to a 7.32 ET and to over 185mph. At the end of the 1992 season, Bob came home with the ECRA Top Fuel championship.

Mountain Motors' one-piece billet primary cover also serves as a cylinder head girdle and front and rear engine mounts. This is the work of a master.

Bob Spina of NitroCycle is shown launching Northern Thunder, which was built around a Truett's Frame Works chassis.

An NOS nitrous kit comes with installation hardware and instructions.

Here is a small sampling of some of the components Northcoast can supply for your project

This FXR has its NOS bottle mounted to the frame, hidden behind the rider's leg.

This purple Shovelhead drag bike was built entirely in Dale Nungesser's shop. Notice the billet aluminum fender struts and the three-spoke modular wheels.

NitroCycle
2100-8 Arctic Avenue
Bohemia, NY 11716
(516) 567-7320

Nitrous Oxide Systems, Inc.

NOS manufactures nitrous oxide injection kits for Big Twins and Sportsters, offering a choice of bottle sizes and shapes and mounting locations.

Nitrous Oxide Systems, Inc.
59030 Lakeshore Drive
Cypress, CA 90630
(714) 821-0580—sales
(714) 821-0592—tech line
FAX (714) 821-8319
Catalog available

Northcoast Thunderbikes

Arlie Becker builds slipper clutches and custom drag racing frames. He sets up carburetors and fuel injection systems for alcohol and nitro, and does custom fabrication and welding. Frames can be built to order for Big Twin or Sportster engines. A typical North Coast frame would be a chrome-moly lay-down design for the strip.

Arlie campaigns an Evolution Big Twin Top Fuel drag bike, and his wife Christine races an Evolution Sportster Super Stock racer.

Northcoast Thunderbikes
8425 180th Street S.E.
Snohomish, WA 98290
(206) 668-1344
(206) 486-0769

Nottingham Custom Cycles

Nottingham builds custom frames, does fabrication and welding, and can build a complete motorcycle.

Nottingham Custom Cycles
4A, Patterson Road
Hyson Green, Nottingham
United Kingdom NG7 6AF
Phone 0602-782871

Nungesser Engineering

Dale Nungesser offers slipper clutches, jackshafts, engine plates, fabrication, custom frames, triple clamps, and modular wheels exclusively for Harley-Davidson drag bikes. Dale campaigns a Harley-Davidson Pro Fuel drag bike, and is the American distributor for Bentec AB transmissions from Sweden.

Nungesser Engineering
515 East Tenth
P.O. Box 829
Belle Plaine, KS 67013-0829
(316) 488-3688

Öhlins

The Swedish-made Öhlins front forks, shock absorbers, and steering dampers are among the world's best. The forks are lightweight and have been used on many road racing bikes. They can be supplied in conventional and upside-down styles. The shocks are available for all current Big Twins and Sportsters, and steering dampers provide fourteen positions of adjustment and can be adapted to any motorcycle.

Öhlins products are distributed in the US by Noleen Racing, who will also rebuild Öhlins and most other makes of shock absorbers.

Noleen Racing
2141 East Philadelphia, Unit T
Ontario, CA 91761-7742
(714) 947-5773
FAX (714) 947-1513

Opcon Autorotor

Opcon Autorotor is a Swedish supercharger manufacturer. Autorotor superchargers have been used successfully on a number of winning Harley-Davidson drag bikes. Unlike traditional superchargers that use rotors with straight blades, these are screw-type superchargers that represent the current state of the art for drag racing.

The exclusive North American distributor for Opcon Autorotor motorcycle superchargers is Advanced Racing Technology.

Opcon Autorotor
Varmdovagen 120
S-131 60 NACKA, Sweden
Phone 46-8-718-3535
FAX 46-8-718-2302

Advanced Racing Technology
5857 Jefferson Avenue
Newport News, VA 23605
(804) 245-3455
FAX (804) 247-3297

Orangeburg Cycles and Dixie Frames

Bill Furr's race operation is based at Orangeburg Cycles, which is also staffed by Roger Ward and Bob Obedzinski. They offer practically anything your Big Twin or Sportster drag bike needs, from custom fabrication of components and lay-down frames to a complete rolling chassis or turn-key race bike. Bill has come up with a unique bottom end for Big Twin drag bikes, designed to provide the extra strength needed in Top Fuel racing.

Orangeburg Cycles
1389 Five Chop Shop Road
Orangeburg, SC 29115
(803) 534-9804
FAX (803) 534-8690

Overseas International Trading

Jan Kennis runs O.I.T., where Kees Beekers builds the "Lowtail" frames that are designed to accept any Big Twin engine.

Overseas International Trading
Liniestraat 121
4816 BG, Breda, Holland
Phone 01031-76710719
FAX 01031-76715423

Owens Racing

Marion Owens built his first Harley-Davidson drag bike in 1974 and went on to become a Top Fuel champion. He builds

Here's Dale Nungesser aboard the Nungesser Engineering Pro Fuel shop bike.

Anybody who hops on a double-engined, 650lb Top Fuel Harley, hammers it, bends the wheelie bars and then jokes about it afterwards gets the author's vote for "Neat Dad of the Month". *Owens Racing*

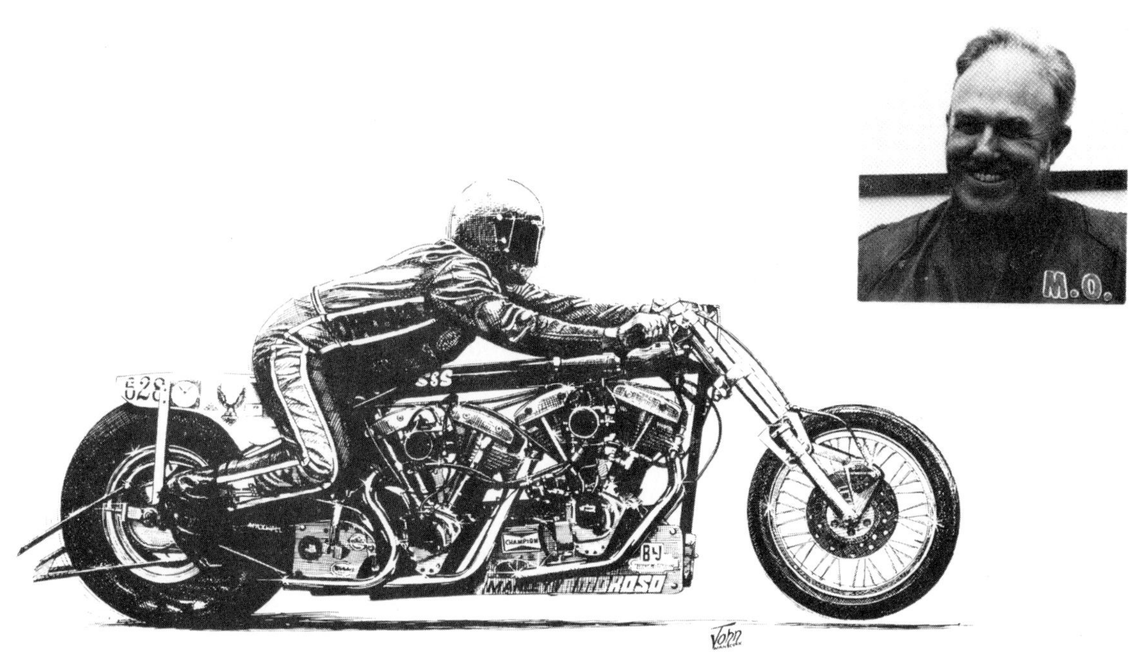

Marion Owens

Race fan John Hancox thought enough of Marion Owens' accomplishments to honor him in this sketch.

cylinder barrels as well as drag racing frames. The barrels are made from your choice of aluminum or steel, with or without cooling fins. Frames are custom built, and a typical Owens laydown 4130 chrome-moly drag frame has an 80in wheelbase and weighs around 34lb.

Owens Racing
13504 S.E. 59
Oklahoma City, OK 73150
(405) 732-0238 or (405) 391-4513

OZMO—Ozark Mountain Cylinder Heads

Don Rothwell at OZMO is a drag racing specialist who can provide cam matching, cylinder head modifications, fabrication, and titanium valves.

The cam matching operation is computerized, using proprietary software. The goal is to find the ideal combination of cam profile and cylinder head porting, and it has paid off well for Don's AMRA Pro Stock Sportster and many of his customers. Fabrication work is available in aluminum, steel, and titanium. Titanium valves are custom-made for particular applications and can be supplied for virtually any Harley-Davidson engine.

OZMO
601 East Calvert Hill Road
Columbia, MO 65202
(314) 442-1560

Panther Precision Machine, Ltd.

Panther is run by Led Szmek, a successful dirt-track racer and master welder who has built racing motorcycle frames since the mid-seventies, formerly under the name of Panther Racing. His workmanship, fabrication, and heli-arc welding are top-notch, and his frames are highly regarded. After building many custom frames for dirt-track racing, most of his current work is for race cars. Led custom builds chrome-moly frames for Big Twin and Sportster engines, but because of his busy schedule, their price can be significant.

Led can fabricate and repair most special race bike components, and offers services such as design work, reinforcing swing arms, custom machining, and welding.

Panther Precision Machine, Ltd.
8116 130th Street, Unit 3
Surrey, British Columbia
Canada V3W 8J9
(604) 599-1542
FAX (604) 594-4265

Parra Performance

Parra O'Siochian specializes in engine modifications for serious Harley-Davidson race bikes, including XR-750s. Cylinder head modifications, valve guides, complete race engine development work, machining, and heli-arc welding are available in addition to cylinder boring, valve seat grinding, and big street engines.

Parra is already busy, so he doesn't advertise. Working alone, he has a small shop doesn't have the time to deal with casual enquiries. An Irish-born nuclear physicist, Parra has an extensive background in Harley-Davidson drag racing and XR-750 dirt-track racing. He is a former Kosman employee and long-time friend of some of the greats of the industry, like C.R. Axtell and Mert Lawwill.

Parra Performance
40 Belvedere Street
San Rafael, CA 94901
(415) 456-5959

Patrick Racing

Patrick Racing is run by Nigel Patrick, who has designed and built his own flow bench and offers expert custom cylinder head modifications for Big Twin, Sportster, and XR-750 engines. A highly successful Pro Stock drag racer, Nigel came to the US from the United Kingdom in 1980.

Patrick Racing
3614 West Pendleton
Santa Ana, CA 92704
(714) 557-9280

Paughco

Ron Paugh at Paughco manufactures a large selection of custom mild steel frames for Big Twins and Sportsters in several styles, and also builds original Big Twin replacement frames that are accurate enough to be used on a restoration project. These can be supplied for most Big Twins all the way back to the 1936 Knuckleheads. Paughco can also provide gas and oil tanks and exhaust systems for many stock frames as well as their own.

While developing his restoration parts, Ron tracked down some vintage bikes to use for reference. The collection kept growing, and Paughco now has a museum with over a hundred classic Harley-Davidsons on display.

Paughco
P.O. Box 3390
Carson City, NV 89702-3390
(702) 246-5738
FAX (702) 246-0372
Catalog available

PBI Sprockets

PBI countershaft sprockets are CNC-machined from solid steel billet, fully heat-treated after machining. The splined area is designed to provide the maximum contact with the countershaft. These sprockets are available for the following applications:

1980-1985 Big Twins—22, 23, 24, and 25 teeth.

1936-1979 Big Twins—22, 23, 24, 25, and 26 teeth.

1984-1989 Sportsters—21, 22, and 23 teeth.

1970-1984 Sportsters—21, 22, and 23 teeth.

1965-1979 Sportsters—21, 22, 23, and 24 teeth.

PBI, in business since 1939, is primarily an OEM supplier who does not usually deal direct, but

Dave Batchelar's work at P&D is found all over this tastefully done FXRS, which was done for a customer.

Perf-form Products' HD-2 and HD-2C replacement filter cartridges.

Dave Batchelar at P&D built this FLH Shovelhead, and it shows his fine workmanship and nice detailing.

Perf-form Products' HD-C filter canister/oil cooler.

their sprockets are distributed by Rivera Engineering.

Rivera Engineering
6416 South Western Avenue
Whittier, CA 90606
(310) 692-8944
FAX (310) 699-3943

PBI Sprockets
P.O. Box 375
Clackamas, OR 97015-0375
(503) 655-5128
FAX (503) 655-9292

P&D Custom Bikes

Dave Batchelar runs P&D in West Sussex in the UK, where he specializes in fabrication and custom frames, gas tanks and oil tanks, seats, and more. While much of his business is for chopper riders, he takes on special projects for racers. Dave can build a frame or component for any application.

P&D Custom Bikes
Unit 1, Lyons Farm Estate
Lyons Road, Slinfold,
West Sussex
United Kingdom RH13 7QP
Phone 0403-791038

Perf-form Products, Inc.

Formerly known as the Douglas Filter Company, Perf-Form manufactures popular oil filters and cartridges for all Harley-Davidsons. These use a Microglass/synthetic-enhanced filtration media to trap and hold contaminants as small as four microns, and they not only trap tiny particles but provide improved dirt holding capacity without increased back pressure caused by flow restriction. Filter cartridges are available in three basic versions for Harley-Davidsons.

HD-1 is a drop-in style filter for 1965-1982 FL and FX models. Its patented design features a built-in temperature-responsive relief valve that limits media bypass on cold starts. HD-2 filters fit all rubber-mounted models, Softails, the Sturgis, and Sportsters from 1984 on. A direct replacement for part numbers 63805-80, 63806-83, and 63812-90, it is 3/4in longer than the stock filter for greater capacity. It is black, and a chrome-plated version (HD-2C) is available.

HD-3 is a smaller version of the HD-2, for the 1983 and 1984 FL, 1983-1986 FXWG, and 1980-1983 Sportster engines. It is a direct replacement for part number 63810-80. It is black and the chrome-plated version is the HD-3C. HD-C filter canister/oil cooler systems work on any motorcycle with external oil lines. Designed to be used with the HD-1 filter cartridge, they feature an aluminum canister with cooling fins. Its inner and outer surfaces are CNC-machined, and the outside of the canister housing is polished and lacquered with chrome-plated fittings. The Clean Change Oil Drain System is designed to make oil changes easier on Big Twins.

Perf-form Products, Inc.
21595 County Road 83 North
Big Lake, MN 55309
(612) 263-6615

Performance Machine, Inc.

Performance Machine manufactures a complete line of brake discs, calipers, and wheels for Big Twins and Sportsters. These components are commonly used on custom bikes, with the machined aluminum brake calipers an especially popular way of improving a bike's stopping power and appearance at once. The calipers come in four-piston and six-piston versions, with stainless steel or cast-iron discs that are floating or rigidly mounted, and a good selection of mounting brackets for front and rear calipers. They also build a variety of front and rear master cylinders machined out of solid aluminum.

Performance Machine wheels are modular, spun aluminum or laced with a choice of rims. They come in several styles that will bolt on to most late-model Harley-Davidsons. Specialized drag racing rear wheels are available in 15in x 7in, 15in x 8in, and 15in x 9in with weights ranging from 12lb, 9oz to 12lb 14oz. The 18in x 1.85in (WM2) drag racing front wheel weighs 6lb.

Performance Machine, Inc.
P.O. Box 1739
15535 Garfield Avenue
Paramount, CA 90723-1739
(310) 634-6532
Catalog available

Pete Hill Motorcycles

Pete and his wife Jackie opened Pete Hill Motorcycles in 1971, and they have become legends in the Harley-Davidson drag racing community. Drag racing Harley-Davidsons since 1962, Pete is known for his engineering know-how, creativity, determination, and race success. His drag racing records have all been set on bikes he built, and he's still running the meanest Knucklehead in the world, a Top Fuel bike with a 3:53 GMC supercharger that Pete rode to the 1981 AMA Dragbike Top Fuel championship and AMRA Top Fuel championship titles in 1988, 1989, 1990, and 1991. A new Evolution drag bike has also been in the works.

Several years ago Pete developed some unique bottom end set-ups using Timken tapered roller bearings. This adds a degree of reliability and consistency that allows a bike to go an entire Top Fuel race season without having the bottom end torn down.

Pete modified Harley-Davidson race engine and can repair any Harley-Davidson ever produced. A member of the AMRA Technical Advisory Committee, he is a fine mechanic, an imaginative design engineer, and a talented machinist who can build a race bike or improve what you have now. Cylinder

Determined to get there on time, Pete Hill guides the Knucklehead Freight Train down the track.

Pete Hill at work in his shop. His resemblance to Don Garlits is a coincidence, but their legendary status in their respective sports came from dedication and hard work.

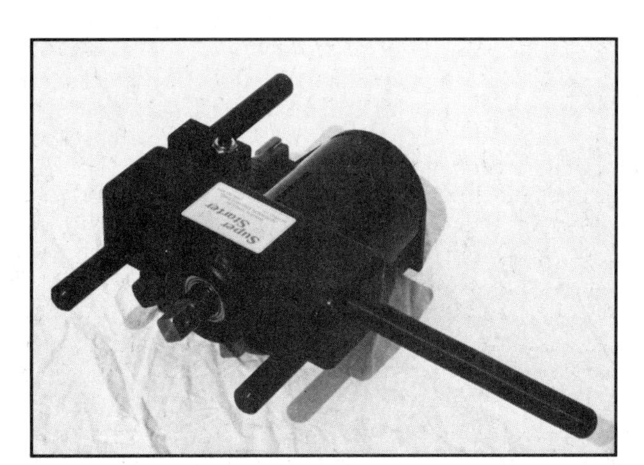

Peterson Engineering's Super Starter.

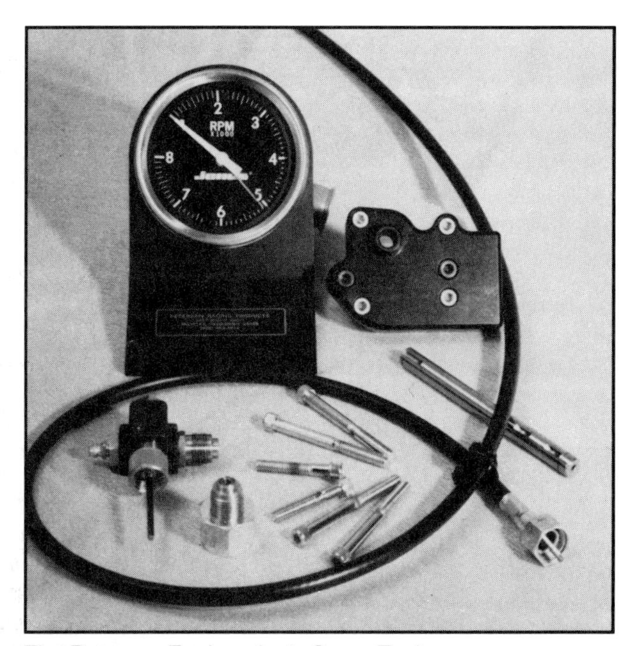

The Peterson Engineering's Super Tach.

head modifications are a specialty, and his shop has facilities for balancing, machining, welding, fabrication, and construction. They also flow fuel injection systems for racers and supply flow charts so you can see and understand your injection system's performance. They especially enjoy challenges from racers and manufacturers needing something new and unusual.

Pete Hill Motorcycles
1401 West Blue Ridge Drive
Greenville, SC 29611
Phone or FAX (803) 271-0528
Catalog available

Peterson Engineering

Tom Peterson at Peterson Engineering manufactures the Super Starter and the Super Tach for Harley-Davidson drag bikes. A slipper clutch has also been in the works and should now be available. Super Starters are battery-powered hand-held units for all drag bike engines using an external starter. These starters operate on 24V DC and spin at 1200rpm with about 85lb-ft of torque. The output shaft is 1in diameter, with a 3/4in (square) drive end ready to accept a socket. Super Tach mechanical tachometers and tach drive kits were designed especially for Big Twin engines.

Peterson Engineering
1817 Houret Court
Milpitas, CA 95035
(408) 263-3778
Literature available

PHD, Inc.

Len Courteney and Bob Koolage at PHD campaign four Harley-Davidson drag bikes. Every one of them is street-legal, and their shop's motto is "we ride what we sell." They specialize in performance engine building for Evolution Big Twins and Sportsters.

PHD, Inc.
686 South US Highway 1
Yonge Street
Ormond Beach, FL 32174
(904) 673-2609
FAX (904) 673-2452

Pingel Enterprise, Inc.

Pingel manufactures and distributes a variety of performance accessories for Harley-Davidson drag bikes, and is best known for its machined fuel valves while also manufacturing centerless-ground axles, electric starters, engine mounts, and wheelie bars.

Fuel valves, available with 90-degree or straight outlets, are designed for high volume and are available with a single or dual outlet. The Power-Flo Nitro Valve is a larger version with Teflon seals that can be supplied with your choice of 1in pipe threads or with nipples to accept a 1in fuel line. The Power-Flo led to the Pingel slogan, "Pass More Gas."

A fuel-line filter is one of their newer products. Nicely machined like all of their products, it has a stainless steel filter that can be cleaned and an aluminum body. Rear engine mounts available for XR-750 and iron Sportster engines are stronger replacements for the stock casting. One version fits all Sportsters up to 1971 and bolts on over the starter shaft and studs on assembled engines; another even beefier model has four top bolts instead of two, which requires removing the studs or splitting the cases to install.

Wheelie bars are heli-arc-welded steel, supplied complete with mounts and struts. They feature adjustable caster height, and can be removed with four bolts. A 65in top tube is standard, with special lengths available on special order.

Pingel Enterprise, Inc.
2076-C Eleventh Avenue
Adams, WI 53910
(608) 339-7999
FAX (608) 339-9164
Catalog available

Pirelli

Pirelli makes tires for street and touring use on many Harley-Davidsons, as well as the MT-53 dirt-track racing tire.

Racing tires include the MT 38 Speedway dirt-track racing tire, which comes only in the 100/80-19 size, 26.33in tall, for rims that rage from 2.15in to 2.75in. Pirelli also makes models designed for dirt racing such as enduro, motocross, rally, and trials competition.

Street tires include the MP 7 Sport performance radial (also available in a sport racing compound), MT 09 and 08 Match sport touring radial, MT 59 and 58 touring, MT 69 and 68 Tour Am touring, MT 69E and 68E sport touring, and the MT 79 and 78 Demon performance (available with Kevlar belts).

Pirelli has played an important role in the development of performance tires. Pirelli played an important role early in this century in race tire development, and by 1950 was building tires for Formula One cars. In 1951 they (and Michelin) began producing radial tires, and in 1956 Pirelli retired unbeaten in Formula One racing. They produced the first radial racing tire in 1975 and the first radial motorcycle tire in 1983. By 1991, Pirelli had won 23 out of a possible 33 world motocross championships.

Pirelli Motorcycle Tire Division
4520 107th Street S.W.
Mukilteo, WA 98275
(206) 347-0864—information
(800) 722-1108—orders only
FAX (206) 353-6760
Brochure available

The Pirelli MT 38. *Pirelli*

A Pirelli MT 28. *Cosmopolitan Motors*

The Pirelli MT 69 front. *Pirelli*

The Pirelli MT 68 rear. *Pirelli*

These Big Twin cam gears were invented by Mike Poole to allow five choices in cam timing.

Pirelli
Viale Sarca, 202
20126 Milano, Italy
(02) 64421
FAX (02) 64423216

Cosmopolitan Motors, Inc.
301 Jacksonville Road
Hatboro, PA 19040
(215) 672-9100—information
(800) 523-2522—orders only

Poole Parts

Long-time drag racer Mike Poole manufactures tools and engine components for racers.

Cam gears for the Big Twin are machined from aluminum and weigh one-third as much as the stock piece; more importantly, they can be installed in five positions for five choices in cam timing (stock, two or four degrees advanced, or retarded). Mike came up with this idea out of necessity while campaigning his turbocharged drag bike a decade ago. Valve timing is especially critical on turbocharged bikes. His idea beats trying ten supposedly "identical" cams and then picking the one that times in the closest to what you need.

Cylinders are cast from 351 aluminum, heat-treated to T6. Liners are centrifugally cast from a chrome-moly alloy that machines like cast iron and wears like chrome-moly. It is compatible with all piston ring configurations and seals well with cast, chrome, or stainless rings. The barrel is cast around the sleeve; and the internal oil drains are cast right into the barrel casting themselves rather than being pressed in afterwards. Poole barrels can be supplied for virtually any Big Twin or Sportster on a special-order basis. They are available from stock for Shovelheads in standard 74in, standard 80in, 3 5/8in, and 3 3/4in bores. They come with liners with greater wall thickness (i.e., to sleeve a 3 3/4in engine down to a 3 5/8in). Barrel height is typically the same as stock but they can be built up to .200in taller.

Gaskets: Inner primary O-ring replacement gaskets are for engines with a broken lip. Designed for use under more extreme conditions, the gasket eliminates the need for time-consuming case repair. Shovelhead rocker box gaskets are made of a material that resists extreme heat and nitro-diluted oil.

Lifters for Big Twins are compatible with solid or hydraulic applications. They are machined from titanium billet and then given a special coating to prevent galling. If these aren't light enough for you, you might try whittling some out of balsa wood. Fuel valves are machined from solid brass with a 3/8in thread. With their unique key lock, when the key is removed it is virtually impossible to turn the fuel on. These valves come with two keys and use no plastic or rubber parts.

Morris wheels are no longer produced, but Poole has a supply in stock to fit 1974-1977 Sportsters. They were cast from 356 aluminum in a permanent mold and look very similar to the factory's current cast seven-spoke wheels. Poole has 19in front wheels for a single disc; 16in and 18in rear wheels with drum brakes; and 18in front and rear sets as used on the XLCR for a single disc each. Pistons work with bore sizes from 3 1/2in-4in, either domed or flat-topped. Rocker arms are made for Shovelheads from cast aluminum, available with bushings or needle roller bearings. Heat-treated tool steel is used for the pushrod inserts and the pins and rollers on the valve ends.

Turbochargers have been one of Mike's specialties since 1976. In the eighties he set four national records and had four Nationals wins with his turbocharged Shovelhead drag bike. Poole Shovelhead turbocharger kits come with exhaust system, all brackets and hardware, and complete instructions. Tools include a rod lapping arbor and a combination arbor for crankcase, transmission, and rod lapping.

Poole Cycle Parts
4801 Peachtree Road
Balch Springs, TX 75180
(214) 286-5351
Catalog available

Precision Balancing Company

Precision Balancing is run by Bob Pickett, who has specialized in custom balancing racing engine components for over thirty years. Bob has balanced flywheels on Indianapolis 500 race cars, and USAC Midget and Sprint cars, as well as over 600 Harley-Davidson flywheel assemblies. Typically, you ship him your assembled and trued flywheel assembly, the pistons, rings, rods (off the crank), and rod bearings (and the crank pin nut locks and screws if your engine uses them). Parts are returned within five working days of their arrival.

In an *Easyriders* magazine article (November 1991) on balancing, a key point Bob made is that dynamic balancing is a good idea any time you change the weight of the pistons, rings, wrist pins, crank pin, or flywheels, or when you change the stroke. Quoting his article: "For example, let's say that the engine is in good balance, but you want to go with a bigger piston. The new pistons, rings, pins, etc. weigh 100 grams more, each, than the pistons you took out. This would mean that the flywheels would be out of balance by 62 grams (8.2 oz. in.) at the outside diameter of the flywheel assembly."

Precision Balancing works to very close tolerances of less than .5 oz. in.

Precision Balancing Company
448 North Holmes Avenue
Indianapolis, IN 46222
(317) 639-2712

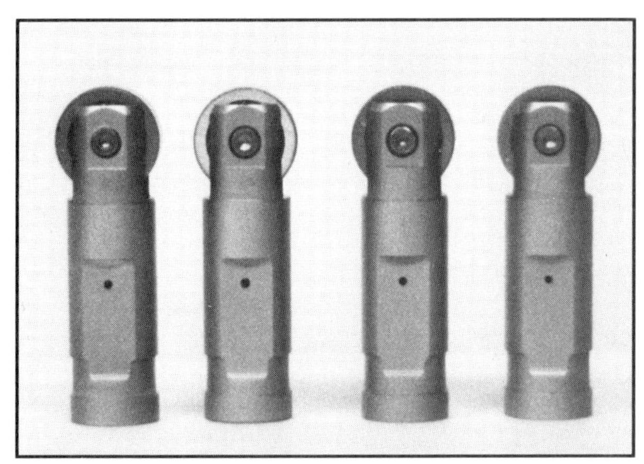

Poole Cycle Parts' lightweight titanium lifters for Big Twin engines are suitable with solids or hydraulics.

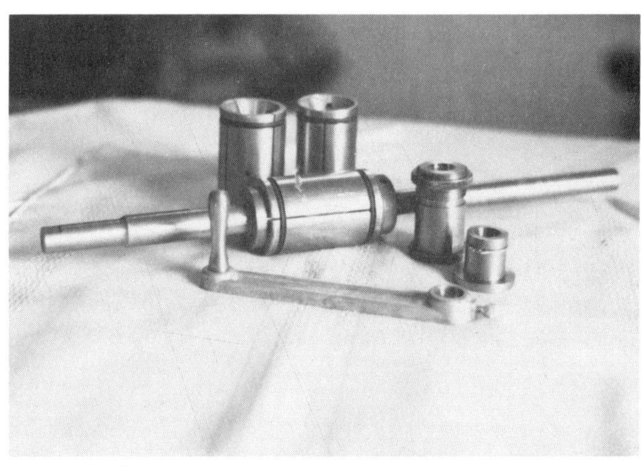

Poole Cycle Parts' lapping tools are machined from solid brass.

Poole barrels are flawlessly cast and polished.

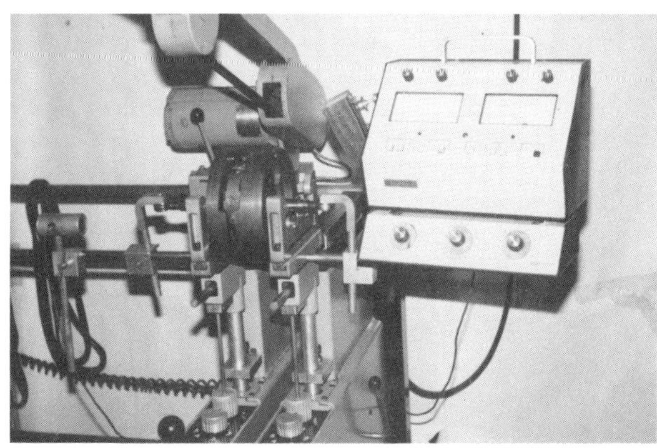

A Harley-Davidson flywheel assembly (with a "bob weight" installed) in the Precision Balancing Company balancing machine, ready for balancing.

The PMC shop prototype bike (shown here mocked-up in primer) is built around a Precision Dual Belt Rigid frame, with a 45-degree head angle and a 4in stretch.

The Precision Motorcycle Concepts shop prototype bike features PMC components throughout and lots of attention to detail.

Precision Machining

Precision Machining manufactures Black Diamond valves for Harley-Davidsons. They feature one-piece stainless steel or titanium construction with extremely hard Stellite tips. Precision Machining has an excellent reputation for its products and its personnel.

Black Diamond valves are also distributed by Hyperformance.

Precision Machining
580-H Crespi Drive
Pacifica, CA 94044
(415) 359-4704
FAX (415) 359-8574

Precision Metal Fab Racing

John Trutnau at Precision Metal Fab specializes in drag racing components. He builds custom frames and wheels and does fabrication and welding.

Precision Metal Fab Racing
100 North Scott Street
Shakopee, MN 55379
(612) 445-3530

Precision Motorcycle Concepts

Precision Motorcycle Concepts manufactures cylinder barrels, exhaust systems, frames, gas tanks, oil tanks, shifters, and their own Big Twin cams. The company is run by Greg Jones and Richard "Peck" Lumpkin. Peck handles the parts department and marketing, and Greg is a talented metal fabricator who built his own tubing bender and frame jigs to build custom frames. He can whip up anything for the street or drag racing, from stainless or aluminum brackets to titanium axles. He specializes in Shovelhead and Evolution engines but handles all Harley-Davidson street and race engine modifications, including balancing.

Cams for Big Twins include the PMC 4, which is compatible with stock heads, springs, and lifters and is guaranteed to outperform the EV 3 cam. It "kicks in" at around 3200rpm and is strong beyond 6500rpm. Cylinder barrels come in stock or big-bore sizes. PMC barrels feature centrifugally-cast sleeves and are available with or with cooling fins. Besides carrying Viper two-into-one exhaust systems, which use SuperTrapp mufflers, custom-built exhaust systems are available. Custom frames can be built for street or strip, Big Twin or Sportster. Gas tanks are along the lines of the classic Sportster tank, with a polished stainless steel bottom and filler cap.

Oil tanks are heli-arc-welded from 1/8in stainless steel plate like the old horseshoe tanks, are rubber-mounted, and include provision for easy oil changes. Custom designs can also be supplied. Shifters include the Red Eye jockey shifter, which is made from polished stainless steel. The shifter is internally wired and lit, and the handle is polished clear polyurethane so it looks like a red eye when lit.

The workmanship on the shop prototype bike Greg and Peck built show that while this may be a small shop, it is run by dedicated perfectionists.

Precision Motorcycle Concepts
8959 1/2 Mission Boulevard
Glen Avon, CA 92509
(714) 681-4420

Primo Belt Drives

Primo Brute II belt primary drive systems are available in six versions for Big Twins: 1979-1984 five-speed; 1979-1984 four-speed; 1965-1984 kickstart; 1965-1984 electric start; 1955-1964; and 1937-1954. They come with a 31-tooth front pulley, a 47-tooth rear pulley, an idler assembly, and a Gates 1 1/2in-wide belt with an 11mm tooth pitch. Complete 8mm kits are also available, in open or closed primary styles, in several versions for all Big Twins from 1937 to 1984.

Brute III belt drive systems fit all Evolution Big Twins. The Primo design uses a Barnett clutch and doubles the clutch surface area. Along with their complete kits, Primo offers individual components, including: Balance Master engine vibration dampers; cast aluminum Equalizer engine plates to maintain structural integrity in open primary set-ups; two styles of bearing supports; idler bearings; starter ring gears; acorn engine nuts; clutch drive plates; stamped aluminum derby and inspection covers; and numerous pulleys and belts in 8mm, 11mm, and 14mm pitches in 1 1/2in, 2in, or 3in widths.

Primo Elite clutch hub assemblies are compatible with belt or chain primary systems. They feature fifty-two ball bearings, a three-stud hub, three retaining springs, an aluminum pressure plate, and their own clutch friction disc and rivets. Primo includes a special high-temperature grease designed to perform well under high temperatures and stay in the bearing surfaces when spinning. A clutch hub bearing kit eliminates the caged roller bearings in 74in and 80in clutches. It also features fifty-two ball bearings, and comes with three retaining springs and the high-temperature grease.

The complete line of Primo products is described in detail in the Rivera catalog.

Rivera Engineering
6416 South Western Avenue
Whittier, CA 90606
(310) 692-8944
FAX (310) 699-3943

Progressive Suspension

Progressive Suspension manufactures a wide variety of shock absorbers and fork springs for new and old Big Twins and Sportsters, and an adjustable spanner wrench that can be adjusted to fit many rear shocks. Rear shocks are gas-charged and come in center-to-center lengths of 11.5in, 12.5in, 13in, 13.5in, and 14.25in. Narrow Glide front suspension can be improved with Progressive's damper rod kits and fork springs.

Progressive Suspension
11129 G Avenue
Hesperia, CA 92345
(619) 948-4012
FAX (619) 948-4307
Catalog available—specify Harley-Davidson

Pro Street Chassis Works

Pro Street Chassis Works is run by Kenny Boyce, who manufactures custom frame kits for Evolution Big Twin engines and five-speed transmissions. They replace stock FXRS series frames and use an FXST oil tank. A stock or aftermarket FXRS swing arm can be used. The specs include a 32.5° head angle, a seat height of 26.5in, and a bare weight of 34lb. With a stock FXRS front end, it provides a 60in wheelbase. Mounts for your choice of gas tank can be installed. Also available are machined aluminum fender struts and an 8in DC Company fiberglass rear fender.

Kenny's frames can also be ordered from Darrell Collier at DC Company in Citrus Heights, CA.

Pro Street Chassis Works
P.O. Box 1136
Orangevale, CA 95662-1136
(916) 987-1864

Prototek

Prototek began in 1980 as an engineering firm and prototype fabrication shop for aerospace, aircraft, and automotive clients, and in 1989 they began manufacturing billet aluminum components for Harley-Davidsons. In 1991 Prototek opened a custom bike shop, Pro-Twin. Also available are custom fabrication services, including performance engine building and complete motorcycle construction, polishing, plating, anodizing, repair, and restoration. Custom frames can be built for drag racing or street use as well as a variety of other parts, all on a special-order basis.

Prototek
11036 Brookville Road
Indianapolis, IN 46239
(317) 861-1000—information
(800) PRO-5759—orders only
FAX (317) 861-1000
Brochure available

Puccio Welding

Ken Puccio and his son Kerry build custom Big Twin and Sportster frames for street use and drag racing. Custom fabrication and heli-arc welding work are available. Aluminum oil tanks are among their specialties.

Puccio Welding
357 North Montgomery
San Jose, CA 95110
(408) 294-1660

Puttin' Parts

Tony at Puttin' Parts builds custom frames for Big Twin and Sportster engines. This shop also provides street and strip Harley-Davidson engine modifications and machining.

Puttin' Parts
16185 South Golden Road
Golden, CO 80401
(303) 279-8893

Quik Silver II

The Quik Silver II carburetor is made specifically for Harley-Davidsons and is distributed by Rivera Engineering. Released in the fall of 1991, the Quik Silver carburetor is the work of Bill "Red" Edmonston.

Rivera Engineering
6416 South Western Avenue
Whittier, CA 90606
(310) 692-8944
FAX (310) 699-3943

RacePak

Ron Armstrong and Spencer Eisenbarth started RacePak in 1985 after developing a computer system for racers. Two models are available for both drag racing and road racing. Each system monitors both crankshaft and transmission output shaft speed, enabling you to chart the differences between them. Suspension travel can be checked up to 250 times per second, along with exhaust gas temperature and throttle position. RacePak computers are designed to be user-friendly to non-technical people. They are especially beneficial for racers using elaborate, multi-stage clutches.

RacePak computers are used by winning motorcycle racers such as Elmer Trett, Jim McClure, Larry McBride, Rob Muzzy's team, and Team Yoshimura.

RacePak
17502 Studebaker Road
Cerritos, CA 90701
(310) 403-7125
FAX (310) 403-7129

Race Technique

Chip Solley runs Race Technique, where he manufactures Solley valves for Big Twin and Sportster engines.

Race Technique
5334 Old Winter Garden Road
Orlando, FL 32811
(407) 298-4958

Race Visions

Race Visions is run by Jim "Puppet" Ditullio, whose specialty is building lay-down drag bike frames. These are built from chrome-moly tubing and can be supplied for Big Twin and Sportster engines. Puppet also builds a rolling chassis or complete bike, and makes billet aluminum triple clamps, engine plates, and other components to order.

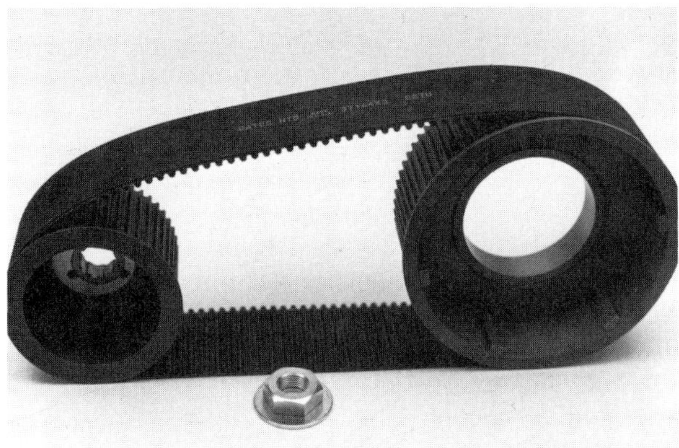

Designed to handle the stress of monster engines and violent launches, this Primo primary kit features a 3in belt.

Progressive's 4000 series shocks are available with black or chrome (as shown here) springs in five lengths.

This Softail street bike features a frame, wheels, and many other aluminum components from Prototek.

Progressive's shocks for Softails have six-stage damping and adjustable spring preload.

This custom Prototek modular wheel has a CNC-machined five-spoke aluminum center section.

Race Visions
350 Hinman Avenue
Buffalo, NY 14216
(716) 875-9010

Ram Jett Retainer

Roger "Ram Jett" Chatelet's product line includes a "mobile dyno" motorcycle computer, cylinder stud kits, intake manifolds, and shop tools.

Cylinder stud kits include a set of eight studs and inserts, a tap, tap guide, and cutting tool. The studs are machined from chrome-moly, and the precision-rolled threads provide additional strength. Intake manifolds are designed to cure the compliance fitting problem of stock manifolds, and provide a five-percent flow increase. They are heat-treated aluminum castings that bolt on with no modifications.

The Ram Jett Performance Computer straps onto the bike, and a sensor snaps onto one spark plug lead. After you enter the weight of the bike and its rider, the overall gear ratio, ignition type (single- or dual-fire), drag coefficient (using information provided), air density, and the maximum rpm at which the engine will be tested, the computer calculates the bike's horsepower and torque in 250rpm increments. It displays it on the screen either graphically or numerically.

Specialized tools for Harley-Davidsons include a wrist pin bushing tool that reduces the time required to size new wrist pin bushings for all models from 1936 to 1993. The Ram Jett clutch retainer works on all 1936-1983 Big Twin clutches, eliminating clutch creep and providing smoother shifting.

Ram Jett Retainer
P.O. Box 1521
Santa Maria, CA 93456-1521
(805) 934-5833

Rat's Whole Place

Bob Taft, the owner of Rat's Whole Place, built the first Evolution drag bike to run in the eight-second bracket on gas. They offer performance engine building for Big Twins and Sportsters, including transmission and racing cylinder head modifications, and custom machining.

Rat's Whole Place sponsors the B/Fuel Harley-Davidson drag bike ridden by Terry Starbody, and the Bob Taft's Top Gas Harley-Davidson.

Rat's Whole Place
2777 North Woodford
Decatur, IL 62526
(217) 875-RACE—information
(800) 421-RATS—orders only

Rawlings Motor Maniacs

Clyde Rawlings, Jr. builds slipper clutches, forks, frames, fuel injection systems, and complete gas, alcohol, and fuel Big Twin and Sportster drag racing engines. He also offers custom fabrication and repair work. He can build just about any component from a fork brace to a complete drag bike.

Clyde is a successful and dedicated Top Fuel racer who was the first rider in history to ride a Big Twin down the quarter-mile into the seven-second bracket. His father, Clyde Sr., began stunt riding at fairs, roaring around inside a huge barrel called the "Ride of Death" back in 1935. Rock on, guys.

Rawlings Motor Maniacs
3755 East Belmont
Fresno, CA 93702
(209) 237-2332

Ray Price Performance Products

Along with his new air shifters, Ray Price has specialized in a variety of transmissions for all-out Big Twin drag bikes since the early eighties. These transmissions are available with two, three, four, or five speeds in machined aluminum cylindrical cases. The two-speed weighs 22lb and its case measures 5 1/4in in diameter by 6 3/4in wide. This company is part of Ray's dealership, Ray Price Harley-Davidson, home of the Top Fuel Sportster drag bike ridden by Chris Forrest.

Ray Price Performance Products
1126 South Saunders Street
Raleigh, NC 27603
(919) 832-2261—information
(800) 39-HARLEY—orders only
FAX (919) 833-6846
Literature available

Razorback Motor Works

Wyatt Fuller does custom design work for manufacturers, and complete motorcycle construction, fabrication, machining and welding. You will see examples of his design talents on most products from KüryAkyn U.S.A. and the Sumax aluminum pushrod covers.

Razorback Motor Works
4100 North Powerline Road,
Suite A3
Pompano Beach, FL 33073
(305) 974-5654

RB Racing/Race Systems Research

Bob Behn at RB Racing/Race Systems Research manufactures exhaust systems, fuel injection systems, and turbochargers for Harley-Davidsons.

Exhaust systems are mostly two-into-one style, available in styles for all Big Twins from 1966 on and all Evolution Sportsters. The two-into-one systems come with a turnout, slash-cut, aluminum, or carbon fiber muffler, and some of the dual systems are available with megaphones.

Race Systems Research fuel injection systems are available for all Evolution engines, with your choice of a 50 or 55mm venturi. These are complete digital fuel injection systems that monitor the way the engine is performing and order corrections as required. Each package includes the intake manifold, an array of

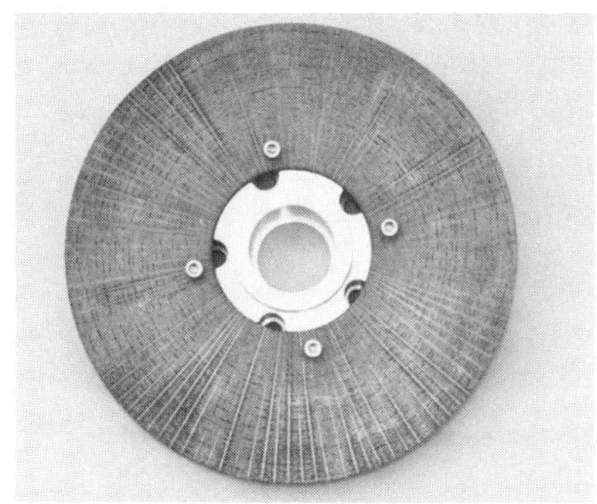

R.B.'s brake discs are carbon/carbon for extremely lightweight, mechanical stability, and good braking under high-temperature conditions. *Connie Baker*

R.B.'s wheels feature two-piece carbon fiber rims with an aluminum center dish that is O-ring sealed to each rim half. *Connie Baker*

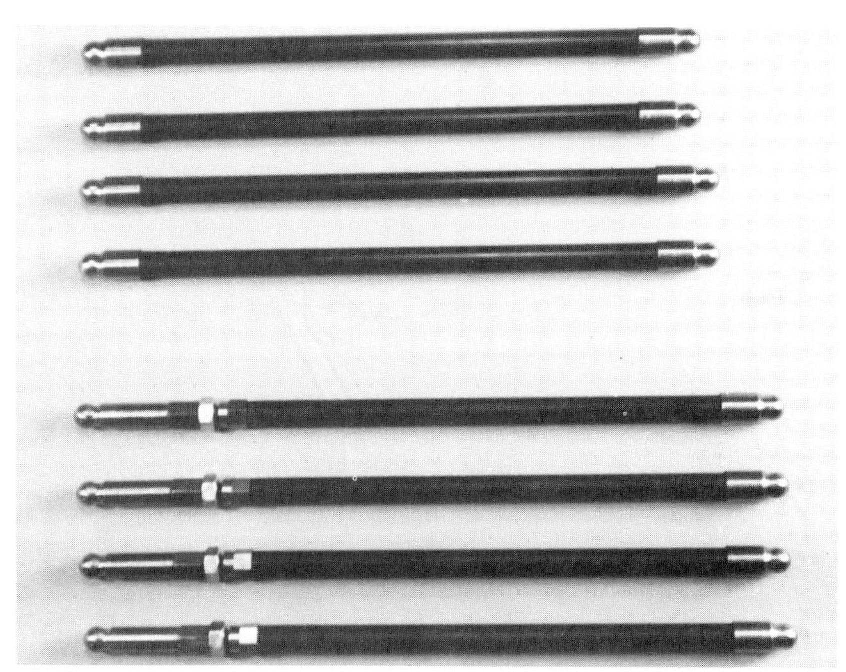

R.B.'s carbon fiber pushrods are popular among top racers. Titanium lifters and complete valvetrain kits are in the works. *Connie Baker*

This V-8 XLCR was an R.B.'s project bike, powered by a 350 Chevy with Hilborn injection. *Connie Baker*

The classic graphics on the packaging give an indication of the long heritage behind Regina chains. *Cosmopolitan Motors*

sensors, and software for your PC. If you have a PC you can reprogram the system by using a modem (the electronic box that allows computers to talk to each other over telephone lines).

Turbochargers are a specialty at RB. They can supply and install complete turbocharger systems for Harley-Davidson for the street, strip, or salt. The 1992 RB catalog says, "Turbocharging is the most efficient way to produce horsepower, and RB Racing has more experience turbocharging Harleys than anyone. You can build your motor to the max with radical cams, solid lifters and high-compression pistons but it's still going to see the taillight of a turbocharged bike. A turbocharger simply allows you to put more air and fuel into your cylinders, and as long as you can burn it, you're going to make more power—it's that simple."

Two basic versions are available for Evolution Big Twins. The 204hp kits come ready to bolt on with a 300cfm turbocharger. The 380hp full-race intercooled kits are strictly for racing, with a 500cfm turbocharger.

The company's catalog and tech manual offer a good explanation of the fundamentals of induction alternatives, including carburetors, fuel injection, and turbochargers.

RB Racing
1625 West 134th Street
Gardena, CA 90249
(310) 515-5831—tech
(310) 515-5720—orders
FAX (310) 515-5782
Catalog available

R.B.'s Performance Technology

R.B.'s Performance Technology is run by Randy and Connie Baker, who manufacture numerous products—many of which are made from carbon fiber—for serious racers.

Brake discs made from carbon/carbon can weigh as little as 6oz. R.B.'s discs have been under development since the mid-eighties. Unlike most other braking systems, R.B.'s makes both the disc and the brake pad from the same carbon/carbon fibers. To do so requires unique manufacturing techniques. Binder resins are normally used in composites of carbon fiber, with the components being made by the mixture of the fibers and the resin. With carbon/carbon brake discs and pads no resin is used. The parts are formed in a mold using extremely high temperature and pressure. R.B.'s feels that these systems reduce both the heat-induced brake fade and the disc's rotating mass; and there is virtually no distortion of the braking surface, even under extreme temperatures. These materials drive the components prices beyond the reach of most of us, but they are becoming standard equipment on Grand Prix road racers and serious drag bikes.

Cam cover needle bearing kits are available for all Harley-Davidson engines. They allow Sportster owners to reduce friction by pulling out the worn, sloppy factory bushings and pressing in the precision needle bearings. Big Twin owners will need access to a vertical milling machine to enlarge the diameter of the bushing recess in the cam cover case to accept the bearing race, which is then pressed into place. R.B.'s can do this work for you if you send in your cam cover.

Pushrods made from carbon fiber are available for all Harley-Davidsons. They are made from an epoxy matrix system that is cured in a proprietary high-temperature, high-pressure molding process to produce pushrods that are stronger than steel and lighter than aluminum. Wheelie bars, also made of carbon fiber, can be made for any drag bike in virtually any length.

Wheels are built around a CNC-machined aluminum center dish mated with O-ring seals to each of the 15in carbon fiber rim halves. These quickly-replaceable rim halves come in widths of 3in, 4in, 5in, and 6in to create a rear wheel width of between 6-12in. Tire changes are a snap: racers unbolt the tire locks, remove the tire, slip on the new tire, and replace the tire locks. Bead locks like these are currently required by several sanctioning bodies for Top Fuel and are expected to become mandatory soon for all Pro classes. R.B.'s wheels are available with grade eight steel bolts, but you might as well spring for the optional titanium and aluminum hardware. R.B.'s was the first company to offer this type of wheel to Harley-Davidson drag racers.

Randy and Connie have worked exclusively for the promotion of the racers, who are the foundation of the sport. Connie's articles and photography appear in American Motorcycle Racing Association programs and in *Handcrafted American Racing Motorcycles*, *Harley Women*, and *Hot Bike* magazines.

They work with composite engineers from Lockheed, McDonnel-Douglas, and NASA, and have over fifty years of combined composite engineering experience that should enable them to continue to define the leading edge in this field.

R.B.'s Performance Technology
Route 1, Box 38A
Beecher City, IL 62414
(618) 487-5885
Catalog available

RC Components

RC aluminum wheels feature spun aluminum rims and CNC-machined center sections. They are distributed by Damon's Motorcycle Creations.

RC Components
13171 Bradley Avenue
Sylmar, CA 91342
(818) 364-9195

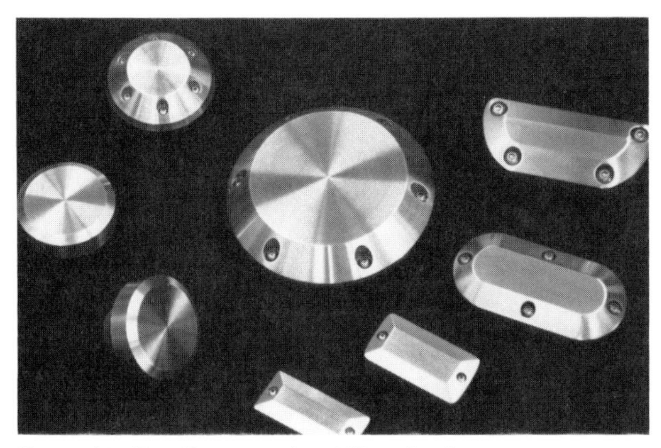

Prototek's Pro-Comp series billet aluminum components include (clockwise from top right) handlebar clamps, inspection covers, front and rear master cylinder covers, vented gas caps, points covers, and (center) derby covers.

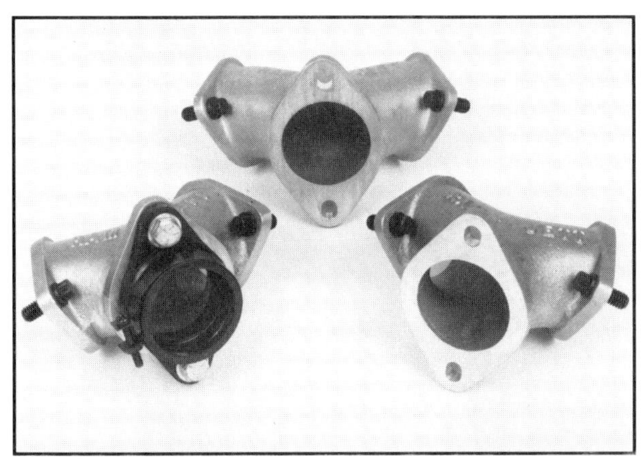

Ram Jett has intake manifolds for Big Twin (top), Sportster spigot-mount (left), and Sportster flange mount (right), and they work with stock or milled cylinder heads and with stroker engines.

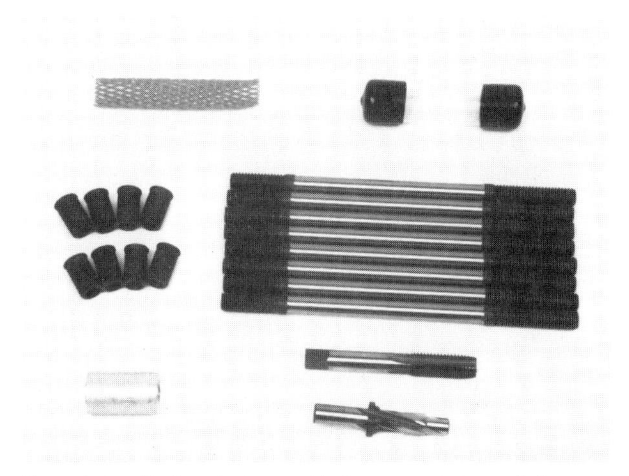

Ram Jett cylinder studs provide increased strength for performance applications and stock engine repair. Tools are provided to let you install these stud kits with the engine in the frame.

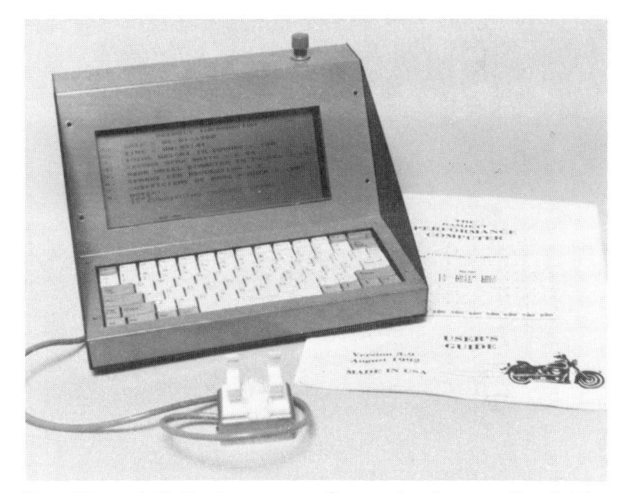

The Ram Jett Performance Computer is an affordable, compact alternative to full-size motorcycle dynos. It gives tuners a reliable way to assess engine performance.

An American legend in action, Clyde Rawlings is late for work again.

Rolling Thunder transmissions use original 1982 (or S.T.D.) cases with Andrews gears, mainshafts, countershafts, shifter forks, and clutches.

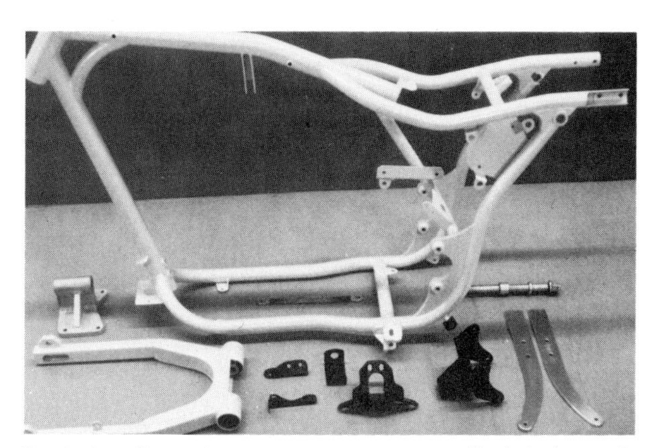

Evolution Sportster owners can mount all of their stock components on this rubber-mounted Rowe frame.

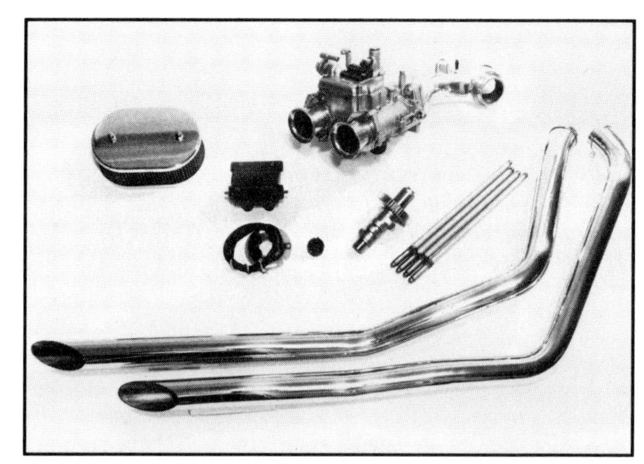

This Rivera engine kit bolts onto all Evolution Big Twins to provide a well-balanced performance improvement. When used with ported heads, Velva-Touch lifters, and a Super-Trapp exhaust system, the combination developed 103hp on the SuperFlow dyno at V-M-O Products.

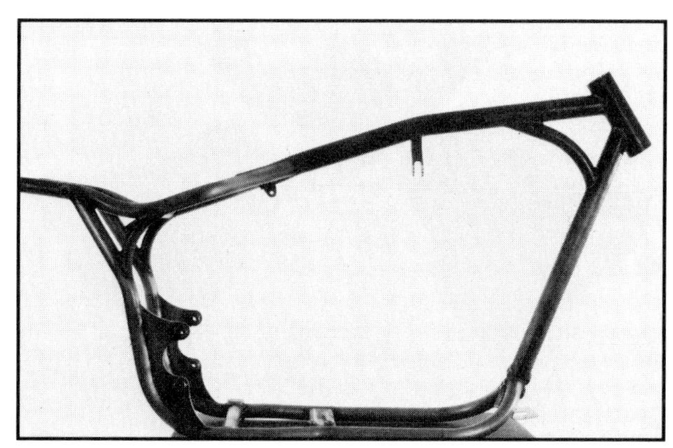

The first motorcycle frame to go into production at Rowe Machine was this single-downtube FXR frame.

Wheels can be trued and statically balanced in this Rowe 09-0004 stand.

Damon's Motorcycle Creations
547 Apollo, Unit C
Brea, CA 92621
(714) 990-1166

R/D Spring Corporation

R/D specializes in manufacturing valvetrain components for motorcycles and race cars. Their products include valve collars, guides, keepers, and springs. Valve collars are available in hard-anodized 7075-T6 aluminum or in titanium.

R/D does not generally sell to the public since they deal mainly with OEM suppliers.

R/D Spring Corporation
P.O. Box 3191
Hesperia, CA 92345-3191
(916) 948-4698
FAX (916) 948-4856
Catalog available to dealers only

Red Neck Cycles

Red Neck is a German shop specializing in building and repairing street and strip Harley-Davidsons.

Red Neck Cycles
Rathausstrabe 48/7
7050 WN-Beinstein, Germany
Phone 07151-35459

Regina

Regina is an Italian manufacturer of final drive chains (in 520, 530, and 630 sizes). Regina chains are high-quality products and perhaps the lightest available. The metals used are second to none and the quality control is impressive.

Regina bicycle chains are considered among the most advanced in the world. They have several extremely lightweight models, and in the seventies they introduced a titanium bicycle chain. Its price keeps it from being used much outside of Olympic competition and record attempts, but it blew some minds when it was unveiled.

Regina Extra motorcycle chains are distributed in North America by Cosmopolitan Motors.

Regini Industria S.p.a.
22052 Cernusco Lombardone (CO)
Via Monza, 90, Italy
(039) 9906512
FAX (039) 9906782

Regina U.S.A., Inc.
P.O. Box 469
Waukesha, WI 53187-0469
(414) 521-1998

Cosmopolitan Motors, Inc.
301 Jacksonville Road
Hatboro, PA 19040
(215) 672-9100—information
(800) 523-2522—orders only

Rich Products Company

Don Rich started Rich Products Company in 1984, and the company is now run by his son Jim. They manufacture engine components, performance kits, and exhaust systems for current Big Twins and Sportsters, the XR-1000, and the XR-750. They also offer parts and service, including dyno and flow bench work.

A typical performance kit includes pistons, cams, an exhaust system, clutch, and final drive gearing changes. In 1988 they installed such a kit in their XR-1000 developmental bike and it ran a 10.19 at 124.60, looking stock except for the laced wheels and a wheelie bar.

Their new Thunderheader two-into-one exhaust system was designed to increase power with a good, wide powerband. Available for Big Twins and Sportsters, it has produced excellent results on everything from commuting bikes to lay-down drag bikes. The system is unique because it uses an exhaust flow director that takes the out-of-phase rear wave into account and minimizes its effects. It was described in detail in *Hot Bike* magazine (September 1991).

Rich now owns the molds used to produce the classic Thunderhead cylinder heads for iron Sportsters.

Rich Products Company
12420 San Pablo Avenue
Richmond, CA 94805
(510) 234-7547
FAX (510) 234-1690

Rickey Racer

Lance Weil produces a limited number of vintage road racers with iron Sportster engines. Equipped with laced wheels, drum brakes, and a hand-formed aluminum tank, the bikes are set in a frame designed along the lines of the classic Norton Featherbed design. A street version is available on a special-order basis.

Rickey Racer
811 North Western Avenue
Hollywood, CA 90029
(213) 461-8238

Rifle

In addition to their color-matched Nightflite fairings for Sportsters, Rifle makes fairings and replacement windshields for Big Twin touring bikes.

Rifle
3140 El Camino Real
Atascadero, CA 93422
(805) 466-5880—information
(800) 262-1237—orders only
(800) 663-1016—Canadian orders

Rivera Engineering

Rivera Engineering is run by the knowledgeable and enthusiastic Mel Magnet, whose contribution to the evolution of the Evolution is considerable. Rivera offers a wide array of performance parts for any Big Twin or Sportster racer.

Rivera distributes the product lines of several top manufacturers, all of whom are covered in the Rivera catalog. Rivera also has its own cams and pistons.

Evolution Big Twin bolt-on high-performance kits are available in FX and Softail versions with your choice of Dell'Orto or SU carburetors, and either Run Roader 1 3/4in drag pipes or SuperTrapp staggered duals. These kits include Rivera's Spirit cam and air cleaner, a set of Sifton pushrods, and a Dyna ignition and coil. The V-M-O dyno showed these kits can provide 35-40 percent more power over a stock engine.

Pistons co-developed by Rivera and Arias Industries are forged from 2618-T6 aluminum and are supplied with 4340 chrome-moly wrist pins and Hastings rings. They can be supplied for Evolution engines with S.T.D. cylinder heads in several versions and for most Big Twin engines in .010in, .020in, .030in oversizes and 9:1, 9.5:1 and 10:1 compression ratios.

Big-bore pistons are available with unfinished domes in 3 5/8in and 3 13/16in bore sizes and in .010in, .020in, and .030in over those sizes; .040in over is available for the 3 13/16in nominal pistons. These come with special Arias rings that include a chrome-faced compression ring. As with all Rivera pistons, they are forged from 2618T-6 aluminum and come with tapered-wall-thickness 4340 chrome-moly wrist pins with spiral-lock clips.

One-piece pushrods are machined from .065in-wall 3/8in 4130 chrome-moly tubing and are heat-treated. They come 11 1/2in long and are left unfinished at one end (with the ball ends separate) to permit a precise fit without adjusters.

Sprockets include 24-tooth offset transmission sprockets (and rear wheel spacers) for five-speed Big Twin chain-drive conversions; aluminum final drive sprockets for FL and FLH models with 48, 49, 51, 54, 55, 56, 57, 58, 59, 60, or 61 teeth; and versions for bikes with offset transmission sprockets in 45 or 46 teeth.

Valve springs for Shovelheads come in sets of four double springs or in kits that include steel keepers, eight shims, and titanium top collars. The kits are designed to be used without bottom collars, and Rivera recommends a Manley cutter and pilot for installation.

Their lifter roller replacement tools are designed to provide a way to hold lifters during repairs. Cylinder head fixtures come in Panhead, Shovelhead, and Evolution versions. Cast from 356 aluminum and accurately milled and tapped, they have provisions for four T-slot clamps and have a rectangular shape that can be held in a vise.

Rivera works with dozens of serious and successful racers and engineers to develop and select quality components for their customers. Their 134-page Rivera catalog is among the most informative of its kind, and is filled with an exceptional array of top-quality performance parts exclusively for Harley-Davidsons.

Rivera Engineering
6416 South Western Avenue
Whittier, CA 90606
(310) 692-8944
FAX (310) 699-3943
Catalog available

Riverside Cycle

Paul Matyka at Riverside Cycle makes billet two-valve cylinder heads for Evolution engines and custom chrome-moly frames for Harley-Davidson drag bikes—all on a special-order basis. Riverside, open since 1979, builds street and drag racing engines, and offers motorcycle repair.

In June of 1992, Paul rode his 140ci Pro Stock Big Twin 151mph in 8.71 seconds on gas, beating the old ECRA national record by eight-tenths of a second.

Riverside Cycle
258 Riverside Avenue
Bristol, CT 06010
(203) 584-2270

Roberson's Cycle

Roberson's produces fork braces, ignition kill switches, and steering dampers for Harley-Davidson drag bikes.

Roberson's Cycle
R.D. 2, Route 8
Centerville, PA 16404
(814) 694-3225

Rolling Thunder Products

Rolling Thunder produces four-speed transmissions for Big Twins and distributes frames manufactured in New Zealand, and other Australian products such as air fork caps, Kevlar fenders, polyurethane handlebar bushings, rebuildable and adjustable shock absorbers for Softails, and steering dampers.

Rolling Thunder four-speed transmissions are built completely from new parts, with Andrews gears and components installed in original 1982 Harley-Davidson castle-top cases. Options include your choice of ratios for first, second, and third gears, kicker kits, and S.T.D. cases.

Rolling Thunder Products
119 Waymouth Street
Adelaide SA 5000, Australia
(08) 231-7335
FAX (08) 231-3363

Romine Racing

Mike Romine offers engine building, custom fabrication, machining, and welding. The 1987 and 1988 AMRA A/F class champion, Mike campaigns a Big Twin Top Fuel drag bike in the AMRA series.

Romine Racing
313 South Clay
Sturgis, MI 49091
(616) 651-9081

Route 66

John Russell at Route 66 specializes in frames, custom fabrication, and performance engine modifications. Engine services include double-plug conversions and rebuilding. Frames range from mild steel versions to laydown drag frames, all built to or-

This Rowe 09-1179 flywheel truing stand has an 80lb capacity and a 10in swing and is the standard of the Harley-Davidson aftermarket.

Liquid-cooled R&R cast cylinders helped the *Easyriders* streamliner reach 322mph at Bonneville in 1991.

A degree of rider safety is added when the barrels are fitted with the R&R water jacket castings, which can also serve as scatter shields.

Bob George of R&R Cycle has built many streamliners and partially streamlined bikes for Bonneville since he started racing there in 1970. *Joe Reily*

der. They also modify and repair existing frames.

Route 66
204A Walsall Wood Road
Aldridge, West Middlesex
United Kingdom WS9 8HB
Phone 0922-59398

Rowe Machine

Rowe Machine is run by Marc Rowe, who produces custom frames and swing arms for FXRs and Evolution Sportsters. Both of these frames use rubber-mounted Dyna Glide engine mounts and feature single front downtubes. The necks are stretched 2in to provide a 33-degree steering head angle.

All frames are heli-arc-welded in jigs, using cold-rolled mild steel tubing. They come with swing arm and swing arm shaft, axle and spacers, front, rear and top engine mounts, rear fender struts, ignition mount, and other brackets

The workmanship on these products is first-rate. Marc is also a SEMA-approved chassis builder who has designed and built IHRA and NHRA dragsters since the early sixties. Dave also runs a company whose products are described under Dave Rowe Performance Products.

Rowe Machine
148 Batchelder Road
Seabrook, NH 03874
(603) 474-3330
FAX (603) 474-9114

Rowe U.S.A.

Ed Rowe and the staff at Rowe U.S.A. have produced quality engine parts and tools since 1970. Rowe manufactures a variety of tools, valves, and valve guides, and also distribute Hastings piston rings. Tools include flywheel assembly jigs and truing stands for flywheel assemblies and wheels.

Rowe U.S.A.
P.O. Box 7409
Santa Maria, CA 93456-7409
(805) 349-1932—information
(800) 531-9901—orders only
FAX (805) 922-0155

R&R Cycle

R&R is owned by Roberta Linn and veteran Bonneville racer Bob George. They manufacture cylinders, fiberglass fairings, and complete streamliner bodies.

Their Big Twin cylinders (with or without water jackets for cooling) come in bore sizes up to 3 13/16in and a 5 1/2in height. Strictly for racing, these barrels normally come as rough castings which are machined for Evolution and Shovelhead engines. They are also available finished and ready to install.

Fairings are built to withstand the pressure of serious speed and have proven themselves at 231mph on the Bonneville Salt Flats. The "world's fastest fairing" weighs in at around 25lb as shown and is split down the middle into two halves when pulled from the mold. Originally designed for a 10in extended wheelbase, these fairings can be trimmed down for your particular application. R&R (or you) can add windows, air ducts, or leg rests.

Streamliner bodies are 23ft long with a 9ft nose section. This wind tunnel-tested design has proven itself in many forms, the most famous of them being the *Easyriders* streamliner, which ran 322mph in 1990.

At Bonneville in 1970 Bob ran 150mph using two Shovelheads. Two years later he added nitro—just to make sure—and ran 217mph. Although he wasn't able to back it up for a record, it remains the fastest pass ever by an "open" (non-streamlined) motorcycle.

Bob started R&R Cycle in 1974 after developing the steel barrels and water-cooled jackets. That year, with Dave Campos at the reins, they ran 208mph on gas and 231mph on fuel—and both are records to this day. Bob received a patent on his cylinder design on August 22, 1976. In 1978 Mil Blair at Jammer took over the ownership of the project and Dave Campos coaxed it to 278mph. And then came the famous 1990 record of 322.149mph with *Easyriders* and a cast of thousands helping out.

Bob has Bob Behn at RB Racing/Race Systems Research handle some of the machining work. R&R provides racing engine building and pattern making services for racers and manufacturers, and a VHS videotape called "The Making of a Motorcycle Streamliner" is available.

R&R Cycle
6622 West 87th Place
Los Angeles, CA 90045
(310) 645-9067
Catalog available

Run Roader

Run Roader has designed and manufactured exhaust systems for Harley-Davidsons for more than thirty years. Even if you don't know their name, chances are you've seen their work since they actually manufacture (and then label) custom motorcycle exhaust system for several "manufacturers."

Drag pipes are available for 1957-1985 Sportsters in 1 3/4in diameter; and in a choice of 1 3/4in or 2in diameters for 1984-and-up FXRs and Softails, 1971-1984 FXs, and all Evolution Sportsters.

Run Roader drag pipes are supplied in Rivera Engineering's engine kits.

Run Roader
9500 Lucas Ranch Road
Cucamonga, CA 91730
(714) 944-0890—information
(800) 448-6826—orders only
FAX (714) 941-7672

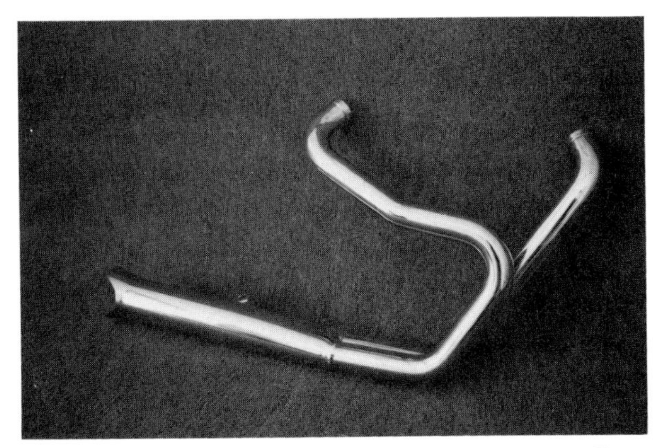

Samson two-into-one systems are available for most Evolution Big Twins.

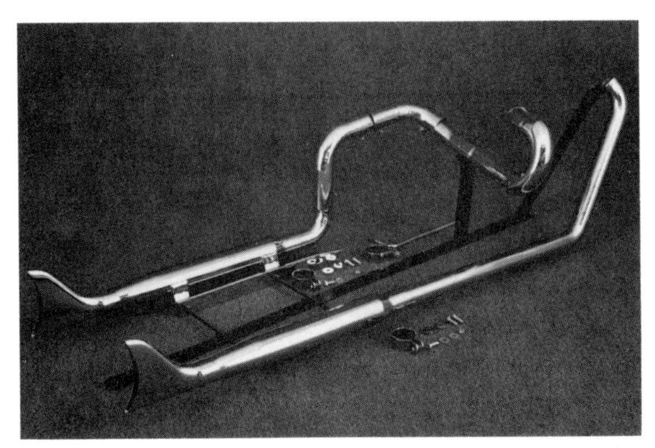

Samson offers five models of fishtail systems for Softails, including this tapered model.

Sam Evans takes his work seriously, as evidenced by a well-equipped shop and some AHDRA records. He carries a variety of high-performance parts for building and maintaining Harley-Davidson drag bikes.

The Schultz Racing bottom end can be used in stock-style cases...

Screamin' Eagle Evolution Sportster cam kits are available in two versions, for 1986-1990, and 1991-and-later Sportsters, and they include titanium upper collars.

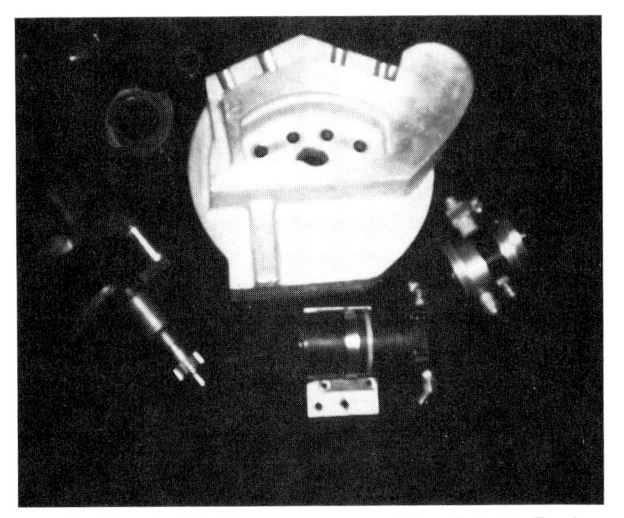

...or in Terry's billet four-cam cases. The Schultz Racing dry-sump oiling system is also shown here. *Terry Schultz*

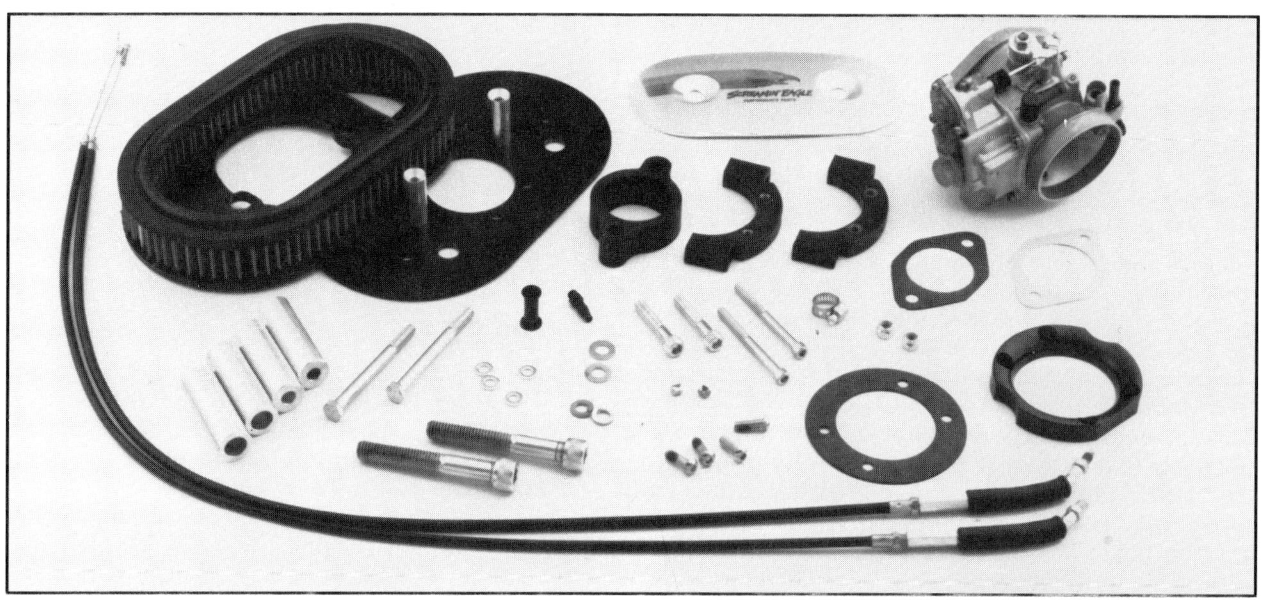

Screamin' Eagle carburetor kits include a higher-performance version of the Keihin carburetor with a 40mm venturi and performance jetting. Part number 29081-90A (shown here) is for Evolution Sportsters.

This Screamin' Eagle cam kit (25490-87) fits all 80in Evolution Big Twins and is intended for use with solid lifters, but it is also compatible with hydraulics. Another version (25493-89) provides peak power at 6000rpm and is intended for use with hydraulic lifters. Bikes produced through early 1986 will require piston notching with either of these kits.

Schultz Racing components have been proven reliable after several years of testing in Terry's Top Fuel bike. *Connie Baker*

Samson Motorcycle Products, Inc.

Samson has a complete line of exhaust systems for Evolution Big Twins, with models for dressers, Dyna Glides, FXRs, and Softails. Most are available as drag pipes or with a choice of slash-cut, tapered, turned-out, or two-into-one collector mufflers. Samson products feature one-piece construction, heli-arc welding, and triple chrome plating. Stock mounting hardware can be used whenever possible. Their staggered dual exhaust systems are "guaranteed to deliver more horsepower throughout the entire rpm range."

Samson Motorcycle Products, Inc.
1180-A North Fountain Way
Anaheim, CA 92806
(714) 630-8086—information
(800) 373-4217—orders only
FAX (714) 630-5023
Literature available

Sam's Performance Specialties

Sam Evans offers his own line of valves and specializes in porting, polishing, and flow-testing cylinder heads exclusively for Harley-Davidsons. In business since 1989, he concentrates on drag bikes and has completely reworked and flow-tested over 200 sets of heads. The shop distributes the Miller Racing Systems crankcase pressure regulator.

Valves are machined from stainless steel and come with a choice of high or low tulips, hardened or Stellite tips, and in polished finishes or black nitrite coatings.

Sam's Stage I heads helped Wayne Miller and Robbie Miley kick down the old AHDRA 5.90-second record in the eighth-mile with a 5.57 on gas. Three weeks later the combination set another AHDRA record of 125.50mph at the eighth-mile strip at Myrtle Beach, South Carolina. Stage II Pro heads are also available for all-out drag racing.

Sam's Performance Specialties
P.O. Box 1624
Summerville, SC 29484-1624
(803) 871-2401

Santee Industries

Santee has a line of exhaust systems for Harley-Davidsons, and also builds custom frames and an oil tank. Frames are mostly rigid chopper designs. Built from mild steel tubing, they're available for Big Twin and Sportster engines. Oil tanks are machined and welded aluminum and take a cartridge oil filter.

Santee Industries
651 Arraya Street
San Fernando, CA 91340
(818) 365-3236
Literature available

SBS

SBS stands for Scandinavian Brake Systems, whose asbestos-free brake pads are available for most 1975-and-later Big Twins and 1982-and-later Sportsters.

SBS brake pads have been used by many winning racers, including the 1991 and 1992 World Superbike champion Doug Polen, 1992 AMA Grand National champion Chris Carr and runner-up Scott Parker, and the 1992 AMRA Top Fuel champion Jim McClure. SBS pads are imported into the United States from Sweden by ProMan in Wisconsin.

ProMan
P.O. Box 5222
3501 Kennedy Road
Janesville, WI 53547-5222
(608) 758-1111

Schafer Manufacturing Company

John Schafer and the staff manufacture a line of fiberglass components for KR and XR-750 Grand National race bikes. Seats, tanks, and fairings are available in black or orange gel-coat finishes. XR-750 gas tanks are made in three versions: a dirt-track 2 1/2gal 1972 style; a road racing 5gal 1972 style; and a dirt-track 2 1/2gal 1980 style.

John has provided custom fiberglass for numerous drag bikes. His work can also be seen on the factory-backed Lucifer's Hammer road racer, which was featured in *American Iron* magazine in April 1992.

Schafer Manufacturing Company
P.O. Box 388
Troutman, NC 28166-0388
(708) 766-8424
Literature available

Schirra Cycle & Machine

Schirra Cycle & Machine manufactures slider clutches and provides engine case repairs and other services exclusively for Harley-Davidson drag racers. They provide engine modifications, machining, and welding services, with an emergency twenty-four-hour turnaround time available.

Schirra stocks many items for drag racers, including quality speed equipment and, for those with a truly serious thirst, nitro.

Schirra Cycle & Machine
R.D. 2
Valencia, PA 16059
(412) 898-9911—information
(800) 875-3401—orders only

Schultz & Shreve Racing Fabrication

Mike Schultz and John Shreve specialize in custom chassis components, frames, machining, and welding for Harley-Davidson drag bikes.

Frames are built to order, and most are lay-down drag frames made from 4130 chrome-moly. Most of the shop's engine work is done by Zipper's Performance Products, allowing Mike and John to concentrate on what they do best—refining the design and construction of pro-class Harley-Davidson drag bike chassis.

Robin Gauthier's love for Harley-Davidsons goes beyond most people's fantasies. Here is the only complete collection in the world of every year of Panhead ever produced. (More fun than baseball cards...) Every one is restored and correctly detailed.

Alan Sputhe built the 1300cc engine for Goliath back in 1980, when Vance Breese rode it to over 176mph at Bonneville. *Team Obsolete*

Another day at the office for Robin Gauthier of Southside Cycles, aboard the fastest Harley-Davidson in Canada.

The Spinning Wheel's safety bead (left) and tire lock (right) carbon fiber wheels are shown along with the Omega Safety-Tow System. *Traci Lovell*

The S&S Hot Setup 96 kit for 80ci Evolution Big Twins will give you a 3 5/8in bore and 4 5/8in stroke. It comes with all necessary gaskets, piston clips, pins and rings, and instructions.

Schultz & Shreve Racing
Fabrication
19700 Crystal Rock Drive
Germantown, MD 28074
(301) 694-0602

Schultz Racing

Terry Schultz at Schultz Racing produces clutches, side-by-side connecting rods, one-piece crankshafts, cylinder heads, dry-sump oiling systems, and engine cases, all designed exclusively for Big Twin drag bikes.

Clutches were developed by Terry along with long-time automotive drag racer Clayton Harris. The Schultz Racing clutch uses the same technology as the multi-stage lockup clutches on current Top Fuel cars, with a fingerless pressure plate that is hydraulically and air operated.

Crankshafts are designed for use with Schultz Racing connecting rods, and can be supplied in a 4in to 6in stroke. The pinion shafts are removable, which allows them to be used in your choice of cases (providing they have clearance for the stroke you're using).

Cylinder heads are two-valve, machined from billet aluminum. They can be supplied for use with up to a 5 1/2in bore. (For your information, a twin-cylinder engine with a "square" 5 1/2in bore and 5 1/2in stroke would be 261ci or 4282cc; a twin with a 5 1/2in bore and a 6in stroke would be 285ci or 4672cc.)

Engine cases are four-cam, designed to accept the Schultz one-piece crankshafts or conventional flywheel and pinion assemblies.

The Schultz Racing bottom end makes sense and solves some inherent engineering problems. Shortly after I dragged home my first motorcycle (a $50 1942 WLC 45, back in 1968), I started asking around about one-piece cranks for Harleys. All of the experts said it was impossible. We can be glad Terry didn't listen to those people and instead just went ahead and did it.

Schultz Racing
P.O. Box 777
Sterling, IL 61081-0777
(815) 537-5775
Catalog available

Screamin' Eagle

Screamin' Eagle is a high-performance division of the Harley-Davidson Motor Company. Their products include air cleaners, slotted brake discs, cams, carburetors, exhaust systems, aluminum fork braces, ignition modules, intake manifolds, mufflers, pistons, pushrods, transmission gears, and valve springs and retainers. All components are available for Big Twins and Sportsters—mostly for Evolution engines, and some for the earlier models as well.

The ignition module provides a higher-performance curve. Its built-in rev limiter lets you preset the cutoff speed to your choice of rpm.

For 1993, fiberglass seats for Twin Sports racing were introduced. These are styled like the classic XR-750 dirt-track seats but are designed to fit the 1982-and-up Sportster frames.

Screamin' Eagle components are all officially designated as being "for racing use." They can be ordered through Harley-Davidson dealers worldwide and are described in the racing section of the Harley-Davidson Accessories catalog.

Harley-Davidson
Motor Company
P.O. Box 653
3700 West Juneau Avenue
Milwaukee, WI 53201-0653
(414) 342-4680
Catalog available; specify
Accessories catalog

Sifton

Greg Brown and the staff at Sifton manufacture cams, lifters, and pushrods for Big Twins and cams and lifter blocks for Sportster engines.

Cams are available in four grinds for Evolution Big Twins, thirteen grinds for Shovelheads and Panheads (with total lifts ranging from .400in to .575in), one for Knuckleheads, two grinds for Evolution Sportsters, and four versions for 1957-1984 Sportsters.

Lifter blocks are for 1957-and-later Sportsters. Precision machined from aluminum billet and polished, they feature a spiral oil groove to help lubrication.

Pushrods and lifters are designed to be used together and are available for Evolution, Shovelhead, and Panhead Big Twins. The pushrods are machined from 7/16in diameter .095in-wall 2024 aluminum tubing and are longer than stock while the lifters have been shortened. This reduces the angle between the front cylinder's exhaust lifter and its pushrod. This system is also designed to eliminate pushrods rubbing against the pushrod covers.

Sifton
943 Bransten Road
San Carlos, CA 94070
(415) 592-2203
Catalog available

Sims & Rohm Performance Products

Richard Sims and Billy Rohm import and distribute a unique version of the Keihin carburetor that is made especially for them—a roller-bearing flat-slide Keihin FCR 41mm carburetor.

S&R have a Dynojet dyno and can also provide custom fabrication in aluminum, steel, and titanium. Their non-related products include performance parts for Italian and Japanese superbikes, including a complete supercharger kit for Suzuki GSX-R sport bikes. One of their shop bikes is a class record holder at the Bonneville Salt Flats.

Sims & Rohm Performance
Products
3265 Industrial Drive
Yuba City, CA 95993
(916) 674-9123

SI / WEN Industries

While most of their products are for race cars, the SI division of WEN Industries manufactures cams, valves, guides, seats, and springs for most models of Big Twin and Sportster engines all the way back to the 1932 flatheads. Valves are available as stock replacements in steel and stainless steel. Some versions come in a swirl-polished finish. Titanium valves are available as blanks in a variety of sizes, to be finish-machined by the customer.

SI / WEN Industries
11310 Hartland Street
North Hollywood, CA 91605
(818) 761-2796—information
(800) 343-4287—orders only
(800) 635-8733—California orders
Catalog available—specify Harley-Davidson

Smith Brothers Pushrods

Smith Brothers is the company that manufactures the pushrods for several aftermarket companies. Primarily an OEM supplier, they do not normally do business with the public.

Smith Brothers Pushrods
1201 North Azusa Canyon Road
West Covina, CA 91790
(818) 338-8026
FAX (818) 960-5255

Soapstone Engineering

Mike McKillip runs Soapstone Engineering, where he specializes in custom fabrication and building frames for serious Harley-Davidson drag racers. Mike works with Clyde Rawlings and other racers to develop trick components that use materials like beryllium and titanium.

Soapstone Engineering
1567 A Alamden Road
San Jose, CA 95125
(408) 297-2028

Southside Cycle

Southside sells and installs high-performance equipment for Big Twin engines. Headed by Robin Gauthier, Southside has a complete machine shop and a flow bench. They are the Canadian distributor for Delkron cases.

In 1991, with some help from Clyde Rawlings, Southside built the first Canadian-built Harley-Davidson Top Fuel drag bike. By mid-1992 Robin had turned a best ET of 7.96 at 170.3 with the bike in its early stages of development.

Southside Cycle
129 Nichol Street
Nanaimo, British Columbia
Canada V9R 4T1
(604) 754-1368
FAX (604) 754-1905

The Spinning Wheel

Mike Burke and Lee Robertson at The Spinning Wheel manufacture custom frames, tow lines, carbon fiber rear wheels, and carbon fiber wheelie bars for serious drag racing. Frames are built to order, often built from 4130 chrome-moly tubing for Big Twin lay-down drag bikes.

The tow line is the Omega Safety-Tow System, the only one of its kind that lets the rider quickly disconnect the line in case of an emergency while the bike is being towed. Materials include three steel rings and nylon webbing that has a tensile strength of 1,500lb.

Wheels are offered only for 15in tires. They have carbon fiber rims that are made in two halves which bolt to a machined aluminum center section. They can be supplied in widths from 8in all the way up to 16in in 1in increments.

All sizes are available in two rim styles: the traditional safety bead; and Tire Lock. The locking versions use carbon fiber rings held to the outside of the rim flanges with aluminum bolts. Available in several colors, these rings are designed to provide better sidewall support. The center sections and hubs are CNC-machined from 7075-7351 aluminum. There are three bearings (with two on the drive side) which are held in place with snap rings. Hubs come in 13in or 13 7/8in to provide a chainline of 6 3/8in or 6 7/8in, respectively.

Aside from the light weight, an advantage of modular wheels is the ease of replacing components. For example, a damaged wheel can be repaired; or you can go to a different rim width without having to buy a complete new wheel.

The Spinning Wheel
1110 East Ash, Unit G
Fullerton, CA 92631
(714) 773-1847
FAX (714) 773-1100
Literature available

Sputhe Engineering, Inc.

Sputhe Engineering is run by Alan Sputhe, who manufactures big-bore cylinders and pistons, cam covers, engine cases, a sixty-degree V-twin engine that accepts some Big Twin parts, a kickstart kit for late Big Twin transmissions, tools, and a transmission case.

Barrels can be supplied for Evolution Big Twin and Sportster engines.

Cam covers are cast from 356-T6 aluminum and allow owners of 1936-1969 Big Twins to fit late-style ignitions.

Engine cases for Big Twins are a recent addition to the Sputhe line, supplementing the replacement cases for iron Sportsters that have been in production for years.

Transmission cases allow you to use five-speed internal components in a case that fits four-speed frames.

The current versions of the legendary S&S Super Carburetors include the 1 7/8in bore Super E, for any single-carburetor Harley-Davidson engine, and the 2 1/16in bore Super G, for engines displacing at least 74ci, especially those with performance mods.

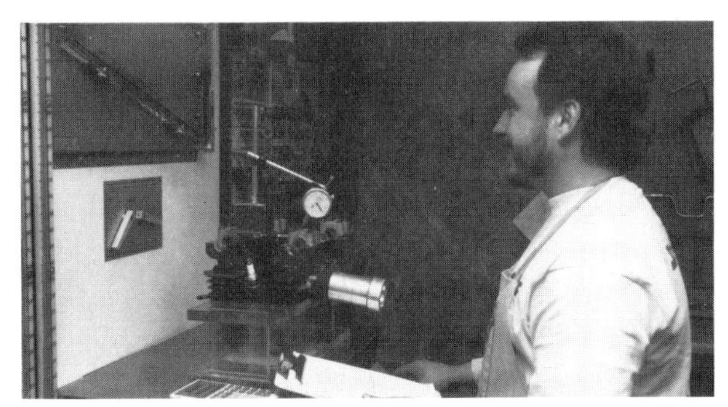

The cylinder heads for some of the world's quickest Gas-class drag bikes have been flow-tested on this Star Racing bench.

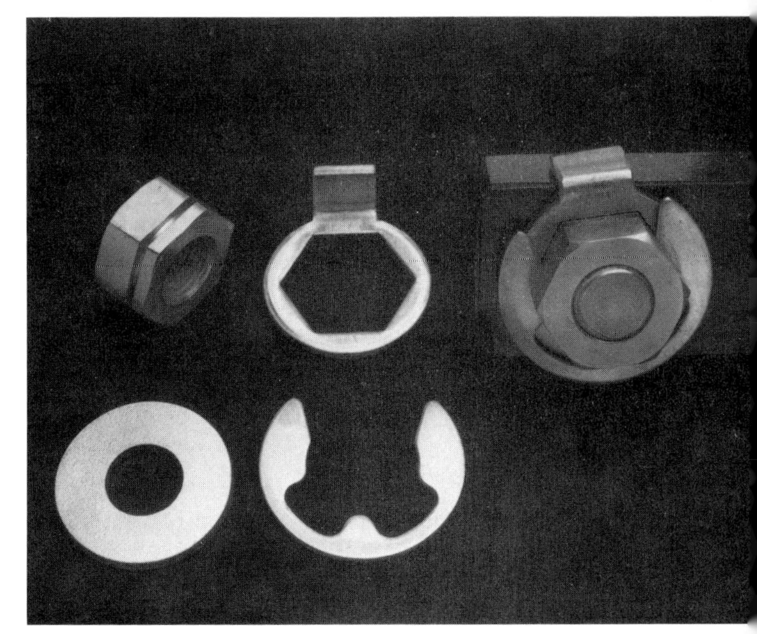

Stage 8 rear axle locking nut kits provide the ideal solution to a dangerous problem.

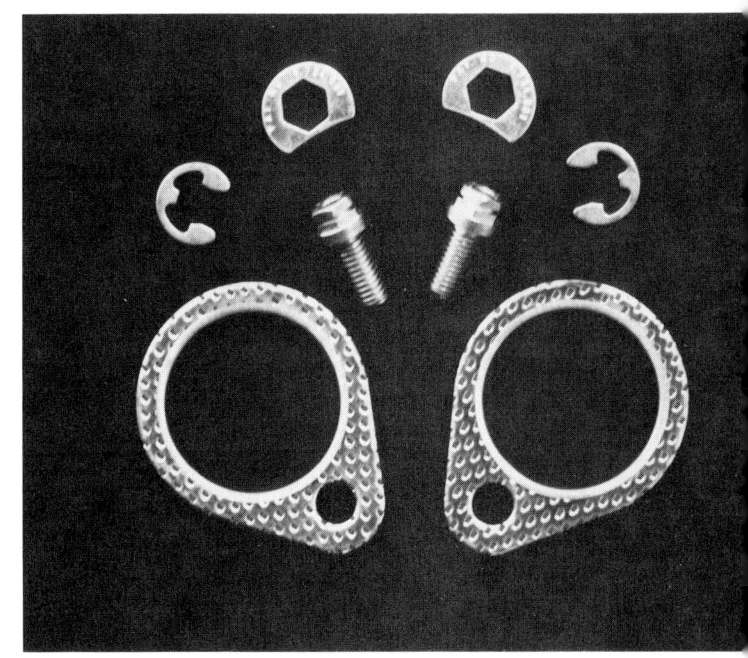

Stage 8 exhaust gasket and locking bolt kits feature special gaskets from Rivera that eliminate corrosion between dissimilar metals.

This SERDI 100 machine gives an indication of how serious George and Jackie Bryce and the Star Racing staff are about wringing the last bit of power out of their racing cylinder heads.

Sputhe Engineering, Inc.
11185 Lime Kiln Road
Grass Valley, CA 95949
(916) 268-0887
FAX (916) 268-3024
Catalog available

S&S Cycle, Inc.

S&S manufactures a great selection of performance parts for all current and vintage Harley-Davidson engines. While they're most famous for their carburetors and stroker engine kits, S&S also produces air cleaners, connecting rods, cylinder barrels, cylinder heads, engine cases, intake manifolds, oil pumps, pistons, pushrods, tools, and valves for Harley-Davidsons.

Cases are made for alternator and generator engines, to accept cylinders with stock and 3 5/8in bore sizes. All styles of cases are available in custom and racing versions. Cylinder heads come with guides, springs, and valves.

Flywheels are available in strokes of 4 1/4, 4 3/8, 4 1/2, 4 5/8, 4 3/4 and 5in for racing or street use; and 5 1/8 or 5 1/4in for racing only.

S&S is one of the original manufacturers of Harley-Davidson speed equipment. Back in 1952, George Smith built a stripped-down, hopped-up Knucklehead drag bike that beat all of the competition at a local drag race. In 1954, he took his bike to the Bonneville Salt Flats and ran 152mph. By 1958, George had begun work on his carburetor, and went into business with Stanley Spankos. The first production S&S carburetor came in 1967. Today, S&S products are tested on the dyno, street, highway, and at Bonneville before going into production.

S&S Cycle, Inc.
Box 215
Route 2, Highway G
Viola, WI 54664
(608) 627-1497
FAX (608) 627-1488
Catalog available

Stage 8 Fasteners, Inc.

Stage 8 manufactures fastener systems for Harley-Davidsons that are designed not to vibrate loose. This is another one of those ideas that will leave you wondering why you never thought of it; and like many good solutions it is elegant in its simplicity. Conceived and patented by Bruce Bennett, Stage 8 systems use a bolt with a groove machined around the circumference of the head. An E-shaped snap ring pops into the groove, and its purpose is to hold a unique, stamped locking retainer (with a hex-shaped cutout for the bolt head) in place.

Stage 8 has locking products available for Evolution and Shovelhead exhaust pipes, gas tanks, rear axle nuts, and upper engine mounts.

Bruce got this idea out of necessity in 1986 when his own Harley-Davidson's tendency to vibrate loose inspired him to come up with a solution. It works well, with over four million units in use on race cars and motorcycles, they've never heard of one coming loose.

Rivera Engineering is the master distributor for all Stage 8 Harley-Davidson components.

Stage 8 Fasteners, Inc.
15 Chestnut Avenue
San Rafael, CA 94901
(415) 485-5340—information
(800) 843-7836—orders only
FAX (415) 485-0552

Rivera Engineering
6416 South Western Avenue
Whittier, CA 90606
(310) 692-8944
FAX (310) 699-3943

Star Racing

George Bryce and his wife Jackie at Star Racing specialize in drag bikes, and although Harley-Davidsons aren't their focus, they offer complete machine shop services for all motorcycles, engine modifications, and SuperFlow dyno time. George also does transmission work, including gear undercutting, which can be provided for Big Twin and Sportster transmissions.

George is a veteran NHRA Pro Stock racer who is also the Pro Stock motorcycle instructor at Frank Hawley's Drag Racing School in Gainesville, Florida.

Star Racing
P.O. Box 1241
New Industrial Park
Americus, GA 31709-1241
(912) 924-0031—tech line
(800) 841-7827—orders only
FAX (912) 928-2321

Starwest, Inc.

Starwest manufactures a single-fire ignition system kit for Big Twin and Sportster engines.

Starwest, Inc.
7712 Lankershim Boulevard
North Hollywood, CA 91605
(818) 764-2226

S.T.D. Development Company, Inc.

Lou Trachtenburg and Tom Sullivan at S.T.D. manufacture engine and transmission cases and cylinder heads for Big Twin engines. Engine cases are available for Evolution, Shovelhead, and Panhead engines, with a variety of options that include ignition type, deck height, cylinder spigot diameter, and the type of aluminum used in the castings. The heads are for Shovelhead engines and provide a number of improvements over the original designs.

S.T.D. Development Company, Inc.
P.O. Box 3583
Chatsworth, CA 91313-3583
(818) 998-8226
FAX (818) 998-0210
Catalog available

Stinger U.S.A.

Stinger manufactures single-fire performance ignition systems for Big Twins from 1970 and up, and Sportster engines from 1971 and up.

Stinger U.S.A.
1013 66th Street
Des Moines, IA 50311
(515) 265-5513

Storz Performance

Storz Performance manufactures several products to improve the handling and performance of Big Twins, Sportsters, XR-750s, and XR-1000s. These include laced aluminum 18in wheels, an upswept stainless steel exhaust system, an XR-style seat, and a bigger tank. When teamed up with the Storz machined aluminum rearset foot controls and some engine, suspension and brake improvements, the result is a very impressive package that Steve calls an "XR-883."

Other products include crank pins for the XR-750 race engine, valve gear for the XR-1000s and XR-750s, and hydraulic steering dampers. Storz distributes the Italian-made Forcella Italia forks (formerly called Ceriani), which are described in the Forcella Italia section.

Steve Storz started Storz Performance in 1986. Prior to that he was Jay Springsteen's tuner on the AMA Camel Pro circuit, and his background with the XR-750 led to his developing the Evolution Sportster components that were inspired by the classic styling of the XR-750.

Storz Performance
239 Olive Street
Ventura, CA 93001
(805) 641-9540
Catalog available

Strader Engineering

Strader manufactures a line of tapered exhaust systems designed to improve the performance of Evolution Big Twins, Sportsters, and Shovelheads.

Walter Strader played an important role in helping the Harley-Davidson factory meet EPA requirements for noise and emissions. He later worked as a defense contractor, and is now back where he belongs, making Harley-Davidsons perform.

Strader Engineering
126 West Santa Barbara Street
P.O. Box 683
Santa Paula, CA 93060-0683
(805) 525-8280

SU

SU carburetors are used on many street and strip Harley-Davidsons. Without a doubt the experts at this are the people at Rivera Engineering, who are known even among many British sports car shops as being the source for SU components.

The bare carburetors can be supplied in the original cast finish, polished, with a chrome dome, or completely chromed; all are available in packages that include your choice of intake manifold and air cleaner. There are so many versions and options available you should consult the Rivera catalog for the full story. Air cleaners are available in two basic styles—the perforated Breather, and the Chrome Front, which has the large SU logo.

The Rivera catalog also shows rebuilding kits that include a new float, throttle shaft, O-ring float bowl seal, needle, seat, and main jet. These components are available separately, as are polished cast aluminum velocity stacks, Grose Jets for increased fuel flow, O-ring float bowl spacers, return springs in three strengths, manifold and air cleaner gaskets, tickler pump rebuild kits, push-pull throttle linkage kits, levelling brackets, and elbow adaptors. The many different Big Twin intake manifolds available come in a choice of cast, polished, or chromed finishes and include versions for stock and stroked engines.

Rivera also offers high-performance kits for Evolution Big Twins that include the carburetor, manifold, cam, pushrods, and a choice of drag pipes or a SuperTrapp exhaust system.

Rivera Engineering
6416 South Western Avenue
Whittier, CA 90606
(310) 692-8944
FAX (310) 699-3943

Sumax

Sumax offers exhaust systems, ignition wires, pushrod covers, and wheel covers.

Exhaust systems are made for Sumax by Run Roader. They're available for any Shovelhead or Evolution engine with your choice of four styles of end cuts, as muffled street systems or drag pipes, in black porcelain enamel or chrome finishes.

Ignition wire kits are made for Sumax by Taylor Cable Products in many models, types, and colors for virtually any application. Most have 24in leads and can be supplied with their Pro ferromagnetic or metallic inner cores with your choice of plug boot angles. Sumax also has composite spark plug wire separator clamps in eight colors. More information on these wires is listed under Taylor Cable Products, Inc.

Pushrod covers are CNC-machined from three pieces of aluminum. A pair of O-rings is provided for each cover to provide a positive seal. Wheel covers are spun from sheet aluminum, along the lines of the classic Moon discs. They are available for 15-, 16-, 18-, 19-, and 21in laced wheels with drop center rims (only), in polished, or painted finishes.

Sumax distributes the products of several top manufacturers, and is the American distributor for the Canadian-built Tripoli frames, which are described in more detail in this book under Tripoli. Their most popular frame is for Evolution engines and five-speed transmissions. Unlike the Softail frame it replaces, it uses rubber mount-

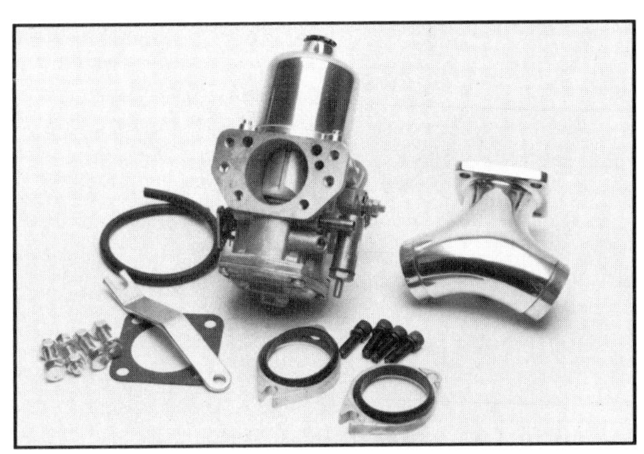

Rivera Engineering can supply the Eliminator II SU carburetors and a wide range of intake manifolds in several styles for Panhad, Shovelhead, and Evolution Big Twins.

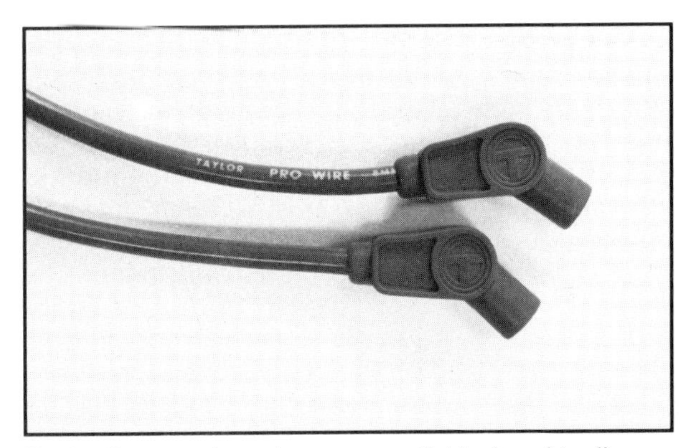

Taylor/Sumax plug wires are available for virtually any Harley-Davidson application.

Super Max belt primary drive systems for Harley-Davidsons have been in production for over twenty years.

Sumax pushrod covers (shown with optional hand engraving by Herb Jerred) are available for Evolution and Shovelhead Big Twins and 1959-1979 iron Sportsters. They come powder coated in clear, black, red, or blue finishes.

Pre-1993 Sportsters can be converted to belt final drive with a Super Max kit, which includes both pulleys, the drive belt, and a new rear axle. Kits are available for 1957-1978 (2.35:1), 1979-1981 (2.35:1), 1982-1988 (2.25:1 or 2.17:1), and 1989-1992 (2.35:1).

ing to isolate engine vibration. Another frame is designed especially for use with stroker engines. Reinforcement has been added at each end along with a stress bar (a second top tube) and the tubing has a heavier wall thickness than usual. Belt drive clearance is provided and you have a choice of a 30-degree or 38-degree head angle.

A high-quality powder coating service is also available. Developed by a division of Eastman Kodak along with Kirk Van Scoten at Sumax, it is available in a wide range of finishes that includes candies and solid colors. Custom hand engraving by master engraver Herb Jerred is also available.

Sumax
337 Clear Road
Oriskany, NY 13424
(315) 768-1058—information
(800) 654-5546—orders only
FAX (315) 768-1046
Catalog available

Sun Metal Products

Sun motorcycle rims are now manufactured by Buchanon's Frame Shop in California. Buchanon's makes a complete line of extruded aluminum rims for building laced wheels, which are available undrilled or drilled.

Buchanon's Frame Shop
629 East Garvey Avenue
Monterey Park, CA 91754
(818) 280-4003
FAX (818) 280-4106

Superbrace

Kelly Tidwell and the staff at Superbrace machine several models of billet aluminum fork braces that provide a noticeable increase in rigidity. Braces are available for 1978-1993 Wide Glide front ends, 39mm 1988-1993 FXRS models and Sportsters, and the 1978-1987 FXRS models and Sportsters with 35mm front ends.

A great deal of research goes into their fork brace development, and Superbrace has received several design patents.

Superbrace
5842 McFadden Avenue, Suite O
Huntington Beach, CA 92649
(800) 322-4783
FAX (714) 894-6344

Super Max Products

Super Max is run by Phil Ross, who manufactures primary and final belt drive systems for practically all Harley-Davidsons. Custom bearing supports for open-primary four-speed Big Twins are also available.

Polyurethane pulleys with steel inserts for all Big Twins that came with belt drive are available with 29, 32, 33, 34, or 35 teeth for transmissions, and rear wheel pulleys with 61, 66, or 68 teeth. Phil also makes pulleys for Sportsters with 27, 28, or 29 teeth.

Super Max Products
200 South D Street
Porterville, CA 93259
(209) 782-8200
Literature available

SuperTrapp Industries, Inc.

SuperTrapp manufactures some of the most popular performance mufflers and exhaust systems for Harley-Davidsons. Made of stainless steel, the exhaust systems are available for Big Twins, Sportsters, and the XR-750 and XR-1000.

SuperTrapp mufflers have a unique system of tunable discs. They were described this way in the May 1992 issue of *Hot Rod* magazine:

"SuperTrapp has the only 'tunable muffler' on the market today. By simply adjusting the number of Diffuser Discs on each end of the muffler, the system can be tuned for the desired performance effect of a particular engine in terms of power, sound, and jetting. Changing the number of discs changes the back pressure. The SuperTrapp creates a suction that actually helps draw residual exhaust gases from the system. This helps create a cleaner, hotter burn in the combustion chamber the next time that cylinder fires. And a better burn creates more horsepower. The diffuser discs also create an anti-reversionary effect that helps exhaust scavenging; particularly in the low-end and midrange rpm by making it easy for the exhaust gases to flow out but difficult to flow back in. In effect, the exhaust system acts like a pump. Increasing the number of discs increases the pumping effect. The exhaust pump concept works to use normally wasted exhaust energy, like a turbocharger; but produces an engine response like a supercharger. On the dyno, we have seen as much as a 5hp difference by adding one disc. It really depends on how the particular engine was built to perform. You need to find its sweet sport or preferred powerband."

Virtually all current Harley-Davidsons can be fitted with either staggered duals or a two-into-one system from SuperTrapp. Mufflers are also available in two basic styles: the tapered-body Universal, which is the more commonly seen performance muffler; and the staggered-dual style which tapers down at each end, which was designed for pre-Evolution engines. Both styles can be supplied for 1 3/4in or 2in pipes.

SuperTrapp exhaust systems for XR-750s are available through the Harley-Davidson factory.

SuperTrapp Industries, Inc.
3910 Seaport Boulevard
West Sacramento, CA 95691
(916) 372-5000
FAX (916) 372-1354
Catalog available

Taylor Cable Products, Inc.

Taylor manufactures ignition wire for racing engines. Taylor's

Super Max rear wheel pulleys are available with 61, 66, or 68 teeth. Flanges come in nine styles and eight colors.

SuperTrapp tunable mufflers like the one on the Sturgis use a number of discs that can be added or removed to vary the engine's power curve and sound pressure level.

This Sportster has a SuperTrapp staggered dual system.

In 1990 and 1991, Team Obsolete won the American Historic Racing Motorcycle Association Formula 750 national championship with their 1972 Harley-Davidson XRTT road racer.

Goliath was built in 1980 and has been ridden on the drag strip, road courses, and the Bonneville Salt Flats. Vance Breese set a Modified Production Streamlined record of 176mph, which still stands today.

This FXR features a bolt-on trike conversion from Texas Frame Works.

409 cable comes with a metallic conductor or a stretch-resistant, spiral-wound Aramid core and a bright blue outer jacket. Built with three silicone layers to prevent arcing, this cable is .409in in diameter with a dielectric strength of over 100,000 volts.

Sumax distributes Taylor ignition wires, and offers several versions for various Harley-Davidsons.

Taylor Cable Products, Inc.
301 Highgrove Road
Grandview, MO 64030
(816) 765-5011

Sumax
337 Clear Road
Oriskany, NY 13424
(315) 768-1058—information
(800) 654-5546—orders only
FAX (315) 768-1046
Catalog available

Team Obsolete

Robert Iannucci and Dave Roper specialize in building and racing classic American, British, and Italian road racers. Robert and Dave might well be able to provide some help with a vintage Harley-Davidson racer project bike. They have considerable experience with the XR-750, and can provide engines, custom fabrication and frames, and complete rolling chassis. This shop can also build or supply a complete XRTT road racer to the customer's specifications.

Their stable of race bikes includes several interesting vintage road racers, including an AJS three-cam single, a Benelli four-cylinder works bike, a 1971 BSA Rocket 3 Formula 750 on which Dick Mann won the 1971 Daytona 500, a 1973 Ducati works bike that won at Imola in 1973, a 1972 Harley-Davidson XRTT, a Matchless, and a Velocette.

Team Obsolete
139 Henry Street
Brooklyn, NY 11201
(718) 596-0504—office
(718) 624-7126—shop
FAX (718) 596-6443

Tech Products

Bob Kemtes at Tech Products makes a handy plate that mounts inside Big Twin primary covers for setting timing. Other versions are available for 1986-1993 Evolution Sportsters and also for bikes with open primary drives.

Tech Products
511 West Mahoney
Mesa, AZ 85202
(602) 649-3901—information
(800) 232-3901—orders only

Tecnomagnesio

Tecnomagnesio cast magnesium wheels are made in a factory that used to belong to Campagnolo, whose wheels were found on Bimota and Ducati superbikes. Designed for road racing, gold-anodized Tecnomagnesio wheels come in 16-, 17-, and 18in sizes, which can then be adapted to Harley-Davidsons.

For decades, Campagnolo has been known for its fine aluminum and magnesium casting, with projects that include aerospace components and transaxle housings for Ferrari Formula One Grand Prix cars.

Prosimet S.p.a.
24040 Filago (BG)
Via Rodi 10, Italy
Phone 035-99-3721

Tek Cycle

Dan Trenholm produces custom frames for Sportster engines, and kits for adapting Velva-Touch lifters to all XR and iron Sportsters. Dan also offers engine building, case modifications and repairs, cylinder head modifications and porting, aluminum and steel fabrication including gas tanks and oil tanks, machining, and welding.

Frames use FXR-series rubber mounts. They accept the stock Sportster oil tank and include new seat pan. Tek Cycle frames can be supplied in mild steel or chrome-moly for any Sportster engine.

Tek Cycle
Route 2, Box 144B
Gill, MA 01376
(413) 863-9215

Tetrick Speed & Custom Motorcycles

Brad Tetrick is a Harley-Davidson drag racing specialist who manufactures fiberglass parts and oil filter mounts. He also provides cylinder head and engine work including blueprinting and performance modifications, custom fabrication, machining, and welding. Complete engines can be built to order for Street Stock or Pro Stock racing, from 80ci to 114ci and beyond.

Fiberglass parts include front fenders, rear fenders that are an 8in version similar to the FXRS, and dummy gas tank shells. All of these are strictly for drag racing, and are supplied in a white gel-coat finish. Oil filter mounts are for all 1986-1992 Softails. They are machined from billet aluminum and come in a polished finish.

Brad campaigns a 114in B/Fuel Big Twin at AHDRA races, and placed first at the Phoenix Pro Nationals.

Tetrick Speed & Custom
Motorcycles
9919 Montana Avenue
El Paso, TX 79925
(915) 590-0055—tech line
(800) 572-2029—orders only
Literature available

Texas Frame Works

Rick Nichols has been building custom Harley-Davidson frames and doing fabrication work for drag bikes since 1975. He can build or repair virtually any motorcycle frame.

Although not usually considered a high-performance item, trike conversion kits for late-model Big Twin and Sportster owners are among Rick's specialties. These kits, and his complete trike frames, have been under development since 1981, when a friend who was confined to a wheelchair asked him to build a bike. The result was a sidecar rig with an automatic transmission, with all of the controls on the handlebars. The project changed both of their lives. The rider, whose birth defects had left him with no use of his legs, gained mobility. When Rick realized he had the resources to allow people to transcend their disability he devoted more energy to the design and fabrication of three-wheeled motorcycles. If you know anyone with a disability who would like to ride a Harley, do them a favor, tell them about Rick.

Texas Frame Works
7900-A Highway 71 West
Austin, TX 78735
(512) 288-6224

Thompson's Cylinder Head Service Company

The name of Jim Thompson's shop tells only a small part of the story. Along with cylinder head modification and restoration, Thompson's specializes in mail-order precision machining of anything related to a high-performance Harley-Davidson, aluminum and magnesium polishing, balancing, precision brake disc grinding, casting repairs, fabrication, failure analysis, frame and fork tube straightening, fork slider bushing replacement, hardness testing, fabricating nitrous oxide systems, Magnaflux and Zyglow non-destructive testing, optical measuring, pressure testing, shot peening, sonic thickness testing, and welding.

Jim is a member of the Automotive Engine Rebuilders Association, Automotive Service Excellence, and Society of Manufacturing Engineers. His shop uses state-of-the-art equipment. He and his staff do development work for numerous aftermarket manufacturers, and they can turn an idea into a finished and tested product.

Jim writes technical articles for various motorcycle magazines, and he is a technical consultant to Sunnen for their tooling and honing techniques, and to other Harley-Davidson aftermarket suppliers.

Thompson's Cylinder Head
Service Company
186 River Street
Dedham, MA 02026
(617) 326-8380
FAX (617) 320-9351

Thunder Tech Performance Products

Thunder Tech is headed by Dan Fitzmaurice, who manufactures Red Shift cams, pushrods and valve spring kits, and the ThunderJet fuel delivery modification system kits.

Developed by Dick Hilferty, Red Shift cams are available in several grinds for serious gas and nitro Evolution engines, Shovelheads, and iron Sportsters. Many successful racers rely on Red Shift cams. (You know you're reading about a serious cam when the catalog says "high gear nitro.")

Red Shift pushrods are fixed length, made from .065in wall chrome-moly tubing. Standard versions are produced for Shovelheads with standard, .125in taller and .200in taller cylinders; and iron Sportsters with standard, .300in taller and .500in taller cylinders. Custom lengths can be specially ordered.

Red Shift Pro dual valve spring kits are made strictly for racing. They are available for all Evolution engines (which must have the spring pockets machined with a 1.570in cutter), Shovelheads (with .375in or thin stems), and iron Sportsters. Chrome-moly keys and titanium collars are included. Red Shift valve springs are also available with a special two-stage surface treatment called Fluoroplate. The first stage, called impingement, involves fine finishing to remove surface imperfections that cause stress points, after which a special coating that includes Teflon is applied to result in decreased heat build-up.

ThunderJet kits are available for Bendix, Keihin, and S&S carburetors. They use a third fuel circuit and have built-in air correction to provide improved response at higher engine speeds.

Thunder Tech Performance
Products
P.O. Box 1005
Laurel, MD 20707-0941
(301) 799-9451
FAX (301) 799-9450
Literature available

Tom Hayden Enterprises

Tom Hayden makes primary chain tensioners for Big Twin Harley-Davidsons from 1985 and up. These simple but important units have proven themselves everywhere from the street to Bonneville. You can eliminate some of the vibration, and more importantly on the street, add a measure of safety when your bike's primary chain isn't slapping around. Many dealers install the M-6 as an option on new bikes and at least one police department is enjoying the benefit of better engine braking when downshifting.

Installation is straightforward. Drain your primary oil; pull the primary cover; remove the stock tensioner; install the first two parts of the M-6; play with some shims; add the final part of the M-6; and reassemble the primary cover with a fresh gasket and primary oil.

Rick Nichols of Texas Frame Works built this Sportster drag trike, the fastest Harley-Davidson trike in America.

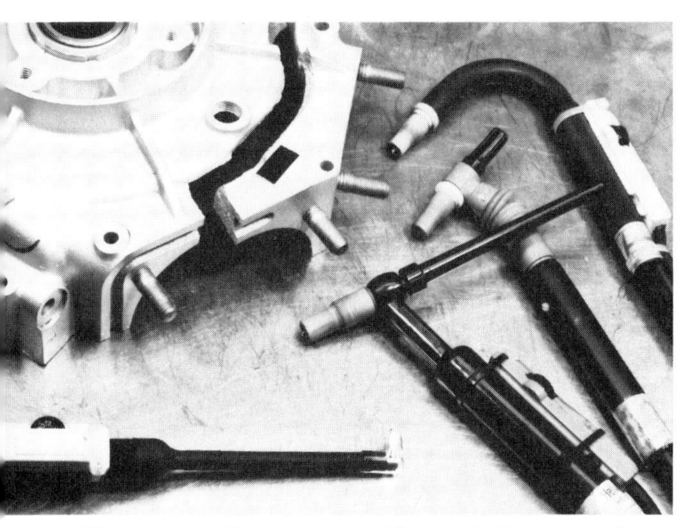

Thompson's offers expert welding, including arc, heli-arc, oxy-acetylene, plasma cutting, and shielded metal arc.

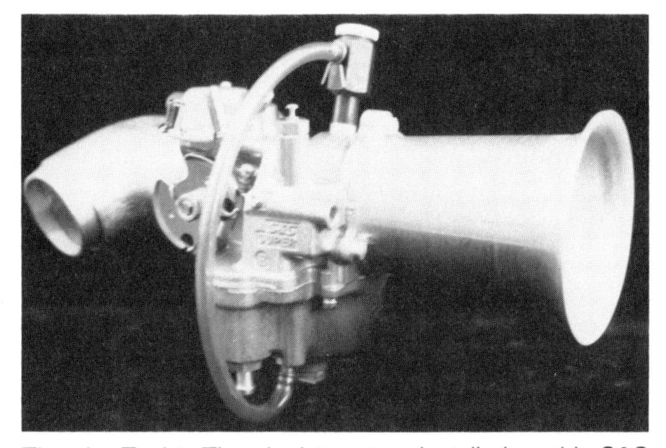

Thunder Tech's ThunderJet system installed on this S&S "E" carburetor provides a noticeable improvement in performance on the racetrack.

This SuperFlow flow bench at Thompson's is just part of what may be the best-equipped machine and welding shop in the Harley-Davidson aftermarket. *Hal Geyer*

Thunder Tech's Red Shift cams for Sportsters are manufactured on an exchange basis to maintain the factory cam gear clearance.

These S&S "B" and "D" carburetors have been equipped with ThunderJet systems from Thunder Tech.

Lightweight valve spring retainers from Trick Titanium are CNC-machined for accuracy.

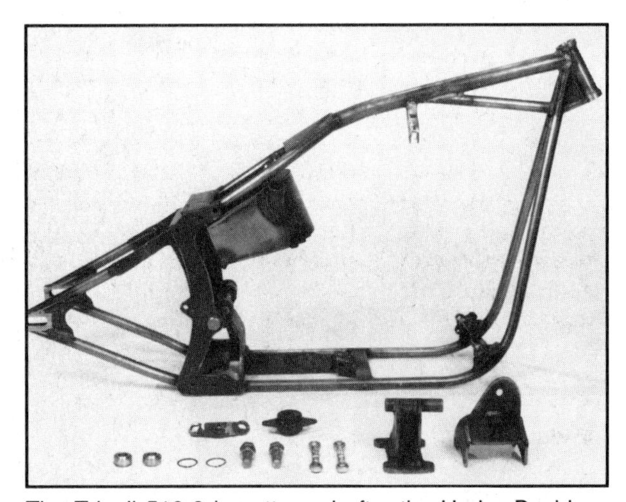

The Tripoli 510-2 is patterned after the Harley-Davidson factory's Softail frame for Big Twins, but provides rubber mounting for Sportster engines. Similar versions are offered for any Big Twin engine and FXR / FLT or FXST transmissions.

In addition to its Gapless rings, Total Seal has an advanced engine research facility in New Hampshire for racers and manufacturers. A system to monitor the cylinder pressure of each cylinder throughout all phases of the combustion process is currently under development.

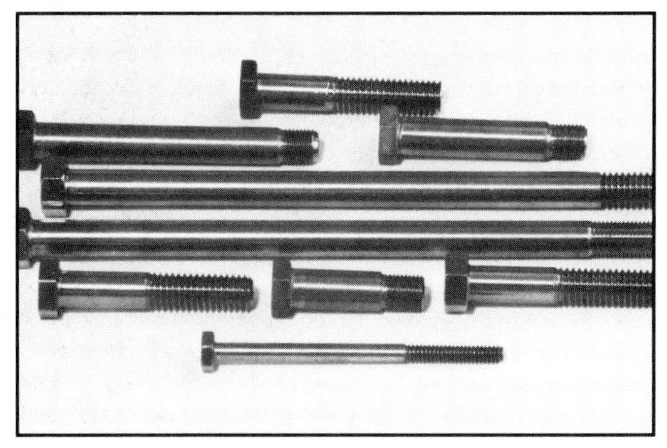

Titanium is undeniably the hot rod of metals, and these Trick Titanium engine bolt sets provide twice the strength of steel bolts with half the weight.

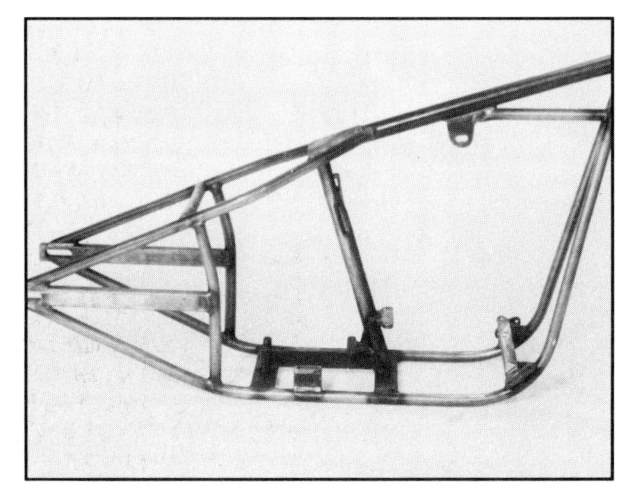

Tripoli rigid frames can be ordered for any Harley-Davidson engine and transmission combination. This one has had reinforcement (available in two sizes) added to the rear triangle.

Tom Hayden Enterprises
11315 Country Club Drive
Anderson Island, WA 98303
(206) 884-2433

Tom's Competition Cycle, Inc.

Tom Caldwell builds custom chrome-moly frames for Harley-Davidson drag bikes and offers Big Twin and Sportster engine building and machining services. He also offers the Brad Foote Gear Works drag racing transmission.

Tom's Competition Cycle, Inc.
6523 Oak Ridge Highway
Knoxville, TN 37921
(615) 584-2101

Total Seal

Since 1969, Total Seal has been making unique, Gapless piston ring sets for most popular engines. They are designed to greatly reduce cylinder leakdown.

Total Seal feels that conventional rings do not seal well enough to prevent combustion blow-by from heating and contaminating oil, which causes accelerated wear on bearing surfaces, crank journals, and cylinder walls. The patented Total Seal two-piece design virtually eliminates combustion blow-by, holds cylinder leakage to less than two percent, and increases midrange torque.

Racers who run these rings may find that the seal is just as good at the end of the season as it was at the beginning. Street riders can benefit from improved long-term power, less dilution, improved economy, and lower emissions.

The Total Seal Development Center in New Hampshire is a state-of-the-art engine shop with a GE eddy-current dynamometer. The staff has over fifty years of combined experience in the areas of horsepower, fuel economy, and endurance. In addition to the standard horsepower, torque, fuel consumption and temperature data, the staff also uses oil consumption and crankcase pressure measurements to come up with complete engine performance profiles. The Development Center also offers flow bench testing, a complete machine shop, and the know-how and equipment required to build and refine racing and prototype engine parts.

Total Seal
2225 West Mountain View, #6
Phoenix, AZ 85021
(602) 678-4977—information
(800) 874-2753—orders only

Total Seal Development Center
Alden Road & Route 101
Greenland, NH 03840
(603) 433-8680

Trett's Speed & Custom

Trett's Speed & Custom is run by Elmer Trett, who offers custom slipper clutches, complete racing engine building, fabrication, and machining services, and custom fuel injection throttle bodies for drag racers.

For years Elmer was one of the quickest and fastest Top Fuel Harley-Davidson riders and builders in the world. He now campaigns an awesome Top Fuel bike with an engine he fabricated himself from scratch; it's built around a Kawasaki inline-four engine layout, and it puts out an estimated 750hp.

Back in 1991 he took a real deep breath and managed to stay on the thing while it shot him down the quarter-mile, reaching 219mph in 6.51 seconds. In a *Cycle World* magazine feature (October 1989), he told how it felt to turn a 6.60-second ET at 213mph.

"The bike lifted its head hard and quick, and almost pulled out from under me. It was an unbelievable run. When it stopped at the end I knew it was faster than I had ever gone in my life. I looked down and the brakes were smoking and the discs were glowing red hot. It definitely got my attention."

For excitement, Elmer does all of his own accounting.

Trett's Speed & Custom
Route #1, Box 1715
Demorest, GA 30535
(404) 754-3393

Trick Titanium

Trick Titanium manufactures titanium bolts and valve spring retainers for Harley-Davidson engines.

In business since 1969, this company has been manufacturing titanium valve spring retainers for race cars for over twenty years. They are best known for their titanium bellhousings and supercharger pulleys for Top Fuel cars. Their race car components include brackets, clutch forks, front wheel hubs, and main journal caps. Their equipment has been used everywhere from the Bonneville Salt Flats to the Indianapolis Motor Speedway. They can fabricate practically any component from titanium, steel, or aluminum.

Trick Titanium
321 Elmwood
Troy, MI 48083-2782
(313) 588-9430
(313) 588-9433

Tripoli Manufacturing (1991), Ltd.

Tripoli manufactures and custom-builds oil tanks, racing frames, street frames, swing arms, and trike conversion kits, exclusively for Harley-Davidsons.

Oil tanks come in the traditional horseshoe design for all Tripoli frames in raw, polished, or chrome-plated steel finishes, or made from stainless steel. The horseshoe tanks hide the battery and use spin-on oil filters; many are rubber-mounted. Other oil tanks can be custom-built for special applications in mild steel, stainless steel, or aluminum.

Racing frames include custom frames and their standard drag racing frame, the Pro Comp. As part of their program to evaluate all of their products Tripoli has been running a gas Big Twin drag bike. This project led to the development of the Pro Comp, available in Big Twin and Sportster versions. Frame tubes are 1in diameter .065in wall chrome-moly tubing, with a 2 1/4in diameter .120in wall top tube that serves as the fuel tank. The frame rails are pressure-tested and can store compressed air for an air shifter. The standard seat height on the Pro Comp is 20in, and the steering head angle is 33 degrees, which will provide a wheelbase from 63 1/2 to 65 1/2in. Other front end geometry, wheelie bar mounts and your choice of custom oil tanks from one to four quarts can be supplied as options.

Street frames include a pair of designs inspired by the factory Softail frames, but rubber-mounted, available for any Big Twin (#515-2) or Sportster (#510-2) engine; a replacement for the factory Softail frame (#520-2) with solid engine mounts for any Big Twin from Knucklehead to Evolution and a four-speed or FXST five-speed; a "swing arm style" frame (#530-2), again for any OHV Big Twin engine but for any Big Twin transmission; a traditional rigid frame (#540-2) for the same; a five-speed rigid frame (#550-2) for any OHV Big Twin engine and an FXR or FLT five-speed; and a rigid frame for any Sportster engine (#560-2). All of these frames can come with your choice of straight-leg or wishbone downtubes. MIG-welded mild steel tubing and a 30-degree steering head angle are standard; with .095in wall chrome-moly tubing and custom steering geometry also available for all frames. You can also select: from three neck styles, stock with or without a neck lock, and custom; chain or belt final drive; vertical stretch for stroker clearance; forward stretch; new or old split gas tank mounts, or no mounts; fender strut style; early, late or no coil mounts; and rear axle plate and rear brake mount choices.

Swing arms for Softail frames are available for chain or belt final drive in three styles, and most come with stock or extended shock mounts which lower the ride height; and a choice of axle plate styles.

Trike conversion kits are also available for Softails and Sportsters.

Tripoli Manufacturing (1991), Ltd.
Box 45, Site 14, RR #1
Red Deer, Alberta
Canada T4N 5E1
(800) 873-1670—tech line
(403) 347-8810—order desk
FAX (403) 343-8848
Price list, catalog available

Trock Cycle Specialties

Master machinist Ron Trock specializes in high-performance engine components for Harley-Davidson drag bikes, including cylinders, engine cases, Sportster transmission components, and shop tools.

Cylinders are custom-built and engine cases use the Sportster four-cam design. They are machined to order from castings composed of a special magnesium and copper alloy.

For Sportster owners, Ron also makes a beefy trap door that adds reliability to 1956-1976 engine cases, taking care of the weak link in the original design. Remember that the Sportster transmission was never intended to handle anywhere near the power and torque some current race engines produce. The Trock trap door adds rigidity to the area around the transmission output shaft. Sportster pawl supports and engine case repair corners are also available.

Rocker arm refacing tools let you reface rocker arms on 1957-and-later engines (except Panheads) with a drill press. Valve checkers help you set the correct guide and spring clearance by accurately measuring the valve travel. Trock valve checkers are made in versions for Shovelheads, all Evolution engines, and 1985-and-earlier Sportsters.

Trock Cycle Specialties
13 North 417 French Road
Hampshire, IL 60140
(708) 683-4010

Truett & Osborn

Bonnie Truett and Paul Osborn manufacture custom stroker flywheel assemblies that can give you up to a 96ci Sportster or a 110ci Big Twin. They come in the following strokes: 4 1/4in, 4 3/8in, 4 1/2in, 4 5/8in, 4 3/4in, and 5in for Big Twins and 4 1/8in, 4 3/8in, 4 1/2in, 4 5/8in, 4 13/16in, and 5in for Sportsters.

Truett & Osborn also offer Sportster cam regrinding, big-bore cylinders for Shovelheads, and forged and cast pistons. They offer complete engine building services for Big Twins and Sportsters for street or strip. Machining for building race engines is available, including connecting rod and cylinder head rebuilding.

Truett & Osborn
3345 East 31st South
Wichita, KS 67216
(313) 682-4871
Catalog available

Truett's Frame Works

Bonnie Truett specializes in building lay-down rigid frames for Harley-Davidson drag bikes. Bonnie's standard lay-down frames are built from 4130 chrome-moly tubing and feature a 72in wheelbase with a 38-degree steering head angle, and custom-built frames may be ordered.

Truett's also offers axles, 24-volt starters, extended swing arms, and wheelie bars.

Pro Comp chrome-moly frames are available for all Big Twin and Sportster engines. This one is the fastest gas Harley-Davidson drag bike in Alberta, sponsored by Tripoli and ridden by Doug Westman.

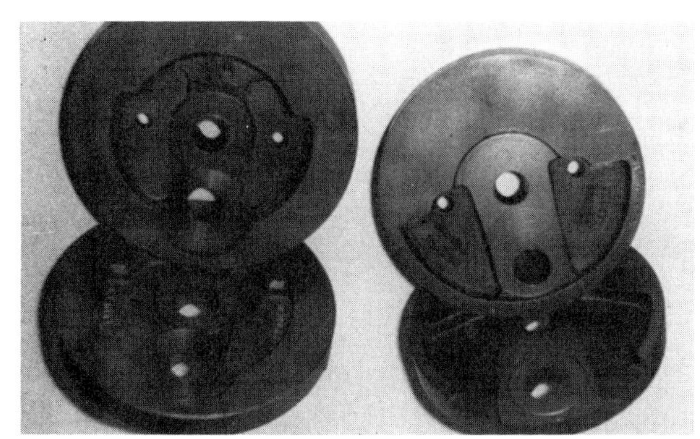

Truett & Osborn flywheel assemblies are crafted from 80,000lb tensile strength steel, which is heat-treated before machining.

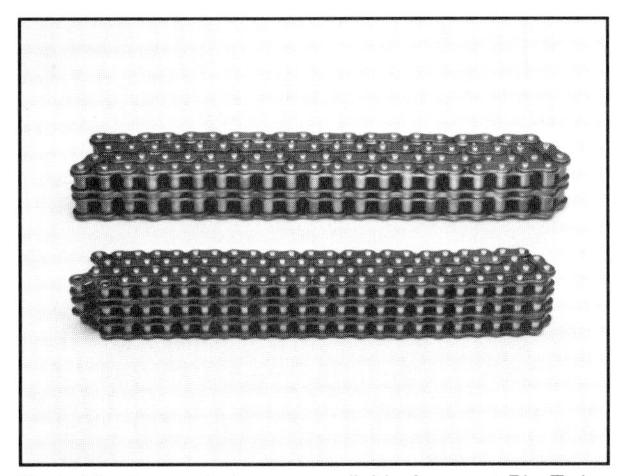

Tsubaki primary chains are available for most Big Twins and Sportsters.

When Steve Flood of Red Deer, Alberta, had trouble getting to work on time he whipped up this bike, based on an Evolution engine and a Pro Comp frame.

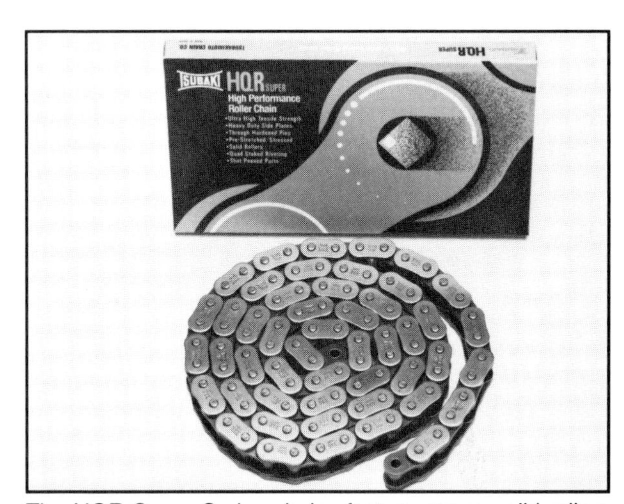

The HQR Super Series chains feature strong solid rollers and other features intended to help them withstand the stress of drag racing

Although 1991 was his first year as a drag racer, Dave Feazell of Two Wheel Travel won the AMRA Pro Stock championship in 1991 and 1992.

Truett's Frame Works
1314 East 31st South
Wichita, KS 67216
(313) 522-2346
Literature available

Tsubaki

Tsubaki manufactures for Harley-Davidsons a line of final drive and primary chains engineered to handle drag racing abuse.

Final drive chains come in several versions. While all of their chains are completely heat-treated, the HQR Super Series chains feature strong solid rollers and other features that are intended to help them withstand the stress of drag racing. Like all #530 Tsubaki final drive chains, 530HQR chains come in lengths of 100, 106, 110, 120, or 150 links, and 25ft reels. Tsubaki also has final drive chains designed for street and touring that share most of the features of their HQR series. The HSL chains are nickel-plated; while the Sigma and Omega versions are O-ring sealed, with the Omega being the #630 size.

Primary chains are also available for most late models. All Tsubaki chain is backed by a one-year limited warranty.

U.S. Tsubaki, Inc.
18031 Cortney Court
City of Industry, CA 91744
(310) 726-8313

Two Wheel Travel

Dave Feazell specializes in custom paint work and in building race engines and frames for Harley-Davidson drag bikes. All work is done to order in his Iowa shop.

Having won three consecutive championships hill-climbing his 106in Sportster, Dave currently campaigns a Pro Stock Sportster drag bike at AMRA events. At press time he held AMRA quarter-mile national records for an 8.89 ET and for running 148.2mph.

Two Wheel Travel
P.O. Box 791
Highway 63 North
Hudson, IA 50643-0791
(319) 988-3144

UNI Filter, Inc.

UNI air filters are available to fit all current Harley-Davidson air cleaners. They have been original equipment on Harley-Davidsons since 1973. Fully washable, the familiar looking green filters provide good air flow.

UNI Filter, Inc.
1630 South Sinclair Street
Anaheim, CA 92806
(714) 939-6300
FAX (714) 634-4935

U.S. Cycle

U.S. Cycle is the largest shop in Australia specializing in Harley-Davidson drag bikes, with engine building and complete race bike construction available. They stock a good selection of parts and equipment for racers.

U.S. Cycle
6 Kyabra Street
Fortitude Valley
4006, Brisbane
Australia

Vance Breese

Vance Breese, an accomplished Isle of Man TT racer, road racer, and salt flats racer, offers design services for racers building bikes to run on the Bonneville Salt Flats. Vance currently races a fully-enclosed streamliner called Mariah that debuted on the salt in 1991. Based on his thorough planning and analysis, Vance will be shifting from first to second at around 123mph, from second to third at 170, and into fourth gear at about 230.

And it's a five-speed...

Vance Breese
Harley-Davidson of Santa Maria
601 West Main Street
Santa Maria, CA 93454
(805) 928-3668

Venolia Pistons

Venolia manufactures forged pistons for Big Twin and Sportster engines. They are available in several bore sizes and dome configurations.

Venolia Pistons
2160 Cherry Industrial Court
Long Beach, CA 90805
(310) 531-8463

V-M-O Products, Inc.

Vern and Vi Ott operate V-M-O. Vern is best known as the inventor of Velva-Touch roller lifters (now made by V-Thunder, a division of Competition Cams).

V-M-O offers complete engine building and machining and dyno work (on their SuperFlow SF-901 dyno). The V-M-O facility can look after anything required to turn a stock engine or a new set of cases into a serious racing engine. Special containers are available for shipping engines, and their race-ready engines have been shipped all over the world.

The shop specializes in Big Twin engines but can also dyno test Sportster and XR-750 engines. They regularly build complete motorcycles from the ground up, doing everything but dynamic balancing, paint, and plating. V-M-O also offers race engine development for serious racers and aftermarket manufacturers.

V-M-O Products, Inc.
218 North State Street
Marion, OH 43302
(614) 383-2396

V-Thunder by Competition Cams

Well-known in stock car and drag racing circles, Competition Cams produces cams and valvetrain components for most

A selection of UNI Filter models, with the stock Harley-Davidson filter element shown at top center.

Vance Breese's development work paid off with a 176.615mph Modified Production Streamlined record that hasn't been broken yet. *Team Obsolete*

Vern Ott operates his Sunnen valve guide honing machine.

With help from the Alan Sputhe (who built the 1300cc engine, with S&S rods and flywheels) and the Harley-Davidson racing department, Vance Breese took Goliath to the salt in 1980. *Team Obsolete*

Vance Breese decided to make his current bike as aerodynamic, compact, and lightweight as possible. Shown here beside a Low Rider Sport, it is 15ft long and weighs only 600lb (compared to the twin-engined *Easyriders* streamliner, which is 24ft long and weighs over 2,400lb). Mike Corbin built the bodywork. Wheels were machined from billet aluminum and tires are from a T-39 jet trainer. *Vance Breese*

Mariah is powered by an Evolution Sportster engine built by Duncan Keller of Yankee Engineuity. Fuel injection was designed and machined by Roger "Ram Jett" Chatelet. Cylinder head work on the S.T.D. heads was provided by Carl Morrow of Carl's Speed Shop. *Vance Breese*

V-M-O provides all machining services associated with building a serious race engine.

Greg Fischer at Harley-Davidson of Texas is the lucky owner of this Weekend Frame beast, completely fabricated by John Storace.

Flawless workmanship and detailing are seen in all of John Storace's Weekend Frame work. Start saving...

White Brothers' Easyboy clutch kits are an inexpensive way to reduce the effort required to operate late-model clutches.

Shown on one of the White Brothers' project bikes with custom triple clamps, the WP Racing MA road race forks are among the world's finest. As if the bike wasn't trick enough, this Softail also features a pair of Performance Machine six-piston calipers.

Harley-Davidsons. Their Harley-Davidson division is known as V-Thunder. It offers cams, springs, steel and titanium retainers, pushrods, Velva-Touch lifters, and an intake manifold for Evolution and Shovelhead Big Twins that accepts dual carburetors.

Cams come in several grinds for Panheads, Shovelheads, and Evolution Big Twins. Sportster cams were still in the development stage at press time.

Velva-Touch roller lifters for Evolution Big Twin and Sportster engines are notable because they are compatible with any cam profile, including radical lifts for all-out drag bikes, but they are patented hydraulic roller lifters that provide all of the performance of solid lifters with none of the drawbacks. Developed by Vern Ott (of V-M-O Products, Inc.), Velva-Touch lifters are found in everything from loaded dressers to Top Fuel bikes; they may have earned more praise than any other aftermarket Harley-Davidson components.

V-Thunder
3406 Democrat Road
Memphis, TN 38118
(800) 967-1066—technical
(901) 794-2833—business
FAX (901) 366-1807
Catalog available

Wayne Loftain

Wayne Loftain does all forms of custom design and fabrication, from custom frames and gas tanks to drag racing clutches and nitro engine building. The bike shown here is his second Top Fuel bike project, which (as of spring 1991) he had ridden to a 7.40 at 182.56mph.

Wayne built the 114ci engine, based on a set of Master Performance four-cam cases and an S&S bottom end with Axtell Sales cylinders, and Venolia pistons with Total Seal rings. Heads are S.T.D. with the full treatment from Baisley, fed by a Hilborn injector. John Storace at Weekend Frame Company looked after the oiling system. Other components include Red Shift cams by Thunder Tech Performance Products, a Dynatech ignition, a Marzocchi front end, Kosman wheels, and Grimeca brakes. Wayne designed, machined, and welded the frame, clutch, and many other components. Dave Perewitz and Roy Mason applied the Wild Cherry paint and hand lettering at Cycle Fabrications in Massachusetts. With an 80in wheelbase, one of Wayne's 30lb chrome-moly frames provides the foundation for one of the quickest and most beautiful Harley-Davidsons ever built.

By day he operates Body Creations, a tattoo shop in East Islip, New York. At press time, a new Top Fuel bike was under construction; although it's hard to imagine, Wayne thinks the new bike will be a lot nicer.

Wayne Loftain
15 Yankee Street
Brentwood, NY 11717
(516) 277-9579

Weekend Frame Company

John Storace at the Weekend Frame Company offers all kinds of components for Harley-Davidson drag bikes, including custom air tanks, sheet aluminum bodywork, slipper clutches, engine mounts, exhaust systems, fork braces, frames, gas and oil tanks, jackshafts, outboard bearing supports, triple clamps, and wheelie bars. A fine craftsman, John uses his fabricating, CNC machining, and heli-arc welding skills to create anything from a hand-formed tank to a complete rolling lay-down drag chassis. Everything he makes is custom-made for the bike it's going on.

Frames are heli-arc-welded 4130 chrome-moly. Customers choose their engines (Big Twin or Sportsters), transmission type, wheelbase, tire size, steering geometry, seat height, and riding position.

Weekend Frame Company
513 Red Oak Street
Allen, TX 75002
(214) 727-1203

Weird Engineering

Owners of early Big Twin engines with flat cam covers can install a Weird Engineering distributor, which accepts your choice of ignition. MC Advantages produces an inverted trigger plate to adapt their Power Arc single-fire ignition system to these engines. Machined from stainless steel, the system provides a clean and simple solution for owners of earlier engines.

The Weird Engineering distributor is described in detail in the March 1993 issue of *Hot Bike* magazine.

Weird Engineering
Route 4, Box 201
Owatonna, MN 55060
(507) 451-4920

White Brothers

White Brothers manufactures a clutch kit, exhaust systems, forks, fork springs, and shocks.

The Easyboy clutch kit is available for 1987-and-later Big Twins and all Evolution Sportsters; it reduces clutch effort by about 40 percent. Porker Pipes fit shotgun style and are available for FXST, FLST, and FLSTF models. They're made from 16-gauge steel 2 1/4in in diameter, "for a burly look and sound compared to wimpy 1 3/4 and two-inch straight pipes."

The WP Racing MA upside-down road race forks from Holland are used by several successful racing teams including the factory-backed XR-750s ridden by Scott Parker (1993 AMA Camel Pro series runner-up and four-time series champion) and Chris Carr, winner of the 1993 AMA Camel Pro and 1993 AMA 600cc dirt-track series.

WP upside-down forks come with or without triple clamps, steering stem, caliper brackets, axle, and spacers; they can be

A peek under the skirt of this Softail shows the White Brothers shocks.

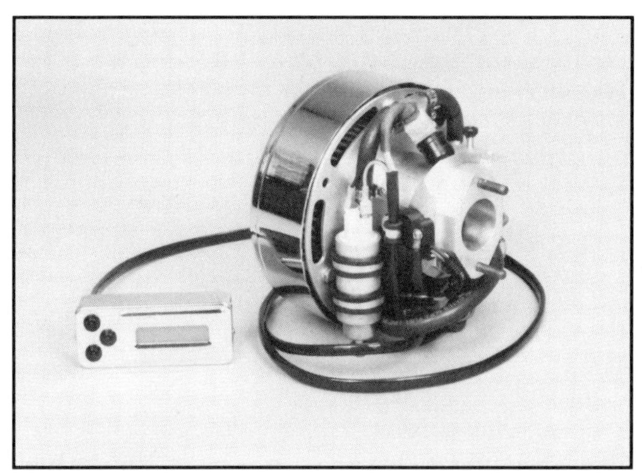
The WhiTek engine control system bolts to most stock and aftermarket intake manifolds.

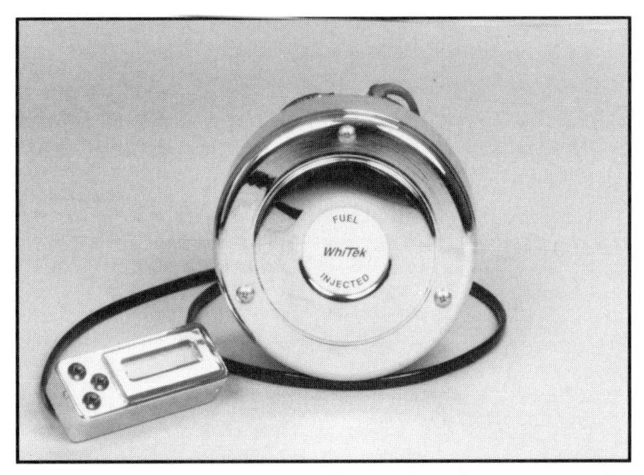

The WhiTek control/display unit permits adjustments to the accelerator pump, cruise leanout (for good highway mileage), mixture, rev limit, timing, and more. It displays the bike's acceleration, battery voltage, engine rpm, and engine temperature, and also displays adjustments and instructions. Optional probes display both cylinder head temperatures and exhaust gas temperatures.

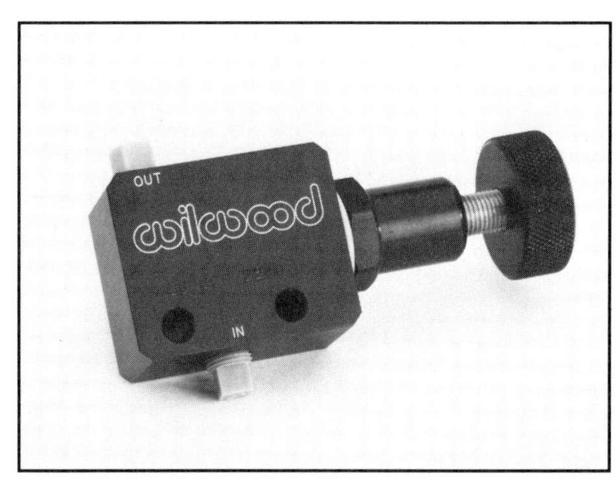

The Wilwood Engineering adjustable brake proportioning valve is CNC-machined from billet aluminum for use on vehicles with a single control operating both front and rear brakes. The knurled knob allows a fine adjustment of brake bias between front and rear, providing infinitely variable reduction of up to 57 percent.

Zipper's engine kits are designed to provide well-balanced performance improvements.

supplied by Kosman Specialties or Performance Machine. White Brothers also has aluminum clip-on bars, a clamp and bracket for a steering damper, and a fiberglass fender in a choice of two widths.

White Brothers rebuilds many brands of forks and shock absorbers, and also offers parts from many leading aftermarket manufacturers.

White Brothers
14241 Commerce Drive
Garden Grove, CA 92643
(714) 554-9442
FAX (714) 554-9622
Street catalog available

WhiTek

Bob White at WhiTek manufactures engine control systems based on his electronic fuel injection system and a built-in single-fire ignition system.

The WhiTek system was designed for use on Harley-Davidsons and was not built up from existing automotive components. A Motorola 68HC11 microprocessor chip (which was developed for controlling small engines) is used, and the system allows future software upgrades by replacing one memory chip. Other components are machined from aluminum, brass, and aircraft-grade steel.

The complete unit is roughly the same size as the stock Keihin and Bendix carburetors (and air cleaners) it replaces. For street riding and many race bikes a choice of 42mm (Shovelheads and Sportsters) and 46mm (for Evolution engines) bore sizes is provided. A third version, with a 2 1/4in (57mm) venturi is also available for racing.

WhiTek
P.O. Box 337
Arroyo Grande, CA 93421-0337
(805) 481-7710
FAX (805) 481-0901
Brochure available

Wiers Racing Company

Paul Wiers started the Wiers Racing Company in 1993 as an after-work venture to produce a variety of custom frames for Big Twin and Sportster engines.

Many of his frames are based on a perimeter design that provides improved rigidity over conventional designs. All frames are made specifically for their particular engine and application, from either mild steel or chrome-moly tubing.

Paul's weekends are often spent on his Super Modified FL drag bike, on which he set seven AMRA national records.

Wiers Racing Company
2339 North 67th Street
Wauwatosa, WI 53213
(414) 476-4240

Wilwood Engineering, Inc.

Wilwood Engineering brake calipers come in several versions that are found on drag bikes, road racers, and custom bikes. Their automotive versions are the most popular calipers used on NASCAR Winston Cup race cars.

Rear caliper mounts for Wilwood Engineering calipers are available from Rivera Engineering; they're made from chrome-plated, blanchard-ground 3/8in steel for the following applications: 1981-1984 swing arm frames with an 11 1/2in brake disc; 1973-1980 swing arm frames with a 10in brake disc; all rigid frames with an 11 1/2in brake disc; and all rigid frames with a 1-in brake disc.

Wilwood makes a residual pressure relief valve designed to maintain pressure in the braking system without brake pad dragging (part number 260-2220). This proportioning valve lets you make fine adjustments in the front-to-rear braking pressure.

Wilwood also supplies their own brake fluid, which is designed to perform well in high-temperature applications. Supplied in 12oz steel cans, it has a 550-degree boiling point.

Wilwood Engineering, Inc.
461 Calle San Pablo
Camarillo, CA 93012
(805) 388-1188
FAX (805) 388-4938
Catalog available

Wink's Custom Cycles

Wink's is run by Wink Eller, a fabricator and drag racer who can build custom frames for street and strip and provide complete motorcycle construction. Performance engine and transmission modifications are also available.

Wink's Custom Cycles
1338 East Wilshire
Santa Ana, CA 92705
(714) 972-2241

Wiseco Piston, Inc.

Wiseco manufactures forged and cast pistons for almost every Big Twin and unit-construction Harley-Davidson engine, in a variety of dome configurations.

The company also has a Special Products Division that will design, forge, and machine custom pistons in your choice of aluminum for racing applications.

White Brothers (one of several Wiseco distributors; see their listing) has Wiseco forged pistons in special versions for Evolution Big Twin and Sportster engines. Big Twin pistons are available in stock 3.5in as well as .020in oversize; they weigh about 60 grams less than stock pistons. Sportster pistons are designed for 883 to 1200 conversions without having to modify the stock 883 cylinder heads. These pistons have a reverse dome that provides 9.5:1 compression, and are offered for 3.5in and 3.52in bore sizes.

Wiseco Piston, Inc.
7201 Industrial Park Boulevard
Mentor, OH 44060
(800) 321-1364

Wiseco Piston, Inc.
720 North Main
Keller, TX 76248
(800) 392-0940

Wiseco Piston Canada, Inc.
P.O. Box 383
Woodstock, Ontario
Canada N4S 7X6
(800) 265-1029

Wood Precision Cycles

Scot Wood and the staff at Wood Precision handle complete motorcycle construction, performance engine and transmission modifications, exhaust systems, custom fabrication, and frames.

Shop services offered to street riders and drag racers include cylinder head porting and polishing, dynamic balancing, and frame modifications, including neck stretching. Custom fabrication work such as engine plates, stroker plates, and triple clamps is available, and they can machine and weld aluminum, chrome-moly, stainless steel, and titanium.

The Wood Precision Cycles staff has been involved in drag racing since 1980.

Wood Precision Cycles
P.O. Box 235
Goldsboro, NC 27530-0235
(919) 751-1100

Works Performance

Gil Vaillancourt heads Works Performance, which manufactures a line of quality shock absorbers and fork springs for most Big Twins and Sportsters.

Works offers their Pro-Racer adjustable shocks for most Harley-Davidsons with dual shocks. Each body is CNC-machined from aluminum and has a remote nitrogen-charged reservoir/gas spring. Ride height is adjusted with a threaded preload collar. These shocks can be supplied with single- or dual-rate springs.

For Softails, Works' dual shock systems feature aluminum bodies but include a remote-mounted adjustment knob to vary ride height over a 2in range. Softail shocks are available for 1984-1988 and 1989-1993 models.

Works also custom-builds shocks for special applications, and they'll rebuild your current shocks.

Works Performance
8730 Shirley Avenue
Northridge, CA 91324
(818) 701-1010
FAX (818) 701-9043
Catalog available

XRV Performance Products

XRV is run by Roger Kallins and Richard Gutterman, who can provide expert dyno work, engine modifications, and chassis improvements for Evolution Big Twins and Sportsters.

The company was formed when Arnie Freeman and Roger saw the Evolution Sportster's hidden potential and they set out to improve its power and handling without sacrificing the stock bike's reliability. Roger had C.R. Axtell lend some of his knowledge towards the project, with impressive results.

After years of development work, they have a line of engine and chassis components whose goal is reliable performance. Their mild Stage I kit provides an honest 72 rear-wheel horsepower. The kit includes a much-needed ignition change with a new module, dual coils and double-plug heads, boring the barrels to accommodate 1200 pistons, C.R. Axtell cams, the popular Mikuni 40mm carburetor, an oil cooler, and a tuneable SuperTrapp two-into-one stainless steel exhaust system.

With C.R. Axtell head modifications and higher-compression pistons, the Stage II engine delivers over 85hp to the ground and runs about 11.7 on the strip (while looking like a stock 883 except for the air cleaner and exhaust). Their main test engine made over 200 runs on their dyno without any bottom-end problems, and is still a reliable ride.

To complement the muscle, XRV adds finesse by reworking the stock Showa 39mm front end. They add a fork brace, a hydraulic steering damper, 15-weight fork oil, new progressive-rate springs, precision bushings, and modified damper rods that provide doubled rebound damping and halved compression damping. They also add rear shocks from Progressive Suspension or Works Performance, a vastly superior front brake setup from Performance Machine, stickier tires, and a bigger tank.

The completed package holds its own around town or on a winding canyon road, with something like a 600 Hurricane not providing much of a threat. And while it snarls, with the chassis dialed in it's now a more civilized piece. The weak links could be rear suspension travel and the solid-mounted engine, but aftermarket shocks and engine balancing can help.

The latest product from XRV is a chrome-moly chassis for the late Sportster, carrying the oil in the frame, with single-shock rear suspension, and XR-750 Grand National-style bodywork. A significant feature is the use of a fuel cell inside the fiberglass tank—a first on a production street bike.

Watch for a chrome-moly perimeter chassis for the Evolution Sportster to be available soon. Somewhat inspired by current Grand Prix frames and intended for serious road racing, it will have more than enough trick features to keep the knee-draggers happy.

Zipper's campaigned this Pro Stock Sportster in races sanctioned by AHDRA, AMRA, ECRA, and ProStar during the 1991 season and won 75 percent of the races they entered.

Regardless of all we hear about trick stuff for the Evolution, Shovelheads are far from forgotten. This one sports a pair of double-plug billet aluminum heads from Zodiac.

Zodiac Wide Glide kits can be supplied in a choice of rake for all models of forks.

Zodiac and Porsche Design worked together on computers, a CNC milling machine, and the dyno to develop the Revolution heads. God Bless the Shovelhead—may she shake and snort forever.

XRV Performance Products
10428 Burbank Boulevard
North Hollywood, CA 91601
(818) 762-5407
FAX (818) 762-1823
Literature available

Yankee Engineuity

Duncan Keller builds high-performance Big Twin, Sportster, and XR-1000 engines to order. This shop also produces CNC-machined billet aluminum coil brackets, which are distributed by Rivera Engineering.

Yankee Engineuity has a long history of racing engine development work for Harley-Davidsons, especially the Evolution and iron Sportsters and XR models.

Yankee Engineuity
1522 West San Carlos
San Jose, CA 95126
(408) 275-0202—parts department
(408) 275-0204—machine shop

Yost Performance Products

1980-and-later Keihin carburetors including the CV40 as well as the S&S B, E, and G carburetors can be fitted with a fuel atomizer that was designed by Bob Yost.

Called the Power Tube, it is a machined part designed to provide a smoother-running engine with a measurable horsepower increase in the midrange. Power Tubes are inexpensive, patented, and guaranteed, and installation is quick and simple. According to Bob, a Sportster that is stock except for an air cleaner and a pair of mufflers from Screamin' Eagle, along with a Power Tube, can deliver an impressive performance improvement. Other trick Yost products for Harley-Davidsons were under development as this book was being fabricated.

Yost Performance Products
P.O. Box 33408
Minneapolis, MN 55433-3408
(612) 755-0398

Zipper's Performance Products

Dan Fitzmaurice and the staff at Zipper's manufacture engine performance packages for Evolution Big Twins that include a carburetor, air cleaner, manifold, heads, cam, pushrods, and pistons. Zipper's offers completed engines, or short block kits that you finish. Their machining service is also available for custom work. Exhaust kits are available as mandrel-formed U-bends. Tubing diameters range from 1 7/8in all the way up to 2 1/2in.

Zipper's Performance Products
8040 Washington Boulevard
Jessup, MD 20794
(410) 799-8989
FAX (410) 799-9450
Catalog available

Zodiac Motorcycle Products

Zodiac manufactures CNC-machined billet aluminum cylinder heads and triple clamps, with more billet products for Harley-Davidsons in the works and due for release soon.

Zodiac Revolution heads are made specifically for Shovelhead engines. They are completely redesigned, with the goal of overcoming the limitations of the factory heads. The first thing you notice is the cooling fins, which were computer-designed to draw heat away from the stock engine They are set up for two plugs per cylinder, with redesigned combustion chambers and improved exhaust flanges. Porsche Design designed the combustion chambers and the ports. Wide Glide kits are available for all hydraulic Harley-Davidson forks.

Zodiac Motorcycle Products
P.O. Box 5
3640 AA Mijdrecht, Netherlands
Phone 31 (0) 2979-88621
FAX 31 (0) 2979-88226
Literature and catalog available

Part II

Component Manufacturer Section

Brakes and Brake Component Manufacturers

The following companies either manufacture or import and distribute high-performance brakes. Some have complete systems ready to be bolted on, while others make universal-type calipers for racing in general, which will call for some machining to adapt to your bike. A few companies listed here don't make calipers designed for Harley-Davidsons—or even motorcycles; they make racing brakes, and it's up to the builder to do what it takes to install them. If you're building an all-out drag bike, that's the way it's often done, but if you're improving a street bike, you may prefer to use something designed to bolt right on.

Regardless of your application, braking is something to pay some attention to. A high-performance bike should really be high-performance—and that includes being able to avoid trouble on the street, shutting it down on the strip, or out-braking the competition on a road course. Great brakes give you confidence when you ride, and for good reason.

Performance Friction isn't listed because they manufacture brake pads most commonly used in IndyCar and NASCAR racing—not motorcycle pads. But if you want to try cutting down their race car pads for your bike, you can find a Performance Friction dealer by calling (800) 521-8874 in the US and Canada or (803) 222-2141 outside North America.

As is the case with all of the following Component Manufacturers sections, descriptions of most of these brakes and brake components are in the main section of the directory.

Arlen Ness
Brembo
Delkron Manufacturing, Inc.
EBC Brakes
Ferodo, Ltd.
Florida Caliper Manufacturers, Inc.
Frentubo
GMA Engineering, Inc.
Graham's Speed & Custom
Grimeca
Harrison Engineering

Hobbsport, Ltd.
I.S.R.
JayBrake
JFZ Engineered Products
Keith Black Systems, Inc.
Ken Maely Enterprises
K&N Engineering
Koenig Engineering
Kosman Specialties, Inc.
Magura
Pat Kennedys Custom Motorcycles
Performance Machine, Inc.
R.B.'s Performance Technology
SBS
Screamin' Eagle
Storz Performance
Wilwood Engineering, Inc.

Cam Grinders and Suppliers

You could say that the cam is the heart of the engine since it controls the way it breathes. If you're new to this game, remember that the cam is one part of a system, and all of the components in the system have to work together. A cam that best suits your needs, that is used with compatible associated components, can give you a solid performance increase. Just make sure you don't make things worse by putting "too much cam" in your engine. Keeps things compatible and balanced.

These companies either manufacture their own high-performance cams or have them made for them.

Andrews Products, Inc.
Bartels' Performance Products
Cam Corp
Crane
C.R. Axtell Company
Custom Chrome, Inc.
Head Quarters
Iskenderian Racing Cams
Johnstone Products
Kateley Performance Products
Leineweber Enterprises
Miller Racing Systems
Precision Motorcycle Concepts
Red Shift Cams (see Thunder Tech)
Rich Products Company
Rivera Engineering
Screamin' Eagle
Sifton
SI / WEN Industries
Storz Performance
V-Thunder by Competition Cams
Wink's Custom Cycles
Zipper's Performance Products

Clutch and Clutch Component Manufacturers

The companies listed here either manufacture or custom-build parts that range from bolt-on replacement clutches to custom slipper clutches for drag bikes.

Advanced Racing Technology
Amp Research
Arlen Ness
Bandit Machine Works
Barnett Tool & Engineering
Competition Drive Lines
Custom Chrome, Inc.
Diversified Product Development
Graham's Speed & Custom
H.E.S. Performance Products
International Engineering Industries, Inc.
Magura
Master Performance Racing
The Motor Shop
Mountain Cycle
Mountain Motors
Northcoast Thunderbikes
Nungesser Engineering
Peterson Engineering
Primo Belt Drives
Rawlings Motor Maniacs
Schirra Cycle & Machine
Schultz Racing
Trett's Speed & Custom
Wayne Loftain
Weekend Frame Company
White Brothers

Computers for Racing

Riders and tuners can benefit from the information that can be measured, stored, recalled, and analyzed with a good racing computer. The companies listed here make computer systems that fall into two basic categories: Suitcase-style computer systems are typically used in the pits at a race, while onboard computers mount right on the bike.

Advanced Racing Technology
B&G Racing Computers
RacePak
Ram Jett Retainer

Connecting Rod Manufacturers

The companies listed here either manufacture or custom-build connecting rods ranging from stock replacement parts to all-out racing designs.

Carrillo Industries
Digger Enterprise
Master Performance Racing
Schultz Racing (for one-piece crankshafts)
S&S Cycle, Inc.

Cylinder Manufacturers

It is said that there is no substitute for cubic inches. For going to a big-bore set-up on your bike, the companies listed here all produce their own barrels. They range from hand-made barrels produced on a special-order basis to kits that are sold complete with pistons, rings, and instructions.

Aftermarket cylinder barrels for general high-performance use don't usually look much different from the stock ones they replace. They can be made from cast or solid aluminum, cast iron, or machined from steel. In the early days it wasn't unusual for somebody running a serious drag bike to machine his own barrels out of a scrap yard railway car axle, and these usually worked fine.

Barrels for Pro category drag racing often have no cooling fins, mainly because the engines are run for only short periods before cooling down, and to a lesser extent because engines run cooler on alcohol than on gas.

There are several different philosophies for increasing the displacement of a Harley-Davidson engine. The most traditional approach leans toward going to a longer stroke, along with the standard hot-rodding techniques. This can improve the engine's torque and horsepower without sacrificing reliability, providing it isn't taken too far.

Another camp believes that since the stock engine already has the longest stroke of any modern production motorcycle engine, and since it doesn't like to rev high anyway, it makes more sense to leave the stroke close to stock and go to a bigger bore size (again along with the other basic hot-rodding techniques).

And then there are the guys who want it all, with their fire-breathing, pavement-shredding 120ci killer engines that idle at something like point three on the Richter scale. More power to all of them.

It is more common to find a custom Harley-Davidson engine with a radical stroke than a radical bore because it's easier to increase the stroke a bunch. A huge bore presents problems with clearance between other components like lifters and pushrods—and moving them out of the way calls for a very special kind of hammer.

If you're new to this game, learn as much as possible from the experts who build and race this kind of equipment before you go nuts. All the companies listed here have supplied their equipment to racers—who have done well with it—and many of these companies are run by people deeply involved in racing themselves.

Axtell Sales, Inc.
Bonneville Engineering
Competition, Inc.
Custom Chrome, Inc.
Dragon Precision Machining
Fantasy Motorcycles
House of Horsepower, Inc.
Hyperformance
International Engineering Industries, Inc.
Los Angeles Sleeve Company
Michael Düx Industries
Owens Racing
Poole Cycle Parts
Precision Motorcycle Concepts
R&R Cycle
Screamin' Eagle
Sputhe Engineering, Inc.
S&S Cycle, Inc.
Trock Cycle Specialties
Truett & Osborn

Cylinder Head Manufacturers

The companies listed below manufacture their own aluminum cylinder heads from scratch. Some of them carry the heads in stock, while others make heads to order for each customer and their particular application. As is the case with frames and many other components, the selection is much better for Big Twins than Sportsters.

Advanced Racing Technology (billet four-valve for Top Fuel Evolution Big Twins)
B&K Cylinder Heads (billet two-valve and multiple-valve for most engines)
Custom Chrome, Inc. (cast two-valve for Evolution engines)
D&S Performance (billet two-valve for four-cam engines)
Fantasy Motorcycles (billet two-valve and multiple-valve for most engines)
Feuling/Rivera (cast four-valve for Evolution engines)
Hyperformance (billet two-valve for Evolution engines)
James Haithcock (billet two-valve for Top Fuel Evolution Big Twins)
Mega-Performance (cast four-valve for Evolution engines)
Mountain Motors (billet four-valve for most Harleys)
Riverside Cycle (billet two-valve for Evolution engines)
S&S Cycle, Inc. (cast two-valve for Evolution Big Twins)
Schultz Racing (billet two-valve for Evolution Big Twins)
S.T.D. Development Company, Inc. (cast two-valve for Big Twins)
Zodiac Motorcycle Products (billet two-valve for Shovelheads)

Engine Case Manufacturers

In some high-performance applications where the engine is going to be spinning faster and putting out more power than stock, it's a good idea to beef up the strength of the cases to handle the loads. If you're building a serious race engine from scratch, you'll probably want to use the strongest cases possible.

These companies produce aluminum cases for high-performance Big Twin engines. Aftermarket cases for Sportster engines are available from at least two manufacturers, but so far only for the iron engines. They can be adapted for use with Evolution components, but it's an involved project. There is a trend among some manufacturers to use the Sportster four-cam system in a Big Twin engine, but that's as close as there is to an all-out design for the Evolution Sportster.

Most of these cases are cast, and some are machined from solid aluminum. A few are virtually the same as the ones they're designed to replace, but most are reinforced in varying degrees for extra strength. Many are designed specifically for racing engines that put much greater loads on components. A few are custom-built to a customer's specific parameters and dimensions to let all of the components work together.

Some companies listed below offer Evolution, Shovelhead, Panhead, or Knucklehead designs, with your choice of ignitions, bore size, deck height, and other options. Don't buy the first set of cases you're offered a deal on; understand what you need. Ask a competent and successful Harley-Davidson race engine builder for help in narrowing down the choices, then contact the manufacturers or their representatives for more complete information.

Competition, Inc.
Delkron Manufacturing, Inc.
House of Horsepower, Inc.
Michael Düx Industries
Morocco Racing
Orangeburg Cycles
Schumaker Racing (listed under Master Performance)
Schultz Racing
Sputhe Engineering, Inc.
S&S Cycle, Inc.
S.T.D. Development Company, Inc.

Engine Case Repair Sources

Below is a list of most of the companies in this directory that are capable of providing expert repairs on broken or cracked engine cases. There are likely other companies that also handle this work, but those listed here specifically mentioned it when submitting information for this directory.

The Chrome Horse, Spencer, Iowa
Daniel's Certified Welding, Inc., Freeman, Virginia
Digger Enterprise, Houston, Texas
H.E.S. Performance Products, Los Angeles, California
House of Horsepower, Inc., Lafayette, Colorado

Mike's Precision Machine Shop, Benicia, California
Mountain Motors, East Windham, New York
Panther Precision Machine, Ltd., Surrey, British Columbia, Canada
Schirra Cycle & Machine, Valencia, Pennsylvania
Tek Cycle, Gill, Massachusetts
Thompson's Cylinder Head Service Co., Dedham, Massachusetts
Trock Cycle Specialties, Hampshire, Illinois
Wood Precision Cycles, Goldsboro, North Carolina

Engine Gasket Manufacturers

Engine gaskets can vary in design, durability, fit, materials, strength, temperature resistance, and thickness. Regardless of the caliber of the engine you're working on, make sure the gaskets you use are ideal for the application.

Bartels' Performance Products
The Chrome Horse
H.E.S. Performance Products
James Gaskets, Inc.
Jan's Cycle Gaskets
Milmeyer Precision
Poole Cycle Parts

Exhaust System Manufacturers

Aftermarket exhaust systems are available in dozens of styles. Pipes are usually made from mild steel tubing that has been chrome plated. Stainless steel is becoming more popular and can offer freedom from corrosion.

Make sure the exhaust system you choose suits your application. With all the variety available, unless you're an expert, you'll want some advice in choosing one. If your going for performance on your street bike, don't just choose the fattest, shiniest drag pipes you can find.

Since exhaust systems are among the components that are usually chrome plated, consider this about plating: There are two basic grades of plating—commercial plating and custom plating. In mass production of products like office furniture, the parts will be dipped without any hand polishing, and only the areas that will show will be significant. Custom-grade plating involves polishing the entire part completely to a smooth finish, and plating it with copper, nickel, and then chrome. That's what is meant by triple chrome plating. Commercial plating is most commonly used on stock exhaust systems, and a decent plated aftermarket exhaust system will be triple chrome plated.

Remember that there is a difference between reducing restriction to let the engine breathe and opening it up too much. Anything other than a full-race engine requires a certain amount of back pressure in the exhaust system for optimum performance. Taking your mufflers off eliminates this back pressure. Some motorcycle exhaust manufacturers will claim their mufflers will give your engine more power than an open exhaust. Ask your engine guru for recommendations for your application.

The following companies all either produce, custom-build, or distribute high-performance exhaust systems for Harley-Davidsons.

Advanced Racing Technology
Alliance Composites, Inc.
Arlen Ness
Bad Bones
Bartels' Performance Products
Bub Enterprises
Carl's Speed Shop
Classified Motorcycle Company
C&L Hog Shop
Cobra Engineering
Cougar Customs
Custom Chrome, Inc.
Cycle Fabrications
Damon's Motorcycle Creations
D&D Performance Enterprises
Drag Specialties—Python
Goodman Engineering, Ltd.
M.A.C. Products
Mototech Enterprises
Mountain Motors
Nungesser Engineering
Pat Kennedys Custom Motorcycles
Paughco
Precision Motorcycle Concepts
RB Racing/Race Systems Research
Rich Products Company
Run Roader
Samson Motorcycle Products, Inc.
Santee Industries
Screamin' Eagle
Soapstone Engineering
Storz Performance
Strader Engineering
Sumax
SuperTrapp Industries, Inc.
Tetrick Speed & Custom Motorcycles
White Brothers
Wink's Custom Cycles
Weekend Frame Company
Wood Precision Cycles
Zipper's Performance Products

Fabricators

When a motorcycle is being scratch-built or modified, the need sometimes arises to have a special part made. Custom-fabricated components can include anything from some aluminum bodywork, a set of triple clamps, or a transmission case for a unique application. Local shops that specialize in machining, sheet metalwork, or welding can sometimes help, but often you need to have the work done by someone who understands high-performance Harleys.

Sometimes the hardest part of having something custom-built is explaining what you want. A neat, simple drawing can provide all of the materials, dimensions, and tolerances needed for the job. Many shops will insist on one, so do your best to provide them with a basic working drawing. If you don't, it's only fair that you pay the fabricator for his time while he figures out exactly what you need.

Besides the companies listed here, you'll find there are other fabricators around such as some companies listed as framebuilders, who can also make custom parts. Consult the framebuilders listings if this list doesn't suffice.

Advanced Racing Technology, Newport News, Virginia
American Classics, Ferndale, Washington
Bernie Willett (listed under Jack Hagemann, Jr.), Victoria, Australia
Bill Wiebler Enterprises, Mapleton, Illinois
Brazos Valley V-Twin, Houston, Texas

Burchinal's Performance, Anaheim, California
Carl's Speed Shop, Santa Fe Springs, California
The Chrome Horse, Spencer, Iowa
C&L Hog Shop, Fort Pierce, Florida
Cougar Customs, Stirling, Scotland
Cycle Fabrications, Brockton, Massachusetts
Cycle Specialists, Newport News, Virginia
Darcy Racing Specialties, Fort Worth, Texas
Departure Bike Works, Richmond, Virginia
Digger Enterprise, Houston, Texas
Don Tilley, Statesville, North Carolina
Dragon Precision Machining, Colorado Springs, Colorado
Dave Rowe Performance Products, Seabrook, New Hampshire
Eagle Engineering, Minneapolis, Minnesota
E.C.S. Engineering, Gastonia, North Carolina
Fantasy Motorcycles, Sumner, Washington
Fast Company, Kirkland, Washington
Finch's Custom Cycles, Inc., Auburn Hills, Michigan
Frame Oddities, North Royalton, Ohio
Full Blast Engineering, Sioux Falls, South Dakota
G&C Racing, Dayton, Ohio
Hannan's Machine Shop, Hayward, California
H-D Performance Specialists, Pinellas Park, Florida
Heavy Duty Cycles, Ltd., Toronto, Ontario, Canada
H.E.S. Performance Products, Los Angeles, California
Howell's, Inc., Denver, Colorado
Jack Hagemann, Jr., Morgan Hill, California
Jørn "Høvding" Jacobsen's MC-rep., Fåvang, Sweden
Keith Peterson, Moheda, Sweden
Ken Maely Enterprises, Corona, California
Kosman Specialties, Inc., San Francisco, California
Lineaweaver Racing, El Sobrante, California
Master Performance Racing, Williamsburg, Virginia
MC Fabrications, Rockford, Illinois
Mike's Frame Shop, Boise, Idaho
Mother's Harley Shop, Vastra Frolunda, Sweden
The Motor Shop, Glendale, Arizona
Nico Bakker Frames BV, Heerhugowaard, Netherlands
NitroCycle, Bohemia, New York
Northcoast Thunderbikes, Snohomish, Washington
Nottingham Custom Cycles, Nottingham, United Kingdom
Nungesser Engineering, Belle Plaine, Kansas
Panther Precision Machine, Inc., Surrey, British Columbia, Canada
Pat Kennedys Custom Motorcycles, Tombstone, Arizona
P&D Custom Bikes, West Sussex, United Kingdom
Precision Metal Fab Racing, Shakopee, Minnesota
Precision Motorcycle Concepts, Glen Avon, California
Puccio Welding, San Jose, California
Rat's Whole Place, Decatur, Illinois
Rawlings Motor Maniacs, Fresno, California
Razorback Motor Works, Pompano Beach, Florida
Red Neck Cycles, WN-Beinstein, Germany
Romine Racing, Sturgis, Michigan
Route 66, West Middlesex, United Kingdom
Rowe Machine, Seabrook, New Hampshire
Schultz & Shreve Racing Fabrication, Germantown, Maryland
Sims & Rohm Performance Products, Yuba City, California
Soapstone Engineering, San Jose, California
Southside Cycle, Nanaimo, British Columbia, Canada
The Spinning Wheel, Fullerton, California
Team Obsolete, Brooklyn, New York
Tek Cycle, Gill, Massachusetts
Tetrick Speed & Custom Motorcycles, El Paso, Texas
Texas Frame Works, Austin, Texas
Thompson's Cylinder Head Service Co., Dedham, Massachusetts
Trett's Speed & Custom, Demorest, Georgia
Wayne Loftain, Brentwood, New York
Weekend Frame Company, Allen, Texas
Wink's Custom Cycles, Santa Ana, California
Wood Precision Cycles, Goldsboro, North Carolina

Fastener Manufacturers

All of the manufacturers of specialized bolts, nuts, and other fasteners that are mentioned in this book are listed below.

Arlen Ness
Classic Chassis
Colony
Gardner-Wescott Company
Lightning Bolt Company
Stage 8 Fasteners, Inc.
Trick Titanium

Fiberglass and Carbon Fiber Component Manufacturers

Fiberglass and carbon fiber parts that are made for Harley-Davidsons include fairings for street riding and roadracing, fenders for street riding and drag racing, gas tanks for dirt-track racing. dummy gas tanks for drag racing, and streamliner bodies for salt flats racing.

Air Tech
Alliance Composites, Inc.
Arlen Ness
Bartels' Performance Products
Bob's Cycle
Competition Motorcycles
Custom FRP
DC Company
R&R Cycle
Schafer Manufacturing Company
Tetrick Speed & Custom Motorcycles
White Brothers

Flywheel Manufacturers

Stroker kits are the traditional way of increasing a Harley-Davidson engine's displacement. The S&S Cycle, Inc., catalog contains a great amount of information on the subject, and can be referred to by readers looking for solid technical information.

Digger Enterprise
Michael Düx Industries
Schultz Racing (one-piece crankshafts)
S&S Cycle, Inc.
Truett & Osborn

Framebuilders

In terms of performance, the main complaints about stock Harley-Davidson frames are usually rigidity, engine vibration, and weight. The stock FXR-series frames provide adequate performance on the street but are heavy and offer no isolation from engine vibration. The Dyna Glide series, including the Sturgis and Daytona models, offer some improvements in rigidity and vibration.

There are lots of aftermarket frames available for Big Twins. The selection isn't nearly as good for Sportsters, with most of what's available being old chopper frames for the (shorter and narrower) pre-1986 iron engine. The significant exceptions are the frames for Evolution Sportsters from Carroll Racing Products, Claymore Racing, Goodman Engineering, Kosman Specialties, Rowe Machine, Tek Cycle, Wiers Racing Company, Wink's Custom Cycles, and XRV Performance Products. The Goodman is built in the United Kingdom from Reynolds 531 tubing; most of the rest are built from 4130 chrome-moly.

The tubing most commonly used for production street motorcycle frames is made of basic mild steel. Chrome-moly (which is short for chromium [and] molybdenum) tubing is stronger so it can be made with a thinner wall thickness for an equivalent application, reducing the weight of the component. But chrome-moly tubing is stocked by fewer steel suppliers and requires more skill to weld properly, usually with heli-arc (also called tungsten inert gas, or TIG) welding.

It should be pointed out that there is some disagreement over the suitability of chrome-moly steel as a material for street frames. Some people say that chrome-moly tubing work-hardens and doesn't stand up as well when subjected to continued vibration as mild steel does. Others say chrome-moly is just fine and they wouldn't use anything else.

High-end bicycle manufacturers, who have made way more chrome-moly frames than motorcycle manufacturers, would say that work-hardening and fatigue are not factors with chrome-moly. Only the cheapest bicycle frames are still made with plain-gauge mild steel tubing.

The people who build aircraft and Pro-category race cars don't use mild steel either. The exception to this is in NASCAR racing, where the structural rigidity of chrome-moly is considered less safe than mild steel, which will bend and crush more readily in a severe crash. Since the chassis of NASCAR race cars must absorb (as opposed to resist) impact to protect the driver, mild steel is the tubing of choice for NASCAR Winston Cup, Busch Series, and Modified race car frames.

Reynolds 531 tubing has a high manganese content and was originally developed for lightweight racing bicycles. In the thirties, the Reynolds Tube Company in the United Kingdom invented the machinery that was needed to manufacture double-butted tubing. This has a thicker wall thickness for about 3in at each end for strength, and a thinner wall thickness in the middle for light weight. Although butted tubing is standard on any decent bicycle frame today, only a handful of framebuilders use it for motorcycle frames.

None of the aforementioned tubing is considered exotic. Aluminum is common on current sport bikes and road racers, but has only been used on a few Harley-Davidsons. Aluminum is one frame material where extended vibration can lead to fatigue problems. Titanium has been used on even fewer custom Harley-Davidsons. Most racing sanctioning bodies don't allow titanium frames on motorcycles, mainly to keep the cost of racing down.

Aluminum and titanium tubes are both more prone to flex than steel of an equivalent diameter, so a larger outside diameter is called for to provide the same degree of rigidity. Aside from their lighter weight (and titanium's corrosion resistance), a further benefit of both aluminum and titanium is their inherent ability to absorb vibration. While neither are as good as cast iron in this regard, they both noticeably surpass steel.

If handling is of any concern to you (and it better be), consider this:

The main function of a motorcycle frame is to rigidly connect the steering head with the swing arm pivot. In the case of a rigid frame, the frame's main function is to rigidly connect the steering head with the rear axle. Any flex here, and in the swing arm and fork tubes, only adds problems. And they're ugly problems, like speed wobble. Sure, the frame holds the components together. But if the steering head and swing arm pivot (or rear axle) are moving torsionally in relation to each other, you're going to have handling problems, and you're going to be a hazard to yourself and your competitors.

In terms of quality, custom frames vary more among manufacturers than any other component in this directory. In fact, there is still no official framebuilder certification program as there is in the automotive drag racing community, where chassis builders have their work inspected and tested to get SEMA approval.

Regardless of what you ride, choose a framebuilder you have confidence in. Make a point of seeing a frame built by a particular builder before you commit yourself. Know your framebuilder. A motorcycle frame is no place to cut corners.

The following companies all either produce, distribute, or will custom-build frames for Harley-Davidsons, varying all the way from flat-track to roadracing to Top Fuel.

Arlen Ness
Atlas Precision Tool & Die
Bandit Machine Works
Billy Budde's Custom Motorcycles
Buell Motor Company
Carroll Racing Products
The Chrome Horse
C&J Precision Products, Inc.
C&L Hog Shop
Claymore Racing
Cougar Customs
Custom Chrome, Inc.
Cycle Fabrications
Cycle Specialists
Daniel's Certified Welding, Inc.
DC Company
Denver's
Departure Bike Works
Digger Enterprise
Dragon Precision Machining
E.C.S. Engineering
Ed Heil
Fantasy Motorcycles
Frame Oddities
Fred's Speed & Sport
Goodman Engineering, Ltd.
Harley-Davidson Motor Company

H-D Performance Specialists
Howell's, Inc.
Keith Peterson
Knight Racing Frames
Koenig Engineering
Kosman Specialties, Inc.
Larson Machine
MC Fabrications
Mike's Frame Shop
Mother's Harley Shop
The Motor Shop
Mountain Motors
Nico Bakker Frames BV
Northcoast Thunderbikes
Nottingham Custom Cycles
Nungesser Engineering
Orangeburg Cycles & Dixie Frames
Overseas International Trading
Owens Racing
Panther Precision Machine, Ltd.
Pat Kennedys Custom Motorcycles
Paughco
P&D Custom Bikes
Precision Metal Fab Racing
Precision Motorcycle Concepts
Pro Street Chassis Works
Prototek
Puccio Welding
Puttin' Parts
Race Visions
Rawlings Motor Maniacs
Rickey Racer
Riverside Cycle
Rolling Thunder Products
Route 66
Rowe Machine
Santee Industries
Schultz & Shreve Racing Fabrication
Soapstone Engineering
The Spinning Wheel
Team Obsolete
Tek Cycle
Texas Frame Works
Tom's Competition Cycle, Inc.
Truett's Frame Works
Tripoli Manufacturing (1991), Ltd.
Two Wheel Travel
Wayne Loftain
Weekend Frame Company
Wiers Racing Company
Wink's Custom Cycles
Wood Precision Cycles
XRV Performance Products

Fuel Valve and Filter Manufacturers

A good fuel valve provides adequate flow to the induction system without leaking or allowing dirt into the engine.

Accel
Perf-form Products, Inc.
Pingel Enterprise
Poole Cycle Parts

Gas Tank and Oil Tank Manufacturers

Descriptions of these tanks and components can be found in the main section of the directory.

Air Tech (fiberglass Sportster, XLCR, and XR-750 gas tanks)
Alliance Composites, Inc. (custom carbon fiber gas tanks)
American Classics (custom aluminum gas and oil tanks)
Arlen Ness (oil tanks)
Bad Bones (oil tanks)
Bartels' Performance Products (fiberglass KR and XRTT 5gal gas tanks)
Classified Motorcycle Company (aluminum Evolution Sportster gas tanks)
Custom Chrome, Inc. (gas and oil tanks)
Cycle Specialists (custom aluminum gas and oil tanks)
Damon's Motorcycle Creations (steel 7gal split gas tanks)
Dave Rowe Performance Products (custom gas and oil tanks)
DC Company (fiberglass dummy gas tanks; drag racing only)
Don's Speed & Custom (custom gas and oil tanks)
Goodman Engineering, Ltd. (aluminum gas tanks)
Harley-Davidson Motor Company (gas and oil tanks)
International Engineering Industries, Inc. (aluminum oil tanks)
Jack Hagemann, Jr. (custom aluminum gas and oil tanks)
Jagg (finned aluminum oil coolers)
Kosman Specialties, Inc. (custom aluminum oil tanks)
Paughco (gas and oil tanks)
P&D Custom Bikes (gas and oil tanks)
Perf-Form Products, Inc. (aluminum oil cooler/canisters, filter cartridges)
Pingel Enterprise, Inc. (fuel filters and valves)
Precision Motorcycle Concepts (gas and oil tanks)
Prototek (vented billet aluminum gas caps)
Puccio Welding (custom aluminum oil tanks)
Santee Industries (aluminum oil tanks)
Schafer Manufacturing Company (fiberglass XR-750 and XRTT gas tanks)
Storz Performance (aluminum Evolution Sportster gas tanks)
Tek Cycle (custom aluminum and steel gas and oil tanks)
Tripoli Manufacturing (1991), Ltd. (aluminum, mild steel, stainless steel oil tanks)
Wayne Loftain (custom aluminum gas and oil tanks)
Weekend Frame Company (custom aluminum gas and oil tanks)

Ignition System and Component Manufacturers

One of the first things to upgrade on a stock bike is the ignition system. There are single-fire, dual-fire, single-plug, dual-plug, points, electronic, and magneto ignition systems. The right system for your bike and application is best left to an experienced engine builder you respect and trust.

Advanced Racing Technology
American Cycle Electronics (see Sumax)
Arlen Ness
Accel Performance Products
Andrews Products, Inc.
Carl's Speed Shop
Crane
Custom Chrome, Inc.
Cycle Performance Products, Inc.
Dynatech
Eagle
Flo Dynamics
HDI Systems
H.E.S. Performance Products
Hunt Magneto
Jacobs Electronics
Jaynes Electric
Karata Enterprises
Ken Maely Enterprises
MC Advantages
Morris Magneto
MSD Ignition
Poole Cycle Parts
Roberson's Cycle
Screamin' Eagle
Starwest, Inc.
Stinger U.S.A.
Sumax
Taylor Cable Products, Inc.
Weird Engineering
WhiTek

Induction System Component Manufacturers

There's almost no limit to how far you can go with aftermarket induction systems. It's all here, from recalibrated stock carburetors (which can help a lot) to the leading edge of fuel injection technology.

But like many other aspects of engine hot-rodding, it's easy for a novice to turn a stock engine into an unreliable and impractical beast that causes its owner more grief than it's worth. If you don't know what you're doing here, get some advice from an expert.

Accel Performance Products (fuel injection systems)

Advanced Racing Technology (intake manifolds, supercharger kits)
Arlen Ness (intake manifold clamps)
Bad Bones (Magnum Jet carburetor)
Bartels' Performance Products (intake manifolds)
Billy Budde's Custom Motorcycles (fuel injection systems)
Brilhante Company, Inc. (supercharger kits)
The Chrome Horse (fuel injection systems)
Custom Chrome, Inc. (carburetors)
Cycle Specialists (custom supercharger belt drives)
Dell'Orto (carburetors)
Don's Speed & Custom (custom supercharger belt drives)
Drag Specialties (air cleaners)
Dynojet Research (Keihin carburetors jetting kits)
Fuel Injection Engineering / Hilborn (Hilborn fuel injection systems)
Full Blast Engineering (nitrous oxide injection system installation)
Hahn Racecraft (fuel injection systems, turbochargers)
H-D Performance Specialists (supercharger, turbocharger system installation)
Head Quarters (S&S two-barrel carburetor custom intake manifolds)
H.E.S. Performance Products (intake manifolds, intake manifold adapter rings)
House of Horsepower, Inc. (pump drives)
Johnstone Products (intake manifolds)
KF Engineering (superchargers)
Kinsler Fuel Injection, Inc. (fuel injection systems)
K&N Engineering (air filters)
KüryAkyn U.S.A. (air cleaners)
Lectron Fuel Systems & Don Vesco Racing (carburetors)
Magura (throttle assemblies)
Master Performance Racing (pump drives, push-pull throttle assemblies)
Majestic Turbo (turbocharger systems)
MB Products (air cleaners)
Mikuni (carburetors, intake manifolds)
Morocco Racing (pump drives)
Morris Magneto (injector pump adapters)
The Motor Shop (fuel injection, nitrous oxide systems, superchargers)
Mountain Motors (custom intake manifold fabrication)
M&T Engineering (System II fuel atomizers)
Nitrous Oxide Systems (nitrous oxide systems)
Northcoast Thunderbikes(alcohol and nitro conversions)
Opcon Autorotor (superchargers)
Poole Cycle Parts (turbocharger systems)
Quik Silver (carburetors)
Ram Jett Retainer (intake manifolds)
Rawlings Motor Maniacs (fuel injection systems)
RB Racing/Race Systems
Research (electronic fuel injection systems, turbochargers)
Rivera Engineering (air cleaners)
Sims & Rohm Performance Products (supercharger kits)
Screamin' Eagle (air cleaners, carburetors, intake manifolds)
S&S Cycle, Inc. (air cleaners, carburetors, intake manifolds)
SU (carburetors)
Sumax (air cleaners)
Thompson's Cylinder Head Service Co. (nitrous oxide injection system design and fabrication)
Thunder Tech Performance Products (ThunderJet carburetor modifications for gas and nitro)
Trett's Speed & Custom (custom fuel injection throttle bodies)
UNI Filter, Inc. (air filters)
V-Thunder by Competition Cams (intake manifolds)
WhiTek (electronic fuel injection systems)
XRV Performance Products (intake manifolds)
Yost Performance Products (S&S carburetor fuel atomizers)

Piston and Ring Manufacturers

The companies here manufacture or distribute pistons or rings for Harley-Davidsons. Some pistons are cast like the stock parts and others are forged for improved durability. Most pistons are available from stock, with some companies making them only on a special-order basis for specific racing applications.

Arias Industries
Axtell Sales, Inc.
Custom Chrome, Inc.
Drag Specialties
Head Quarters
Hyperformance
Kateley Performance Products
Poole Cycle Parts
Rich Products Company
Rivera Engineering
Screamin' Eagle
Sputhe Engineering, Inc.
S&S Cycle, Inc.
Total Seal
Venolia Pistons
White Brothers
Wiseco Piston, Inc.
XRV Performance Products

Pushrod Manufacturers

Lighter reciprocating weight and improved durability are the main reasons to upgrade pushrods. Some companies manufacture their pushrods in-house, while others have them made to their specifications by outside suppliers. All of the companies listed here sell pushrods under their own name.

Andrews Products, Inc.
Bartels' Performance Products
Colony
Crane
C.R. Axtell Company
Head Quarters
Kateley Performance Products
Leineweber Enterprises
R.B.'s Performance Technology
Red Shift (listed under Thunder Tech)
Rivera Engineering
Screamin' Eagle
Sifton
Smith Brothers Pushrods
S&S Cycle, Inc.
Storz Performance
V-Thunder by Competition Cams
Zipper's Performance Products

Salt Flats Racing Specialists

This type of racing, where talented backyard mechanics on low budgets still have a decent shot at a record, has always appealed to me, and it deserves a lot more publicity, participation and support.

For coverage of land speed record racing in general, one publication that covers the sport in detail monthly is *Bonneville Racing News* (P.O. Box 730, Hemet, California 92546-0730, 714-926-2277, FAX 714-926-4619). This is a salt flats racing newspaper.

The sanctioning body that governs the sport is the Utah Salt Flat Racers Association (USFRA, 540 East 500 North, Pleasant Grove, Utah 84062). This group handles the Bonneville Speed Trials each July, September, and October at the Bonneville Salt Flats in Wendover, Utah. Two volunteers to contact are Rick Vesco at (801) 723-6934 and Mary West at (801) 785-5364.

In one way or another, the companies here have all been involved in racing at the Bonneville Salt Flats.

Bonneville Engineering
Bub Enterprises
Competition Motorcycles
Carl's Speed Shop
Don Vesco Racing (described under Lectron)

Fast Company
H.E.S. Performance Products
Mickey Thompson Enterprises
Mike's Frame Shop
Performance Machine, Inc.
RB Racing/Race Systems
Research
R&R Cycle
Sims & Rohm Performance Products
Sputhe Engineering, Inc.
S&S Cycle, Inc.
Tom Hayden Enterprises
Trick Titanium
Vance Breese
Yankee Engineuity

Sportster Twin Sports Component Manufacturers

The well-deserved popularity of the AMA Twin Sports class for 883 Sportsters brings us to this brief listing of some of the more popular sources for components and services that can make the 883 more competitive. This list is not complete, but it is representative of what some of the front runners are running.

For information about the rules for this class, contact the AMA (P.O. Box 6114, Westerville, OH 43081-6114, 800-AMA-JOIN). You might also consult the ***Harley-Davidson Sportster Performance Handbook*** by Buzz Buzzelli (published by Motorbooks International). Chapter 7 contains detailed tuning tips for Twin Sports class racers.

Auto Meter Products, Inc.
Barnett Tool & Engineering
Bartels' Performance Products
Bill Wiebler Enterprises
Blackmon Racing Products
Carl's Speed Shop
Continental Tire
D&D Performance Enterprises
Don Tilley
Dunlop Tire Corporation
Dynojet Research
Fox Factory, Inc.
Goodyear Tire
Harley-Davidson Motor Company
I.S.R.
JW Racing
Koni America, Inc.
Lineaweaver Racing
Magura
Marzocchi
Mert Lawwill Racing
Öhlins
Parra Performance
Progressive Suspension
SBS
Screamin' Eagle
Stage 8 Fasteners, Inc.
Storz Performance
Superbrace
SuperTrapp Industries, Inc.
Thompson's Cylinder Head Service Co.
Works Performance
XRV Performance Products
Yankee Engineuity
Yost Performance Products

Suspension Component Manufacturers

These companies manufacture or supply suspension components either made specifically for Harley-Davidsons or that can be adapted to them. Some also offer suspension modification services for original components.

Accutronix Racing Products (billet aluminum triple clamps)
Arlen Ness (billet aluminum triple clamps)
Bartels' Performance Products (Evolution Sportster shock absorbers)
BW Billets (billet aluminum triple clamps)
Cougar Customs (billet aluminum triple clamps)
Custom Chrome, Inc. (fork springs)
Custom Cycle Engineering Company (billet aluminum triple clamps)
Cycle Specialists (billet aluminum triple clamps)
Delkron Manufacturing, Inc. (billet aluminum triple clamps)
Forcella Italia / Ceriani (conventional and upside-down forks)
Fournales Suspension (shock absorbers)
Fox Factory, Inc. (shock absorbers)
Frank's Maintenance and Engineering, Inc. (fork tubes—all models, any length)
Graham's Speed & Custom (billet aluminum fork braces, triple clamps)
GMA Engineering, Inc. (billet aluminum triple clamps)
International Engineering Industries, Inc. (billet aluminum triple clamps)
I.S.R. (steering dampers)
Koenig Engineering (drag racing forks, billet aluminum triple clamps)
Koni America, Inc. (shock absorbers, fork springs)
Kosman Specialties, Inc. (billet aluminum triple clamps, fork braces, forks)
Marzocchi (conventional and upside-down forks, shocks)
MB Products (Mike's Short Shocks)
Motorrad Müller GMBH (billet aluminum triple clamps)
Mountain Motors (billet aluminum fork braces, triple clamps)
Nungesser Engineering (billet aluminum fork braces, triple clamps)
Öhlins (forks, shock absorbers, steering dampers)
Progressive Suspension (fork springs, shock absorbers)
Race Visions (billet aluminum triple clamps)
Rawlings Motor Maniacs (billet aluminum fork braces, drag racing forks)
R.B.'s Performance Technology (carbon laminate fork braces)
Roberson's Cycle (fork braces, steering dampers)
Screamin' Eagle (forged aluminum fork braces)
Storz Performance (steering dampers, brackets)
Superbrace (billet aluminum fork braces)
Weekend Frame Company (billet aluminum fork braces, triple clamps)
White Brothers (upside-down forks, lowering kits)
Wood Precision Cycles (billet aluminum triple clamps)
Works Performance (fork springs, shock absorbers)
XRV Performance Products (fork modifications)

Tire Manufacturers

Upgrading your tires is an excellent way to improve performance, but you have to choose them wisely. Some tires in this directory and in the marketplace were not designed to be put on Harley-Davidsons or used on the street. Tire manufacturers are very concerned that their products are used only for their designated purpose. Several tire manufacturers requested that readers be reminded of the importance of getting expert advice when changing tires.

Avon Tires, Ltd.
Contine
ntal Tire
Dunlop Tire Corporation
Goodyear Racing Tire Division
Metzeler Motorcycle Tire
Michelin Tire Corporation
Mickey Thompson Enterprises
Pirelli

Tire Size Conversion Chart

Imperial	Metric
2.50/2.75	80/90
3.00/3.25	90/90
3.50	100/90
4.00	110/90
4.25	120/90
4.50/5.00	130/90

Tools for Maintenance and Repair

Listed below are the companies that manufacture specialized shop tools for assembling, modifying, and repairing Harley-Davidsons.

Advanced Racing Technology
Baisley Hi-Performance
Barnett Tool & Engineering
Bartels' Performance Products
B&G Racing Computers
Crane
Custom Chrome, Inc.
Delkron Manufacturing, Inc.
Diversified Product Development
Dynatech
Dynojet Research
Harley-Davidson Motor Company
Holeshot Performance
Jim's Machining
Keith Black Systems, Inc.
Manley Performance Products
Peterson Engineering
Pingel Enterprise, Inc.
Poole Cycle Parts
Progressive Suspension
RacePak
Ram Jett Retainer
Rivera Engineering
Rowe U.S.A.
Sputhe Engineering, Inc.
S&S Cycle, Inc.
Tech Products
Trock Cycle Specialties
Vance Breese

Transmission and Powertrain Component Manufacturers

All the manufacturers of transmissions and transmission components in the directory are listed here, along with belt drives, chains, chain drive conversion parts, kickstart kits, and sprockets. For each supplier named below, the listed components are only a sampling of what's available, not a complete list. More complete lists and descriptions are found in the main body of the directory.

American Classics (custom aluminum primary covers)
Andrews Products, Inc. (transmission gears, pulleys, shafts)
Arlen Ness (sprockets, chain drive conversions)
Bandit Machine Works (drag race transmissions, Sportster trap doors)
Bartels' Performance Products (chain final drive kits, sprockets, KR sprocket shafts)
Bentec AB (two-speed drag race transmissions)
Billet Bilt (five-speed Big Twin kickstart kits)
B&J Transmissions (air shifters, drag race transmissions)
Brad Foote Gear Works, Inc. (Big Twin drag racing transmissions, sprockets)
BW Billets (belt final drive guards, transmission mount plates)
Cal-Products (four-speed Big Twin shift levers, transmission cases)
The Chrome Horse (custom aluminum primary covers, engine plates)
Competition Drive Lines (belt drives)
Custom Chrome, Inc. (kickstart kits, four-speed Big Twin transmission gears)
Cycle Specialists (belt primary drives, Top Fuel high gear shafts)
Digger Enterprise (custom aluminum primary covers, engine plates)
Diversified Product Development (Big Twin transmission end doors)
Don's Speed & Custom (custom aluminum primary covers, engine plates)
Frame Oddities (custom aluminum primary covers, engine plates)
Graham's Speed & Custom (sprockets, chain drive conversions)
H.E.S. Performance Products (chain drive conversions, primary covers, sprockets)
Holeshot Performance (electric shifters)
International Engineering Industries (air shifters)
Karata Enterprises (belt drive systems)
Kosman Specialties, Inc. (sprockets, engine plates)
Larson Machine (five-speed automatic Big Twin transmissions)
Mike's Precision Machine Shop (transmission repairs)
Mountain Motors (custom drag racing transmission component fabrication)
MRE—Murdoch Racing Enterprises (air shifters, Big Twin drag race transmissions)
PBI Sprockets (countershaft sprockets)
Poole Cycle Parts (Shovelhead belt drive primary covers, engine plates)
Precision Motorcycle Concepts (belt drive primary covers, Red Eye jockey shifters)
Primo (belt primary drive systems for 1937-and-later Big Twins)
Race Visions (custom aluminum primary covers)
Rat's Whole Place (transmission modifications)
Ray Price Performance Products (air shifters, drag racing transmissions)
Rawlings Motor Maniacs (custom aluminum primary covers)
R.B.'s Performance Technology (carbon fiber sprocket spacers)
Regina (final drive chains)
Rivera Engineering (kickstart kits, final drive and transmission sprockets)
Rolling Thunder Products (four-speed castle-top transmissions)
Screamin' Eagle (Sportster transmission gears)
Soapstone Engineering (custom aluminum primary covers)
Sputhe Engineering, Inc. (Big Twin transmission cases, Sportster trap doors)
S.T.D. Development Company, Inc. (four-speed Big Twin transmission cases)
Super Max Products (belt drive systems, belts, pulleys, primary covers)
Tom Hayden Enterprises (primary chain tensioners)
Trock Cycle Specialties (Sportster pawl supports, trap doors)
Tsubaki (final drive and primary chains)
Wayne Loftain (custom aluminum primary covers)
Weekend Frame Company (custom aluminum primarycovers)
Wood Precision Cycles (engine plates, transmission modifications)
Zipper's Performance Products (drag racing transmission modifications)

Valve Manufacturers

The companies listed here manufacture or distribute valves for Harley-Davidson engines. (As in the case of cams, exhaust systems, and some other parts, they are not necessarily manufactured by the companies whose names are on them.) Valves are available for a variety of applications, ranging from stock replacement valves to lightweight titanium valves for serious competition.

Andrews Products, Inc.
Baisley Hi-Performance
Bellucci Racing, Inc.
Black Diamond (listed under Precision Machining)
Custom Chrome, Inc.
Del West Engineering, Inc.
Flo Dynamics
Florida Caliper Manufacturers, Inc.
Hyperformance
Manley Performance Products
Rowe U.S.A.
Sam's Performance Specialties
SI / WEN Industries
S&S Cycle, Inc.
Storz Performance
V-Thunder by Competition Cams

Valve Lifter Manufacturers

Descriptions of these lifters can be found in the main section of the directory.

Crane
H-D Performance Specialists

Jim's Machining
Poole Cycle Parts
R.B.'s Performance Technology
Sifton
Tek Cycle (Velva-Touch adapter kits for XL and XR)
V-Thunder by Competition Cams (Velva-Touch)

Valve Spring Manufacturers

Descriptions of these springs can be found in the main section of the directory.

Baisley Hi-Performance
C.R. Axtell Company
Iskenderian Racing Cams
Kateley Performance Products
Leineweber Enterprises
Manley Performance Products
Miller Racing Systems
R/D Spring Corporation
Red Shift (listed under Thunder Tech)
Rivera Engineering
V-Thunder by Competition Cams

Wheel Manufacturers

The companies listed here manufacture or distribute custom wheels either made specifically for Harley-Davidsons or adaptable to them, for applications ranging from Top Fuel to flat-track to street.

Changing to significantly lighter wheels can theoretically improve your bike's acceleration, braking, handling, and appearance all at once. All motorcycle wheels fit into one of the following six basic types of construction:

Carbon fiber is a relatively new material for building wheels; in motorcycling, it is only being used in drag racing and road racing. Carbon fiber wheels should be considered exotic equipment for serious racing only.

Cast wheels can be either aluminum or magnesium. Cast aluminum wheels are among the strongest, and can be either heavy or quite light, depending on how much material is used. Magnesium should be considered an exotic metal, for serious racing only. Magnesium wheels are sold without D.O.T. approval because they are generally more brittle, and potentially flammable. Magnesium is also more difficult to weld. Aluminum is the way to go unless you're racing in a Pro category, and careful.

Cast aluminum wheels are quite reliable, unless you really smack something with them. Generally speaking, cast wheels work well with tubeless tires when treated with a sealer intended for making them airtight (available at motorcycle shops and automotive supply stores). The first production motorcycle with cast aluminum wheels was the 1973 Yamaha RD-350 two-stroke street bike.

Composite wheels, made of carbon fiber or other synthetic material, are relatively new. Composite products offer a superb strength-to-weight ratio. The fibers can be arranged to concentrate strength and distribute stress, somewhat similar to the way the grain structure of a metal forging can be controlled to conform to the shape of what is being made.

In developmental work on Grand Prix road racing motorcycles and Formula One race cars, composite wheels have produced some success and some problems, mainly with brittleness. The potential weight savings is phenomenal—a South African company has built composite wheels for a Grand Prix bike that weighed around 4 1/2lb apiece.

As of this writing, very few companies make composite wheels, which are in their infancy and will develop and gain popularity in time. Even the $2,000 composite wheels for professional racing bicycles are generally intended only for straight-line time trial racing.

Laced wheels offer the advantages of light weight, reparability, some limited shock absorption, and that great traditional appearance. Their disadvantages are flex, due to the spokes' relative lack of mechanical integrity compared to a cast wheel; the necessity of running inner tubes, which adds weight and can generate heat in prolonged use; and reliability, since they must be trued occasionally when subjected to hard lateral loads.

Considering weight only, steel rims are dated for high-performance use, although a laced wheel with a steel rim could conceivably be lighter than a heavy cast aluminum wheel. Laced wheels with aluminum rims and polished stainless steel spokes can be lightweight, beautiful, and reasonably reliable provided they are not abused.

Modular wheels share an advantage with laced wheels: the components can be replaced separately, allowing you to change to another rim width or to repair damage. The strength of the connection between the "disc" section (that replaces the traditional spokes) and the rim is a potential weak point. Don't let those bolts come loose. The Stage 8 Fasteners locking fastener system is ideal for this application.

Modular wheels usually have aluminum rims, with center sections that are cast, machined from solid stock, or forged. These wheels are sometimes called composites (they're composed of several parts), but modular is a more correct term, except in cases where some of the wheel's components are actually made from composite (plastic) material. Their main drawback today is the relatively small selection of manufacturers to choose from.

Spun wheels are popular for their appearance and light weight. In the early seventies, Center Line Racing Wheel Company started spinning aluminum automotive wheels that were riveted to smooth, machined aluminum center sections. A word of caution, though—with a solid front wheel on a light bike you will notice crosswinds more. The lighter the bike, the worse the problem.

Motorcycle builders started adapting the Center Line 15in x 3.5in front wheel (designed for the front ends of drag cars) to run on the back of custom Harley-Davidsons. By the late seventies companies like Mitchell produced spun aluminum wheels for motorcycles. They look great, they're strong and reliable, they're simple to clean, and they usually seal well.

Akront (aluminum rims for laced and modular wheels)
Alliance Composites, Inc. (carbon fiber for road racing)
Avenger Wheels (modular aluminum for drag racing)
Buchanon's Frame Shop (laced to order)
Classified Motorcycle Company (laced with aluminum rims)
Custom Chrome, Inc. (laced and spun aluminum)
hyPerTek, Inc. (modular aluminum and magnesium for road racing)
International Engineering
Industries, Inc. (spun aluminum for drag racing)
Jay Company (cast magnesium for road racing)
Jim's Aero Glide Racing, Ltd. (spun aluminum for drag racing)
Keith Peterson (spun aluminum)
Koenig Engineering (modular aluminum for drag racing)
Kosman Specialties, Inc. (laced and modular for dirt-track and drag racing)
Marchesini S.R.L. (cast magnesium for road racing)
MC Tuning (laced 40- and 80-spoke for street use)
Michael Düx Industries (laced stainless steel for street use)
Morris (from Poole Cycle Parts) (cast aluminum)
Motorrad Müller GMBH (laced—rear only)
Nungesser Engineering
(modular aluminum 15in rear for drag racing)
Pat Kennedys Custom
Motorcycles (laced 40-, 80- and 120-spoke)
Performance Machine, Inc. (laced, modular and spun aluminum)
Precision Metal Fab Racing (modular aluminum for drag racing)
R.B.'s Performance Technology (carbon fiber and aluminum composite for drag racing)
RC Components (modular aluminum)
The Spinning Wheel (carbon fiber and aluminum composite for drag racing)
Storz Performance (laced to order for dirt-track, drag racing and street use)
Sun Metal Products (aluminum rims for laced and modular wheels)
Tecnomagnesio (cast magnesium for road racing)

Rim Width Measurement Chart

WM 1	1.600in
WM 2	1.850in
WM 3	2.150in
WM 4	2.500in
WM 4.5	2.750in
WM 5	3.000in
WM 6	3.500in
WM 7	3.750in
WM 8	4.000in
WM 9	4.250in
WM 10	4.500in
WM 11	4.750in
WM 12	5.000in
WM 13	5.250in
WM 14	5.500in
WM 15	5.750in
WM 15.5	5.875in
WM 16	6.000in

XR-750 Component Sources

Anyone with an interest in XR-750s (or the earlier KR and WR models) would do well to sign up with the Competition Network for Harleys. In early 1992, Greg Duray started this organization. For nominal annual dues, members get six newsletters with information about classic Harley-Davidson race bikes like the XR, KR, and WR models as well as the XR-1000 and XLCR street bikes. You can reach Greg at: Competition Network for Harleys, P.O. Box 95881, Hoffman Estates, IL 60195-5881, (708) 884-6033.

Air Tech (XRTT fairings, XR-750 gas tanks)
Andrews Products, Inc. (custom-ground cams)
Baisley Hi-Performance (XR-750 roller-bearing rocker arms)
Bartels' Performance Products (XR-750 engine components, fiberglass)
Bellucci Racing, Inc. (XR-750 titanium valves)
Bill Wiebler Enterprises (XR-750 engine components, modifications)
Branch Flometrics (XR-750 dyno work, porting)
Brembo (disc brakes)
Buchanon's Frame Shop (laced wheels)
Champion Racing Frames (XR-750 frames, swingarms)
C&J Precision Products, Inc. (XR-750 frames, swingarms)
Darcy Racing Specialties (cylinder head, engine modifications)
DC Company (fiberglass seats)
Del West Engineering, Inc. (XR-750 titanium valves)
Don Tilley (XR-750 engine modifications, fabrication, tuning)
Forcella Italia / Ceriani (conventional and upside-down forks)
G&C Racing (XR-750 fabrication, restoration)
Goodyear Racing Tire Division (dirt-track tires)
Grimeca (disc brakes)
Gustafsson Plastics (XRTT windshields)
Hank Scott Racing (XR-750 construction, head work, engine building)
Harley-Davidson Motor Company (XR-750 engines, components)
H-D Performance Specialists (XR-750 engine work, dyno work, fabrication)
Hunt Magneto (magnetos, parts, rebuilding)
Jack Hagemann, Jr. (custom aluminum gas and oil tanks)
Jim's Machining (crank pins, pinion gear shafts, sprocket shafts)
Ken Maely Enterprises (boot plates, disc brakes, kill switches, welding)
K&N Engineering (air filters)
Knight Racing Frames (XR-750 frames, swing arms)
Kosman Specialties, Inc. (XR-750 frames, oil tanks, triple clamps, wheels)
Leineweber Enterprises (XR-750 cams, pushrods, valve spring kits)
Lineaweaver Racing (XR-750 dyno work, engine components, fabrication)
Marzocchi (forks, shocks)
Mert Lawwill Racing (consulting work, engine building)
Mountain Motors (cylinder head work, fabrication)
Parra Performance (head work, engine development, valve guides)
Pingel Enterprise, Inc. (engine mounts, fuel valves, filters)
Pirelli (dirt-track tires)
Rich Products Company (XR-750 engine components)
Schafer Manufacturing Company (XR-750 and KR fiberglass fairings, seats, tanks)
Storz Performance (engine and chassis components)
Team Obsolete (XR-750 and XRTT engines, frames, complete bikes)
Tek Cycle (adapters for installing Velva-Touch lifters in XR-750s)
Thompson's Cylinder Head Service Co. (case repairs, development work, machining, welding)
Thunder Tech Performance Products (Red Shift cams made from your exchanged core cams)
White Brothers (forks)
Works Performance (fork springs, shocks)

HARLEY-DAVIDSON ENGINE DISPLACEMENT CHART

Big Twin Engines
(bore & stroke in inches)

80in Evolution	1985 and later	3.500 bore	4.250 stroke	81.77ci	1340cc
74in Evolution	1985 and later	3.437 bore	3.968 stroke	73.63ci	1206cc
80in Shovelhead	1966-1985	3.500 bore	4.250 stroke	81.77ci	1340cc
74in Shovelhead	1966-1985	3.437 bore	3.968 stroke	73.63ci	1206cc
74in Panhead	1948-1965	3.437 bore	3.968 stroke	73.63ci	1206cc
61in Panhead	1948-1965	3.312 bore	3.500 stroke	60.32ci	988cc
74in Knucklehead	1936-1947	3.437 bore	3.968 stroke	73.63ci	1206cc
61in Knucklehead	1936-1947	3.312 bore	3.500 stroke	60.32ci	988cc
80in flathead	1936-1947	3.422 bore	4.250 stroke	78.17ci	1281cc
74in flathead	1936-1947	3.437 bore	3.968 stroke	73.63ci	1206cc
45in flathead	1929-1951	2.750 bore	3.812 stroke	45.28ci	742cc

Unit Construction Engines

XL-1000 Sportster	1972-1985	3.187 bore	3.812 stroke	60.84ci	997cc
XLCH and XLH Sportster	1957-1971	3.000 bore	3.812 stroke	53.89ci	883cc
XLH-1200 Sportster	1988 and later	3.500 bore	3.812 stroke	73.36ci	1202cc
XLH-1100 Sportster	1986 and 1987	3.350 bore	3.812 stroke	67.20ci	1101cc
XLH-883 Sportster	1986 and later	3.000 bore	3.812 stroke	53.89ci	883cc
XR-750 dirt-track racer	1973 and later	3.125 bore	2.980 stroke	45.71ci	749cc
XR-750 dirt-track racer	1970-1972	3.000 bore	3.219 stroke	45.50ci	745cc
XR-1000 street bike	1983 and 1984	3.187 bore	3.812 stroke	60.84ci	997cc

Calculating two-cylinder engine displacement

bore x bore x stroke x 1.5708 = displacement
cubic inches x 16.387 = cc
cc x .061 = cubic inches

CHAIN FINAL DRIVE RATIO CHART

	11	12	13	14	15	16	17	18	19	20	21	22	23	24	25	26	
38	3.45	3.17	2.92	2.71	2.53	2.38	2.24	2.11	**2.00**	1.90	1.81	1.73	1.65	1.58	1.52	1.46	**38**
39	3.55	3.25	**3.00**	2.79	2.60	2.44	2.29	2.17	2.05	1.95	1.85	1.77	1.70	1.63	1.56	1.50	**39**
40	3.64	3.33	3.08	2.86	2.67	2.50	2.35	2.22	2.10	**2.00**	1.90	1.81	1.74	1.66	1.60	1.54	**40**
41	3.73	3.42	3.15	2.93	2.73	2.56	2.41	2.28	2.16	2.05	1.95	1.86	1.78	1.70	1.64	1.58	**41**
42	3.82	3.50	3.23	**3.00**	2.80	2.63	2.47	2.34	2.21	2.10	**2.00**	1.91	1.83	1.75	1.68	1.61	**42**
43	3.91	3.58	3.31	3.07	2.87	2.69	2.53	2.39	2.26	2.15	2.05	1.95	1.87	1.79	1.72	1.65	**43**
44	**4.00**	3.67	3.38	3.14	2.93	2.75	2.59	2.44	2.32	2.20	2.10	**2.00**	1.91	1.83	1.76	1.69	**44**
45	4.09	3.75	3.46	3.21	**3.00**	2.81	2.65	2.50	2.37	2.25	2.14	2.05	1.96	1.88	1.80	1.73	**45**
46	4.81	3.83	3.54	3.29	3.07	2.88	2.71	2.56	2.42	2.30	2.19	2.09	**2.00**	1.92	1.84	1.77	**46**
47	4.27	3.92	3.62	3.36	3.13	2.94	2.76	2.61	2.47	2.35	2.24	2.14	2.04	1.96	1.88	1.80	**47**
48	4.36	**4.00**	3.69	3.43	3.20	**3.00**	2.82	2.67	2.53	2.40	2.29	2.18	2.09	**2.00**	1.92	1.85	**48**
49	4.45	4.08	3.77	3.50	3.27	3.06	2.88	2.72	2.58	2.45	2.33	2.23	2.13	2.04	1.96	1.88	**49**
50	4.55	4.17	3.85	3.57	3.33	3.13	2.94	2.78	2.63	2.50	2.38	2.27	2.17	2.08	**2.00**	1.92	**50**
51	4.64	4.25	3.92	3.64	3.40	3.19	**3.00**	2.83	2.68	2.55	2.43	2.32	2.22	2.13	2.04	1.96	**51**
52	4.73	4.33	**4.00**	3.71	3.47	3.25	3.06	2.89	2.74	2.60	2.48	2.36	2.26	2.17	2.08	**2.00**	**52**
53	4.82	4.42	4.08	3.79	3.53	3.31	3.12	2.94	2.79	2.65	2.52	2.41	2.30	2.21	2.12	2.04	**53**
54	4.91	4.50	4.15	3.86	3.60	3.38	3.18	**3.00**	2.84	2.70	2.57	2.45	2.35	2.25	2.16	2.07	**54**
55	**5.00**	4.58	4.23	3.93	3.67	3.44	3.24	3.06	2.89	2.75	2.62	2.50	2.39	2.29	2.20	2.11	**55**
56	5.09	4.67	4.31	**4.00**	3.73	3.50	3.29	3.11	2.95	2.80	2.67	2.55	2.43	2.33	2.24	2.15	**56**
57	5.18	4.75	4.38	4.07	3.80	3.56	3.35	3.17	**3.00**	2.85	2.71	2.59	2.48	2.38	2.28	2.19	**57**
58	5.27	4.83	4.46	4.14	3.87	3.63	3.41	3.22	3.05	2.90	2.76	2.64	2.52	2.42	2.32	2.23	**58**
59	5.36	4.92	4.54	4.21	3.93	3.69	3.47	3.28	3.11	2.95	2.81	2.68	2.57	2.46	2.36	2.27	**59**
60	5.45	**5.00**	4.61	4.28	**4.00**	3.75	3.53	3.34	3.16	**3.00**	2.86	2.73	2.61	2.50	2.40	2.30	**60**
61	5.55	5.08	4.69	4.36	4.06	3.81	3.59	3.39	3.21	3.05	2.90	2.77	2.65	2.54	2.44	2.35	**61**
62	5.63	5.17	4.77	4.43	4.13	3.88	3.64	3.44	3.26	3.10	2.95	2.82	2.70	2.58	2.48	2.38	**62**
	11	**12**	**13**	**14**	**15**	**16**	**17**	**18**	**19**	**20**	**21**	**22**	**23**	**24**	**25**	**26**	

BELT FINAL DRIVE RATIO CHART

	25	26	27	28	29	30	31	32	33	34	35	36	
60	2.40	2.31	2.22	2.14	2.07	**2.00**	1.94	1.88	1.82	1.76	1.71	1.67	**60**
61	2.44	2.35	2.26	2.18	2.10	2.03	1.97	1.91	1.85	1.79	1.74	1.69	**61**
62	2.48	2.38	2.30	2.21	2.14	2.06	**2.00**	1.94	1.88	1.82	1.77	1.72	**62**
63	2.52	2.42	2.33	2.25	2.17	2.10	2.03	1.97	1.91	1.85	1.80	1.75	**63**
64	2.56	2.46	2.37	2.29	2.20	2.13	2.06	**2.00**	1.94	1.88	1.83	1.77	**64**
65	2.60	2.50	2.41	2.32	2.24	2.17	2.10	2.03	1.97	1.91	1.86	1.80	**65**
66	2.64	2.54	2.44	2.36	2.28	2.20	2.13	2.06	**2.00**	1.94	1.89	1.83	**66**
67	2.68	2.58	2.48	2.39	2.31	2.23	2.16	2.09	2.03	1.97	1.91	1.86	**67**
68	2.72	2.62	2.52	2.42	2.34	2.27	2.19	2.13	2.06	**2.00**	1.94	1.89	**68**
69	2.76	2.66	2.55	2.46	2.38	2.30	2.22	2.16	2.09	2.03	1.97	1.92	**69**
70	2.80	2.69	2.59	2.50	2.41	2.33	2.26	2.19	2.12	2.06	**2.00**	1.94	**70**
	25	**26**	**27**	**28**	**29**	**30**	**31**	**32**	**33**	**34**	**35**	**36**	

Racing Associations and Sanctioning Bodies

All-Harley Drag Racing Association
P.O. Box 1429
Elon College, NC 27244-1429
(919) 229-4877
FAX (919) 227-4630
all-Harley drag racing sanctioning body

American Dirt Racers Association
57346 Cowling Road
Three Rivers, MI 49093
(616) 279-9774 or (616) 383-0039
dirt-track drag racing sanctioning body

American Historic Racing Motorcycle Association
P.O. Box L
Mount Jewett, PA 16740
(814) 778-2291—Jeff Smith, Executive Director
FAX (814) 778-5375
"dedicated to preserving historic American racing motorcycles and providing events for them to be seen and heard in action"

American Motorcyclists Association (AMA)
P.O. Box 6114
Westerville, OH 43081-6114
(800) AMA-JOIN—in US;
(800) AMA-4567—in Ohio;
(614) 891-2425—outside US
883 Dirtster, Camel Pro Grand National, superbike and Harley-Davidson Twin Sports racing sanctioning body

American Motorcyclists Association Championship Cup Series
P.O. Box 447
Skyland, NC 28776-0447
(704) 684-4297
Harley-Davidson Twin Sports road racing sanctioning body

American Motorcycle Racing Association
P.O. Box 50
Itasca, IL 60143-0050
(708) 250-0838—Richard Wegner
all-Harley drag racing sanctioning body

Dragbike! U.S.A.
2100 Baker Avenue
Utica, NY 13501
(315) 735-7223 or
(315) 735-1661—East Coast
(214) 581-8011—South Central
(619) 292-4444—West Coast
drag racing sanctioning body

East Coast Racing Association
219 White House Pike
Galloway Township, NJ 08201
(609) 652-1159—Ben and Brenda Petrovick
drag racing sanctioning body

Eastern Dirt Racing Association
Pennsylvania
(717) 658-9601 or (717) 248-7676
dirt-track drag racing sanctioning body

Harley-Davidson Southern Racing Circuit
3914 South Shiloh, Suite 200
Garland, TX 75041
(214) 864-4647
all-Harley drag racing sanctioning body

International Cycle Events, Inc.
ICE, Inc.
P.O. Box 1690
Hickory, NC 28603-1690
(704) 328-2453—
Ted Cummings, President
FAX (704) 322-3207
organizes and promotes road racing at the Charlotte Motor Speedway in May and the Atlanta Motor Speedway in October

International Drag Bike Association
3936 Raceway Park Road
Mount Olive, AL 35117
(205) 849-7886; or
(205) 849-IDBA
FAX (205) 841-0553
drag racing sanctioning body

J&P Promotions
P.O. Box 138, R.R. #3
Anamosa, IA 52205-0135
(319) 462-4605
organizes dirt-track racing, drag racing, hillclimbs, rodeos, shows, swap meets, and vintage racing

Motorcycle Asphalt Racing Series
MARS, c/o On Track Promotions
P.O. Box 3499
Myrtle Beach, SC 29578-3499
(803) 626-7959—Ken Lilly
600cc and 883cc racing sanctioning body

ProStar
P.O. Box 182
Atco, NJ 08004-0182
(609) 768-4624
FAX (609) 753-9604
drag racing sanctioning body

Rawlings Dirt Drags, Inc.
Rawlings, Maryland
(301) 729-3532 or (301) 729-6131
dirt-track drag racing sanctioning body

Southern California Timing Association
22048 Vivienda
Grand Terrace, CA 92324
(714) 783-8293—Jim Lindsley;
(714) 676-2099—Don Vesco; or
(714) 662-9260—Elmo Gillette
Bonneville and El Mirage salt flats racing sanctioning body

Southeastern Sportbike Association
P.O. Box 420683
Atlanta, GA 30342-0683
(404) 984-2606
road racing sanctioning body

SuperTwins Drag Racing Series
SuperTwins, c/o Avon Park Raceway
Stratford-On-Avon,
Warwickshire
United Kingdom
Phone 0789-414119
all-Harley drag racing sanctioning body

Scandinavian SuperTwins Drag Racing Series
SuperTwins,
c/o Mother's Harley Shop
Box 194
421 22 Vastra Frolunda
Sweden 011-46-31-474746
FAX 011-46-31-474708
drag racing sanctioning body for Harleys and other four-stroke twins

Utah Salt Flat Racers Association
540 East 500 North
Pleasant Grove, UT 84062
(801) 723-6934—Rick Vesco; or
(801) 785-5364—Mary West
Bonneville Speed Trials racing sanctioning body

Western Eastern Roadracers' Association
WERA
P.O. Box 21960
Hilton Head Island, SC
29926-1960
(803) 681-9372
road racing sanctioning body

Riding Associations and Schools

All kinds of associations, clubs, and riding schools exist to help motorcyclists, and here you will find how to contact many of them. Some other names and addresses of interest—motorcycle museums, for instance—are also included in this section.

Unlike virtually everything else in this book, I have not personally verified most of the information in this section and assumed it was correct where I found it printed. If you notice any information in this book that is dated, incomplete, or just plain wrong, let me know so we can get it right in the next edition (but don't write to ask questions).

ABATE
ABATE of California—Local #1
11021 Hesby #3
North Hollywood, California 91061
Alaska ....(907) 248-7828
Arizona........................(602) 968-8985
Arkansas......................(501) 756-3761
California.....................(818) 769-3684
Colorado......................(303) 833-3195
Connecticut..................(203) 229-1638
Delaware......................(302) 453-0490
Florida.........................(813) 646-3106
Georgia........................(404) 294-8982
Idaho...........................(208) 784-4382
Illinois.........................(309) 343-6588
Indiana........................(317) 647-4286
Iowa............................(712) 328-9443
Kansas.........................(913) 597-5140
Louisiana.....................(504) 273-3405
Maryland.....................(301) 658-6675
Michigan......................(313) 427-3244
Minnesota....................(612) 541-1704
Mississippi...................(601) 957-9163
Missouri.......................(816) 238-3132
Montana.......................(406) 721-3937
Nebraska......................(402) 796-2523
Nevada.........................(702) 635-2817
New Jersey...................(201) 442-2788
New Mexico..................(505) 585-9789
New York.....................(716) 557-8859
North Carolina.............(704) 455-6245
North Dakota...............(701) 223-5609
Ohio.............................(216) 645-6931
Oregon.........................(503) 771-0188
Pennsylvania................(717) 761-6880
South Dakota...............(605) 335-8772
Tennessee.....................(615) 361-6023
Texas...........................(713) 353-9500
Utah............................(801) 943-1306
Virginia.......................(703) 780-4948
Washington..................(206) 772-1913
West Virginia...............(304) 425-0769
Wisconsin.....................(414) 367-1188
Wyoming......................(307) 856-4659
"Alliance of Bikers Aimed Towards Education"

Adult Motorcycle Riders Association
6070 Sea Isle
Galveston, TX 77554
no kids, no pets

AMRA
P.O. Box 64
Squamish, WA 98392-0064
legislative action group for street riders

Advanstar Expositions
1700 East Dyer Road, Suite 250
Santa Ana, CA 92704
(714) 252-5300—Ruth Andreaz
organizes the February Cincinnati motorcycle trade show, the March Daytona consumer motorcycle show and the September Las Vegas distributor motorcycle trade show

Aid to Injured Motorcyclists
Suite 202, 14888 104th Avenue
Surrey, British Columbia
Canada V3R 1M4
(604) 582-0140 or (800) 662-BIKE
"a non-partisan political action group lobbying for responsible motorcycle legislation"

Americade East
P.O. Box 2205
Glens Fall, NY 12801
(518) 656-9367—William Dutcher
annual June motorcycle rally at Lake George, New York

American Motorcycle Heritage Museum
33 Collegeview Road
Westerville, OH 43081-6114
(614) 891-2425
vintage American motorcycle museum

AMA Race Results Line
AMA Pro Racing
P.O. Box 6114
Westerville, OH 43081-6114
(900) 884-CYCLE (fee per minutes on-line)

American Sport Touring Riders Association
P.O. Box 32114
Knoxville, TN 37390-2114
(615) 690-4618—Jeff Adams

Annual Harley vs. Jap Bike Drags
Marty Aanstoos
2022 Woodland Shores Road
Charleston, SC 29412
(803) 795-7551—Marty Aanstoos; or
(803) 766-1648—Kerry Yates

Antique Motorcycle Club of America, Inc.
Dottie Wood, AMCA, Inc.
14943 York Road
Sparks, MD 21152
(319) 359-1545—Bob McClean

Associated Rodeo Riders on Wheels
ARROW
California
(818) 889-8740, ex. 226

Bikers Against Manslaughter
5455 Wilshire Boulevard
Suite 1600
Los Angeles, CA 90036
(800) 4-BIKERS—Russ Brown
legislative action group for street riders

British Motorcyclists Federation
United Kingdom
0533-548818—Mike Fairhead
legislative action group for street riders

Canadian Vintage Motorcycle Group
111 Elmer Avenue
Toronto, Ontario
Canada M4L 3R6
membership includes a subscription to The Link, *the CVMG newsletter*

Christian Motorcyclists Association
P.O. Box 9
Hatfield, AR 71945-0009
(501) 389-6196

CLASS
1495 Palma Drive, B
Ventura, CA 93003
(800) 235-7228 or
(805) 642-7228—Reg Pridmore
FAX (805) 642-5856
traveling motorcycle safety school

Competition Network for Harleys
P.O. Box 95881
Hoffman Estates, IL 60195-5881
(708) 884-6033—Greg Duray
an association for the restoration and appreciation of XR-750s and other classic racing Harleys

Concerned Bikers Association
P.O. Box 26445
Charlotte, NC 28221-6445
(704) 455-6245 or
(704) 391-1222—Rick Nail
legislative action group for street riders; holds annual Freedom Run in May

Dale Walker's Drag Racing School
311 Chestnut Street
Santa Cruz, CA 95060
(408) 427-3625 or (408) 427-0299
Pro Stock motorcycle drag racing school

Dixie Bikers Association
P.O. Box 196
Wetumpka, AL 36092-0196
(205) 569-3381
legislative action group for street riders

The Drag Racing School, Inc.
P.O. Box 140369
Gainesville, FL 32614-0369
(904) 373-7223
race car and motorcycle drag racing school run by Frank Hawley, with Pro Stock motorcycle racing taught by George Bryce

Easyriders Bros Club
P.O. Box 525
Mount Morris, IL 60154-0525
(800) 547-2767—Bill Bish, National Director;
(800) 247-6246—membership information
provides insurance for custom bikes, a state-by-state touring guide, and emergency road service all across the US

Fairview College
P.O. Box 3000
Fairview, Alberta
Canada T0H 1L0
(403) 835-6605
FAX (403) 835-6698
training for Harley-Davidson mechanics

Federation of European Motorcyclists
Ave. Marius Meuree 89
6001 Marcinelle, Charleroi
Belgium

FEM
45 Saint Katherines Road
Whipton, Exeter, Devon
United Kingdom
legislative action group

Forgotten Motorcyclist Association
Tracy Connell, FMA
20 Barlow Street
Radcliffe, Manchester
United Kingdom M26 9SU
for disabled motorcycle riders

Fossil Riders
P.O. Box 913
Point Pleasant, NJ 08742-0913
antique motorcycle owners' club

Handcrafted American Racing Motorcycles (HARM)
141 North Meridian Road
Youngstown, OH 44509
(216) 793-0425—Larry Smith, Editor
the bimonthly newspaper about all-Harley drag racing

Harley-Davidson Motor Company Assembly Plant and Museum
1425 Eden Road
York, PA 17402
(717) 848-1177

Harley-Davidson Motor Company Engine and Transmission Plant
11700 West Capitol Drive
Wauwatosa, WI 53222
(414) 535-3666—tour information

Harley Knucklehead Owners Club
Route 1, Box 267
Seagrove, NC 27341

Harley Owners Group (HOG)
P.O. Box 453
3700 West Juneau Avenue
Milwaukee, WI 53201-0453
(800) CLUB-HOG

Harley Owners Group Canada
55 Penn Drive
Weston, Ontario
Canada M9L 2A6
(416) 741-5510—from Toronto;
(800) 668-4836—rest of Canada

Illinois Motorcycle Dealers Association
2000 East Cornell
Springfield, IL 62703
(217) 753-8866
Springfield Mile AMA Camel Pro race sponsor

Indianapolis Motor Speedway Museum
4790 West 16th Street
Indianapolis, IN 46224
(317) 241-2500

Iowa All-Harley Drags
The Chrome Horse
18 Fourth Avenue East
Spencer, IA 51301
(712) 262-8910—Tator Gilmore
held every Fourth of July weekend in Humboldt, Iowa

Jam-On Productions
(301) 779-3235
organizes annual Daytona Motorcycle Swap Meet in March

Ladies Harley Riders Association
LHRA
P.O. Box 162
Holly Hill, FL 32017-0162

Leather Ladies Motorcycle Club
Annabelle Jacobs
P.O. Box 6041
Ashland, VA 23005-6041

LLMC
1207 East Caperton
Lancaster, CA 93535

Mike Baldwin Pro School
P.O. Box 3446
Noroton, CT 06820-3446
motorcycle road racing school

Modified Motorcycle Association (MMA)
4625 East Broadway, Suite 215
Tucson, AZ 85711
(602) 322-5511

MMA
P.O. Box 23
Dorchester, MA 02122-0023

MMA
P.O. Box 26566
Las Vegas, NV 89126-6566
(702) 870-6121
legislative action group for street riders

Motorcycle Action Group
P.O. Box 750
Birmingham, United Kingdom
B30 3BA
021-459-5860
legislative action group for street riders

Motorcycle Industry Council
2 Jenner Street, Suite 150
Irvine, CA 92718-3820
(714) 727-4211

Motorcycle Mechanics Institute (MMI)
2844 West Deer Valley Road
Phoenix, AZ 85027
(800) 528-7995

MMI
9751 Delegates Drive
Orlando, FL 32821
(407) 240-2422 or (800) 342-9253
training for Harley-Davidson mechanics

Motorcycle Riders Foundation
P.O. Box 11153
Minneapolis, MN 55411-1153
(612) 522-8024 (Minnesota),
(202) 546-0917 (District of Columbia),
(203) 869-6060 (Connecticut),
(207) 257-2061 (Maine),
(309) 833-3898 (Illinois),
(316) 942-2915 (Kansas),
(617) 770-3803 (Massachusetts),
(702) 870-6121 (Nevada),
(717) 299-7374 (Pennsylvania),
(816) 358-6632 (Missouri) or
(908) 906-7643 (New Jersey)
legislative action group for street riders

Motorcycle Safety Foundation
2 Jenner Street, Suite 150
Irvine, CA 92718-3820
(714) 727-3227 or (800) 447-4700
educational information and training for street riders

Motorcyclists Legal Action Committee
MLAC, c/o Lascher & Lascher
158 Fir Street
Ventura, CA 93001
attorneys challenging helmet laws

Motorsports International Services
5601 West Slauson, Suite 250
Culver City, CA 90230
(800) 266-1933
specializes in insurance for race cars and motorcycles traveling between race tracks and shows

National Coalition of Motorcyclists
Richard Lester and Pepper Massey
601 Pennsylvania Avenue, Suite 700
Washington, DC 20500
(800) 238-0080 or (800) 525-5355
legislative action group for street riders

National Dragster
2035 Financial Way, Box 5555
Glendora, CA 91740
(818) 963-8475—information;
(800) 678-4630—subscription orders
weekly newspaper about NHRA drag racing, with some motorcycle coverage

National Handicapped Motorcyclist Association
35-34 84th Street, Apt. F8
Jackson Heights, NY 11372
(718) 565-1243—Bob Nevola
Bob publishes a newsletter called The Gimp Exchange

National Handicapped Motorcyclists Association
4 Seymour Street
Highfields, Leicester
United Kingdom LE2 OLB

National Motorcycle Museum and Hall of Fame
2438 South Junction Avenue
P.O. Box 602
Sturgis, SD 57785-0602
(605) 347-6570 or (605) 347-4875
vintage motorcycle museum

Nevada Association of Concerned Motorcyclists
P.O. Box 2566
Las Vegas, NV 85126-2566
(702) 870-6121—Fred Harrell
legislative action group for street riders

North American Racing Insurance, Inc.
P.O. Box 2240
Independence, MO 64055-2240
(816) 373-0505—George England
FAX (816) 373-6145
specializes in insurance and appraisals for racers, race teams, and race tracks

Paralyzed Wheels Foundation (PWF)
435 Clover Street
Athens, GA 30606
(404) 548-9806—Dell Tiller

PWF
4703 South Division
Wayland, MI 49348
(616) 877-4749
disabled motorcyclist group

Paughco Museum
P.O. Box 3390
Carson City, NV 89702-3390
(702) 246-5738
FAX (702) 246-0372
over 100 vintage Harley-Davidsons on display

Ride for Kids Foundation
Mail Stop 100-4C-3B
1919 Torrance Boulevard
Torrance, CA 90501-2746
(404) 394-7870—Mike and Dianne Traynor; (800) 673-7220
organizes fund-raising rides in America to benefit children with brain tumors

Rochester Road Racers
P.O. Box 60998
Rochester, NY 14606-0998
(716) 482-1080
helps riders of all makes of motorcycles get involved in road racing

The Shop Museum
6541 Ventura Boulevard
Ventura, CA 93003
(805) 656-6777
FAX (805) 644-6448

Sons of God Motorcycle Club
48 Bush Avenue
West Paterson, NJ 07505
(201) 279-3770

Southern California Motorcycle Association
P.O. Box 1516
Fullerton, CA 92632-1516
(714) 879-9432
organizes annual Three Flags Classic tour of Canada, US, and Mexico in September

Southern California Sidecar Experience
17116 Goya Street
Granada Hills, CA 91334

Sportys
P.O. Box 593
East Bridgewater, MA 02333-0593
(508) 378-2233—Bruce Lupien
international club with a newsletter for Sportster enthusiasts

Streetbike Drag Club
17 Southampton Road
London, United Kingdom
Phone 0789-414119
SuperTwins and Street Bike class drag racing club

Team Suzuki Endurance Advanced Riding School
P.O. Box 964
Guasti, CA 91743-0964
(909) 245-6414
FAX (909) 245-6417
motorcycle road racing school

Turbo Motorcycle International
Route 1, Box 436
Penlaird, VA 22846
(703) 433-7916—Allen Lough
club for owners of all turbocharged motorcycles

United Sidecar Association
130 South Michigan Avenue
Villa Park, IL 60181
(312) 833-6732—Al Roach, Membership Secretary

White Plate Flat Trackers Association
Al Burke
7345 Blaisdell Avenue South
Richfield, MN 55423
for retired AMA Expert racers

White Rose Motorcycle Club
(717) 229-2691
organizes Pennsylvania hillclimbs

Women in the Wind
P.O. Box 640
Edmonton, Alberta
Canada T5J 2K8

Women in the Wind, Inc.
P.O. Box 8392
Toledo, OH 43605-8392

Women in the Wind Motorcycle Club
P.O. Box 143
Newbury, Berkshire
United Kingdom RG13 3HE

Women On Wheels, Inc.
P.O. Box 5147
Topeka, KS 66605-5147
(913) 267-3779—Kansas;
(815) 942-2736—Illinois

Women's Motorcyclist Foundation
7 Lent Avenue
LeRoy, NY 14482
(716) 768-6054

INDEX

ABOUT THE AUTHOR

It costs $44 to make a Honda 50, and it costs $275 in advertising to get rid of it."

—Cliff Majhor, founder of *Scrambler*, which later became *Cycle News*

Dave Mann bought his first Harley-Davidson back in 1968. The need for a directory such as this became apparent to him in 1987, when he began work on an Evolution Sportster roadracer. Discovering there was no single source for information about every company making performance parts for Harley-Davidsons, and recognizing the need for the Whole Earth Catalog of Harley muscle parts, he began work on this directory.

With products from over 350 manufacturers and fabricators from Australia, Canada, France, Germany, Holland, Italy, Japan, New Zealand, Scotland, Sweden, the United Kingdom, and the US, this is by far the most complete listing of Harley-Davidson high-performance equipment ever compiled or published.

As Dave points out, "If you can't find it here, you must have left it somewhere else."

In addition to his ongoing Evolution Sportster roadracer project, Dave is building up a 1940 Ford Deluxe sedan delivery street rod. He has compiled a directory of over 350 Corvette specialists, and has written dozens of articles about satellite television. Dave has also written Car Movies: A Complete Guide, which covers more than 300 movies that feature motorcycles, hot rods, muscle cars, race cars, sports cars, races, and great chase scenes—including more than 105 motorcycle movies. It will be published by Motorbooks International in March 1994.